THE MERCERS' SERIES

Oil Paintings in Public Ownership in West Wales

Y mae'r gyfres o gatalogau *Oil Paintings in Public Ownership* yn enghraifft eithriadol o waith yn mynd rhagddo. Cyhoeddwyd y fenter hon gan y Sefydliad Catalog Cyhoeddus, ac mae'n cynrychioli ffrwyth llafur ac ymdrechion diflino tîm bach o staff gweinyddol, ymchwilwyr a ffotograffwyr ar draws y Deyrnas Gyfunol.

Y mae'n debyg bod ein casgliad cenedlaethol o baentiadau olew sydd mewn meddiant cyhoeddus ymhlith y gorau yn y byd. Cedwir y casgliad, nid yn unig gan orielau ac amgueddfeydd, ond hefyd gan ysbytai, prifysgolion ac adeiladau cyhoeddus ymhob cwr o'r Deyrnas Gyfunol. Y mae llawer o'r darluniau hyn allan o olwg y cyhoedd ac y mae llawer ohonynt heb eu hatgynhyrchu erioed o'r blaen.

Galluoga'r gyfres hon o lyfrau i'r cyhoedd weld casgliad ffotograffig cyflawn o'r gweithiau hyn am y tro cyntaf – casgliad sydd yn debyg o gyrraedd cyfanswm o ryw 200,000 o eitemau. Drwy'r fenter hon, bydd y cyfrolau'n darparu golwg unigryw ar hanes celfyddydol a diwylliannol ein gwlad.

Fel Noddwr y Sefydliad Catalog Cyhoeddus, y mae fy ymweliadau â chasgliadau ledled y wlad wedi pwysleisio imi nid yn unig awydd y curaduron i dynnu sylw at y darluniau o dan eu gofal, ond hefyd yr adnoddau cyfyng sydd ar gael iddynt. Y mae gwaith y Sefydliad yn mynd cryn bellter tuag at greu mynediad at y casgliadau hyn, ac yn rhoi cyfle i bobl Prydain weld a mwynhau yr *holl* luniau y maen nhw'n berchen arnynt ar yr un pryd.

Y mae'n rhoi pleser neilltuol imi bod y catalogau hyn yn cael eu hargraffu gan Wasg Gomer a dymunaf bob llwyddiant i'r Sefydliad Catalog Cyhoeddus yn ei waith yn y dyfodol.

Camilla

The *Oil Paintings in Public Ownership* series of catalogues is an extraordinary work in progress. Published by The Public Catalogue Foundation, it is the result of the determined efforts of a small team of administrative staff, researchers and photographers spread across the United Kingdom.

Our national collection of oil paintings in public ownership is probably one of the finest anywhere in the world. It is held not just by our museums and galleries but is also to be found in hospitals, universities and other civic buildings throughout the United Kingdom. A large proportion of these paintings are not on display and many have never before been reproduced.

This series of books for the first time allows the public to see an entire photographic record of these works – a collection likely to number some 200,000 in total. In doing so, these volumes provide a unique insight into our nation's artistic and cultural history.

As Patron of The Public Catalogue Foundation, my visits to collections across the country have highlighted to me not only the desire of curators to publicise their paintings, but also the limited resources at their disposal. The Foundation's work goes a long way towards helping to create access to these collections, while at the same time giving the British public the opportunity to see and enjoy *all* the paintings that they own.

I wish The Public Catalogue Foundation every success in its continuing endeavours.

Camilla

Oil Paintings in Public Ownership

in

West Wales

Funding Patron
The Mercers' Company

Coordinators: Jessica Baudey & Pat Lacy
Photographers: Dan Brown & David Griffin

The Public Catalogue Foundation

Patron
HRH The Duchess of Cornwall

Contents

Image opposite HRH The Duchess of Cornwall's Welsh statement: Carlson, Ron, 1936–2002, *Daffodil Bulbs*, Neath Port Talbot County Borough Council (p. 75)
Image opposite HRH The Duchess of Cornwall's English statement: Williams, Christopher, 1873–1934, *Family on Barmouth Island*, Glynn Vivian Art Gallery (p. 227)

Facing page: Panting, Arlie, 1914–1994, *Still Life with Leeks*, Glynn Vivian Art Gallery, (p. 197)

Image opposite title page: Richards, Ceri Giraldus, 1903–1971, *The Artist's Wife*, 1932, Glynn Vivian Art Gallery (p. 201)

Christie's is proud to be the sponsor of The Public Catalogue Foundation in its pursuit to improve public access to paintings held in public collections in the UK.

Christie's is a name and place that speaks of extraordinary art. Founded in 1766 by James Christie, the company is now the world's leading art business. Many of the finest works of art in UK public collections have safely passed through Christie's, as the company has had the privilege of handling the safe cultural passage of some of the greatest paintings and objects ever created. Christie's today remains a popular showcase for the unique and the beautiful.

In addition to acquisition through auction sales, Christie's regularly negotiates private sales to the nation, often in lieu of tax, and remains committed to leading the auction world in the area of Heritage sales.

CHRISTIE'S

Foreword

It is with a very real sense of pride that the Foundation has been able not just to bring the printing of the Welsh catalogue series to Wales, but also to launch the Welsh series at Gomer's printworks in Llandysul, in the presence of our Patron, Her Royal Highness The Duchess of Cornwall.

Ever since Her Royal Highness first lent us her support for our volume covering Cornwall and the Scilly Isles, she has been a generous and affectionate follower of our work, and an enthusiastic visitor to participating galleries up and down the country. The Foundation is proud of her association with us, grateful for all the support she has given us over the past years and delighted to be able formally to record this in this Foreword.

The Foundation is grateful to all those who have funded its work in Wales but most especially to the Mercers' Company, without whose generous contribution the printed version of the project as a whole would not have been completed.

We are also grateful for all the help provided to our team by the staff in the participating collections; in particular to our Coordinators, Jessica Baudey and Pat Lacey, to our photographers, Dan Brown and David Griffin, and to our Series Editor, Sophie Kullmann, whose excellent work is manifest in this volume.

Fred Hohler, Founder

Facing page: John, Gwen, 1876–1939, *The Nun*, late 1910s, Glynn Vivian Art Gallery (p. 187)

The Public Catalogue Foundation: People Involved

Catalogue Scope and Organisation

Medium and Support

The principal focus of this series is oil paintings. However, tempera and acrylic are also included as well as mixed media, where oil is the predominant constituent. Paintings on all forms of support (e.g. canvas, panel, etc.) are included as long as the support is portable. The principal exclusions are miniatures, hatchments or other purely heraldic paintings and wall paintings *in situ*.

Public Ownership

Public ownership has been taken to mean any paintings that are directly owned by the public purse, made accessible to the public by means of public subsidy or generally perceived to be in public ownership. The term 'public' refers to both central government and local government. Paintings held by national museums, local authority museums, English Heritage and independent museums, where there is at least some form of public subsidy, are included. Paintings held in civic buildings such as local government offices, town halls, guildhalls, public libraries, universities, hospitals, crematoria, fire stations and police stations are also included.

Geographical Boundaries of Catalogues

The geographical boundary of each county is the 'ceremonial county' boundary. This county definition includes all unitary authorities. Counties that have a particularly large number of paintings are divided between two or more catalogues on a geographical basis.

Criteria for Inclusion

As long as paintings meet the requirements above, all paintings are included irrespective of their condition and perceived quality. However, painting reproductions can only be included with the agreement of the participating collections and, where appropriate, the relevant copyright owner. It is rare that a collection forbids the inclusion of its paintings. Where this is the case and it is possible to obtain a list of paintings, this list is given in the Paintings Without Reproductions section. Where copyright consent is refused, the paintings are also listed in the Paintings Without Reproductions section. All paintings in collections' stacks and stores are included, as well as those on display. Paintings which have been lent to other institutions, whether for short-term exhibition or long-term loan, are listed under the owner collection. In addition, paintings on long-term loan are also included under the borrowing institution when they are likely to remain there for at least another five years from the date of publication of this catalogue. Information relating to owners and borrowers is listed in the Further Information section.

Layout

Collections are grouped together under their home town. These locations are listed in alphabetical order. In some cases collections that are spread over a number of locations are included under a single owner collection. A number of collections, principally the larger ones, are preceded by curatorial forewords. Within each collection paintings are listed in order of artist surname. Where there is more than one painting by the same artist, the paintings are listed chronologically, according to their execution date.

The few paintings that are not accompanied by photographs are listed in the Paintings Without Reproductions section.

There is additional reference material in the Further Information section at the back of the catalogue. This gives the full names of artists, titles and media if it has not been possible to include these in full in the main section. It also provides acquisition credit lines and information about loans in and out, as well as copyright and photographic credits for each painting. Finally, there is an index of artists' surnames.

Key to Painting Information

Almost all paintings are reproduced in the catalogue. Where this is not the case they are listed in the Paintings Without Reproductions section. Where paintings are missing or have been stolen, the best possible photograph on record has been reproduced. In some cases this may be black and white. Paintings that have been stolen are highlighted with a red border. Some paintings are shown with conservation tissue attached to parts of the painting surface.

Adam, **Patrick William** 1854–1929

Interior, Rutland Lodge: Vista through Open Doors 1920

oil on canvas 67.3 × 45.7

LEEAG.PA.1925.0671.LACF 🐝

Artist name This is shown with the surname first. Where the artist is listed on the Getty Union List of Artist Names (ULAN), ULAN's preferred presentation of the name is given. In a number of cases the name may not be a firm attribution and this is made clear. Where the artist name is not known, a school may be given instead. Where the school is not known, the painter name is listed as *unknown artist*. If the artist name is too long for the space, as much of the name is given as possible followed by (…). This indicates the full name is given at the rear of the catalogue in the Further Information section.

Painting title A painting title followed by *(?)* indicates that the title is in doubt. Where the alternative title to the painting is considered to be better known than the original, the alternative title is given in parentheses. Where the collection has not given a painting a title, the publisher does so instead and marks this with an asterisk. If the title is too long for the space, as much of the title is given as possible followed by (…) and the full title is given in the Further Information section.

Execution date In some cases the precise year of execution may not be known for certain. Instead an approximate date will be given or no date at all.

Artist dates Where known, the years of birth and death of the artist are given. In some cases one or both dates may not be known with certainty, and this is marked. No date indicates that even an approximate date is not known. Where only the period in which the artist was active is known, these dates are given and preceded with the word *active*.

Medium and support Where the precise material used in the support is known, this is given.

Dimensions All measurements refer to the unframed painting and are given in cm with up to one decimal point. In all cases the height is shown before the width. An (E) indicates where a painting has not been measured and its size has been calculated by sight only. If the painting is circular, the single dimension is the diameter. If the painting is oval, the dimensions are height and width.

Collection inventory number In the case of paintings owned by museums, this number will always be the accession number. In all other cases it will be a unique inventory number of the owner institution. (P) indicates that a painting is a private loan. Details can be found in the Further Information section. Accession numbers preceded by 'PCF' indicate that the collection did not have an accession number at the time of catalogue production and therefore the number given has been temporarily allocated by The Public Catalogue Foundation. The 🐝 symbol indicates that the reproduction is based on a Bridgeman Art Library transparency (go to www.bridgemanart.com) or that Bridgeman administers the copyright for that artist.

Facing page: Nicholson, Ben, 1894–1982, *12 October 1952* (detail), 1952, Glynn Vivian Art Gallery, (p. 196)

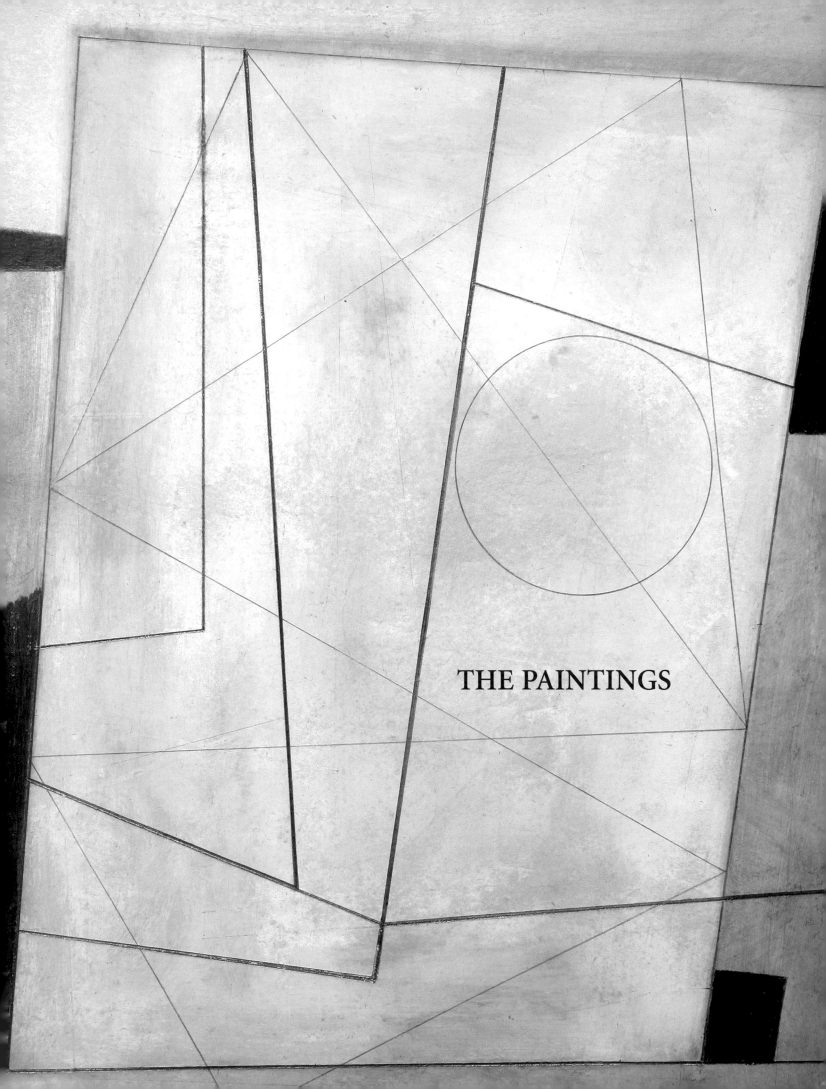

THE PAINTINGS

Carmarthenshire Museums Service Collection

The Carmarthenshire collection of paintings has been brought together by purchase and gift. In the main, the works represent the achievements of artists from the county and those working within it. There are three distinct collections: Carmarthenshire County Museum, Parc Howard Museum and Art Gallery and the County Hall collection.

Carmarthenshire County Museum's collection represents the art of the county and contains work by significant artists such as Edward Morland Lewis, who came from Carmarthen. Parc Howard's collection represents the art of Llanelli and contains paintings by artists from the town, such as James Dickson Innes and Charles William Mansel Lewis. The County Hall collection was largely purchased between the 1950s and 1996 as a contemporary art collection for hanging in public spaces. The landscape of the county has been the inspiration for many artists, although the collections also contain interesting portraits of local gentry. Twentieth century artist are well represented in the collections.

The museums are managed by Carmarthenshire County Council, which is proud of its artistic heritage. Paintings from their collections can be seen at both Carmarthenshire County Museum and at Parc Howard on permanent display and in occasional temporary exhibitions. Entry to both museums is free.

Ann Dorsett, County Museums Manager

Alison, J. active 1900s
Sir James Williams-Drummond (1857–1913), of Edwinsford, Llandeilo, 4th Bt Hawthornden, CB, Lord-Lieutenant of Carmarthenshire 1902
oil on canvas 97 x 56
1976.1514

Anthony, Sonia active 1960s
Llygad Llwchwr 1963
oil on board 96.5 x 127.3
1981.0067

Aplin, Herbert Lawrence 1907–1993
Gelli Aur, Autumn c.1988
oil on board 50.4 x 68.2
1988.0112

Ardron, Annette Matilda 1875–1952
Portrait of an Unknown Boy 1904
oil on canvas 155 x 76
1976.1434

Barham, George active c.1850–1858
Laugharne Castle 1858
oil on panel 28 x 29
1976.1524

Barham, George active c.1850–1858
Laugharne Church 1858
oil on panel 28 x 29
1976.1525

Barnard, J. Langton 1853–1902
The Makers of England
oil on canvas 134 x 166
1997.0572

Bevan, J. G. active 1950s–1960s
Deserted Farm, Coedcae 1955–1965
oil on canvas 125.7 x 193
1981.0085

Beynon, E. B. active 1970s
St Paul's Depot
acrylic on board 41 x 71
1997.1603

Blanchard, Jacques 1912–1992
Still Life with Cherries c.1957
oil on board 58.2 x 68.9
1980.0107

Bonnor, Rose Dempster 1875–1967
Ernest Trubshaw 1909
oil on canvas 174 x 125
1997.056

Bonville, William
Bridge over River Taff, Pontypridd c.1800
oil on canvas 21 x 27
1976.1521

Bowen, John 1914–2006
Self Portrait c.1938
oil on canvas 49 x 40
1997.1729

Bowen, John 1914–2006
Mediterranean Fishing Boat 1959
oil on board 45 x 100
1980.0106

Bowen, John 1914–2006
Aegean Variations II, Temple Ruins 1961
oil on board 152.4 x 228.6
1981.0068

Bowen, John 1914–2006
Sunset 1965
oil on board 57 x 121
1997.1445

Bowen, John 1914–2006
Melting Snow Evening 1967
oil on canvas 71 x 96
1997.1431

Bowen, John 1914–2006
Farmer in a Field 1968
oil on board 102.5 x 62
1997.1432

Bowen, John 1914–2006
Nevills Channel 1968
oil on board 92 x 76
1997.143

Bowen, John 1914–2006
April Morning Wet Pavements 1960s–1970s
oil on board 93 x 60
2003.1263

Bowen, John 1914–2006
Terrace near Bridge with Pole 1960s–1970s
oil on board 72 x 65
1997.1442

Bowen, John 1914–2006
Winter Landscape 1960s–1970s
oil on board 56 x 106
1997.1435

Bowen, John 1914–2006
Autumn Evening 1970
oil on board 82 x 90
1997.1439

Bowen, John 1914–2006
Landscape with Tiger Moth 1970–1980
oil on canvas 35 x 46
1997.1441

Bowen, John 1914–2006
Woman in Lamplight (1) 1970–1980
oil on board 63.5 x 76
1997.1429

Bowen, John 1914–2006
Woman in Lamplight (2) 1970–1980
oil on board 76 x 81
1997.144

Bowen, John 1914–2006
Autumn Mist, Llanelli Beach 1970s
oil on canvas board 63 x 77
1997.1446

Bowen, John 1914–2006
Chapel No.3 1970s
oil on board 67 x 90
1997.1444

Bowen, John 1914–2006
Elegy Autumn 1970s
oil on board 62 x 111
1997.1438

Bowen, John 1914–2006
Park in Autumn 1970s–1980s
oil on board 75 x 72.5
1997.1437

Bowen, John 1914–2006
The Blue Shirt (Graffiti) 1970s–1980s
oil on canvas board 63 x 76
1997.1436

Bowen, John 1914–2006
Spanish Hill Village, Twilight (recto) c.1983
oil on canvas 85 x 82.5
2003.1261

Bowen, John 1914–2006
Colour Abstract (verso)
oil on board 85 x 82.5
2003.1261

Bowen, John 1914–2006
Breezes from the Sea 1985
oil on board 51 x 61
1988.0109

Bowen, John 1914–2006
A Window: Tossa de Mar 1980s
oil on canvas board 76.5 x 63
1997.1443

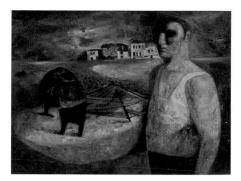

Bowen, John 1914–2006
Evening Thunder, Tossa 1980s
oil on canvas 64 x 76
1997.1434

Bowen, John 1914–2006
Woman Packing Flowers, Nice 1980s
oil on board 76.5 x 76
1997.1433

Bowen, John 1914–2006
Still Life with Fruit and Peppers 1988–1989
oil on board 51 x 61
1997.0965

Bowen, John 1914–2006
Noonday Heat, Provence 1998
oil on board 51 x 61
1997.0964

Bowen, Leslie
Devon Lane 1950s
oil on canvas 41.5 x 61.5
1988.0091

Brenton, Ruth 1922–2007
Local Derby 1964
oil on board 44 x 29
1981.0089

Brenton, Ruth 1922–2007
Autumn Scene 1966
oil on board 52 x 79.3
2003.2971

Brenton, Ruth 1922–2007
View from Libanus, Pwll 1973
oil on board 39 x 82
2003.1289

Brenton, Ruth 1922–2007
Daniel's Cottage, Pwll 1980
oil on board 37 x 49
1997.1551

Brenton, Ruth 1922–2007
Penwlch Farm, Pwll 1983
oil on board 40 x 79
1997.1033

Brenton, Ruth 1922–2007
Burry Port Harbour
oil on board 42 x 59
1997.12

Brigstocke, Thomas 1809–1881
John Jones, Esq. (1777–1842), MP, of Ystrad
c.1830
oil on canvas 215 x 120
1991.0003

Brigstocke, Thomas 1809–1881
General Sir William Nott (1782–1845) 1845
oil on canvas 220 x 150
1992.0032

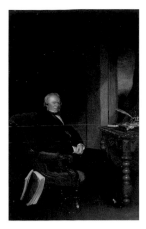

Brigstocke, Thomas 1809–1881
David Morris (1800–1869), MP and Whig
Politician 1859
oil on canvas 200 x 120 (E)
1992.0031

Brigstocke, Thomas (attributed to)
1809–1881
John Jones, Esq. (1777–1842), MP, of Ystrad
c.1854
oil on canvas 72 x 57
1997.0576

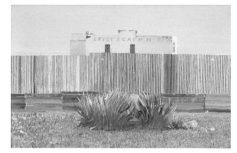

Brown, Geoff b.1948
Jersey Beach Hotel 1988
oil on canvas 50.5 x 76
1990.0566

Brown, Julian b.1934
Free Fibres c.1960
acrylic on canvas 34.4 x 38.5
1983.0402

Bush, Reginald Edgar James 1869–1956
J. E. Jones 1906
oil on canvas 194 x 126
1997.0583

Chalmers, George (attributed to)
c.1720–c.1791
Lady Maude of Westmead (1697–1779)
c.1705–1710
oil on canvas 127.3 x 101.1
1981.0434

Charles, Anthony Stephen
Garnant 1 1975
oil on canvas 74.5 x 99.5
2002.0761

Charles, Anthony Stephen
Garnant 2 1975
oil on canvas 74 x 89
2002.0782

Charles, Julian Peter
The Stranger 1962
oil on board 194.3 x 114.3
1981.0083

Cole, Philip Tennyson 1862–1939
Owen Cosley Philipps, 1st Baron Kylsant, MP
1920
oil on canvas 155 x 96
1976.1431

Cole, Walter Stevens 1883–1967
Aneurin Bevan (1897–1960) 1942
oil on board 50 x 40
1997.1585

Cole, Walter Stevens 1883–1967
Winston Churchill (1874–1965) 1942
oil on panel 51 x 40.5
1997.1586

Cole, Walter Stevens 1883–1967
Our Factory in Winter 1947
oil on canvas 68 x 92
2000.0084

Cole, Walter Stevens 1883–1967
Henry Giles 1957
oil on canvas 50 x 37
1997.0573

Cole, Walter Stevens 1883–1967
Old Welsh Woman
oil on paper 114.3 x 86.4
1981.0047

Cole, Walter Stevens 1883–1967
Still Life, Musical Corner
oil on board 61 x 47
1983.0007

Collier, Ernest Vale 1859–1932
The Gate at the Vicarage, St Ishmael's 1904
oil on canvas 42.5 x 34.7
1995.0222

Collier, Ernest Vale 1859–1932
The Parsonage Garden 1916
oil on card 27 x 36.5
1992.0254

Facing page: Vaughan, John Keith, 1912–1977, *Warrior*, 1959, Glynn Vivian Art Gallery (p. 212)

Collier, Ernest Vale 1859–1932
The Palace, St David's 1922
oil on canvas 56.5 x 46
1976.1515

Collier, John 1850–1934
William Rosser 1884
oil on canvas 124 x 101
1997.0585

Crabtree, Jack b.1938
Pithead Scene 1974
oil on canvas 123.5 x 123.5
1990.0446

Davies, Arthur
La Perdix, Dordogne c.1980
acrylic on paper 25.4 x 31.7
1997.1641

Davies, D. J.
James Buckley c.1895
oil on canvas 199 x 116
1997.0558

Davies, Gareth
Ned Kelly's Ball 1980s
acrylic on canvas 59 x 76
1989.0237

Davies, Gareth
Y Clwb Rygbi 1993
oil on board 72 x 92
2003.2996

Davies, Gareth Hugh b.1962
Bwlch yr Oernant 2005
oil on canvas 25.5 x 35.5
2005.0938

Davies, Gareth Hugh b.1962
Monkey Puzzle Tree, Abergwili 2005
oil on canvas 85 x 70
2005.0939

Davies, Paul 1947–1993
Wooded Valley c.1990
oil on canvas (?) 18 x 28
1991.164

Davies, S. T. Wynford active 20th C
An Impression of Llanelli Church in 1566
oil on board 50 x 91
1997.1604

Davies, S. T. Wynford active 20th C
Eglwys Sant Elli
oil on board 60.5 x 91
2003.1278

Davies, Verona active 20th C
St Teilo Talybont Church
oil on canvas 43 x 47
1997.1587

Dobson, William (attributed to)
1611–1646
Richard, Lord Vaughan (1600–1686), 2nd Earl of Carbery c.1640–1645
oil on canvas 75.4 x 63.8
1981.0436

Dobson, William (attributed to)
1611–1646
Rachel Wriothesley (1636–1723) c.1645–1650
oil on canvas 75.1 x 63
1981.0435

Dudley, Hiram active 1954–1978
Wild Wales 1962
oil on board 30.8 x 68.5
1986.0123

Dudley, Hiram active 1954–1978
The Miner 1978
oil on board 69.9 x 50.8
1978.0378

Dyck, Anthony van (after) 1599–1641
Lady Dorothy Sidney c.1650
oil on canvas 122 x 100
1996.008

Etheridge, Ken 1911–1981
Culwch ac Olwen c.1970
acrylic on canvas 180 x 145
1979.1308

Etheridge, Ken 1911–1981
Gorwelion Myrddin 1974
oil on canvas 241.5 x 165.4
1981.0188

Evans, D. active 1980s
Emlyn Owen Jones 1981
oil on canvas 61.5 x 57.5
1997.1614

Evans, David active 1970s
Town Hall, Reflections at Night 1970
oil on canvas 60 x 85
2003.3093

Evans, Elfin active 1970s
Yr Hen Bont (The Old Bridge) 1977
oil on board 60 x 86.5
2002.0753

Evans, Emily active 1890s
Still Life – Pitcher with Fruit 1893
oil on canvas 40.5 x 51
1976.1442

Evans, Herbert (attributed to) 1807–1850
*Sergeant Andrews Capturing the French
Colours at Waterloo or the Fight for the
Standard* c.1850
oil on canvas 150 x 123
1976.1435

Evans, Isobel active c.1900–1910
River Scene c.1900–1910
oil on canvas 21 x 27
1976.1522

Evans, Isobel active c.1900–1910
Laugharne c.1910
oil on panel 23 x 40
1976.15

Evans, John active 20th C
Llanstephan Castle
oil on canvas 46 x 66
1997.1454

Evans, John active 20th C
'Stag's Head' and Coastal Scene (copy of an earlier watercolour)
oil on canvas 41 x 61
2003.1274

Evans, Peter Culpitt 1926–2009
Early Snow, Brecon 1961
oil on board 52 x 62.5
1975.0698

Evans, Philip Michael active 20th C
North Dock, Llanelli, Winter 1963 1974
oil on board 75 x 61
2003.127

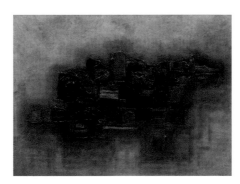

Evans, Philip Michael active 20th C
Armageddon
oil on board 91 x 122
1997.1465

Evans, Tony 1920–2001
The Haulier c.1975
oil on canvas 38 x 72
1997.1463

Evans, Tony 1920–2001
The Machinist 1970s
oil on board 91 x 51
2003.1277

Evans, Tony 1920–2001
Quartet 1970s–1980s
oil on canvas 55 x 93
1997.1565

Evans, Tony 1920–2001
At the Bus Stop 1982
oil on board 59 x 47
2003.1306

Evans, Tony 1920–2001
The Furnace Man c.1988
oil on board 75.7 x 101.3
1988.0143

Evans, Tony 1920–2001
Opening Plates 1980s
oil on board 76 x 62
2003.289

Evans, Tony 1920–2001
Cutting the Post 1980s–1990s
oil on canvas 61 x 61
2003.1312

Evans, Tony 1920–2001
Into the Light 1980s–1990s
oil on canvas 54 x 71.3
2003.1287

Evans, Tony 1920–2001
Low Seam 1980s–1990s
oil on panel 69 x 111
2003.1311

Evans, Tony 1920–2001
On the Dole 1980s–1990s
oil on canvas 83.5 x 41.5
2003.1307

Evans, Tony 1920–2001
The Coracles (recto) 1980s–1990s
oil on panel 60 x 77
2003.1309

Evans, Tony 1920–2001
A View of Colliers Underground (verso)
1980s–1990s
oil on panel 60 x 77
2003.1309B

Evans, Tony 1920–2001
The Harbour at Night 1980s–1990s
acrylic on canvas 76 x 61
2003.1313

Evans, Tony 1920–2001
The Jay 1980s–1990s
oil on canvas 51 x 60
2003.1308

Evans, Tony 1920–2001
Triptych No.1 No.3 Drilling 1980s–1990s
oil on panel 104 x 81
2003.131

Evans, Tony 1920–2001
Triptych No.1 No.5 At the Bus Stop
1980s–1990s
oil on panel 106.7 x 83.6
2003.1315

Evans, Tony 1920–2001
Triptych No.13 Pit Pony 1980s–1990s
oil on panel 84 x 112
2003.1316

Evans, Tony 1920–2001
Triptych No.14 At the Face 1980s–1990s
oil on panel 84 x 84
2003.1317

Evans, Tony 1920–2001
Triptych No.2 No.12 Cutting the Post
1980s–1990s
oil on panel 85.5 x 84
2003.1314

Evans, Tony 1920–2001
Donkey Island
oil on canvas 53 x 73.5
1988_0108

Eyers, John active 1974–1976
Tracks 1974–1976
oil on canvas 49.5 x 43.7
2002.0759

Eyers, John active 1974–1976
Llansawel 1976
oil on canvas 30 x 35
2002.0728

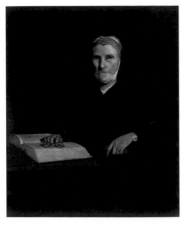

Francis, John Deffett 1815–1901
Sarah Jones 1845
oil on canvas 72.6 x 63.5
1979.0549

Fripp, Paul 1890–1945
A Summer Lane, Penycoed 1940
oil on board 36 x 46
1991.017

Fripp, Paul 1890–1945
Towy Valley Farm 1942
oil on canvas 33 x 37
1992.0239

Galloway, Mary Gwendolyn 1906–1999
Rita c.1925
oil on canvas 19.5 x 14.3
1996.0101

Galloway, Mary Gwendolyn 1906–1999
Alltycnap Road Flannel Mill 1930–1950
oil on board 30 x 40
2004.0156

Galloway, Mary Gwendolyn 1906–1999
Jones' Alley, The Quay, Carmarthen 1958
oil on canvas board 35.5 x 25.5
1990.0113

Galloway, Mary Gwendolyn 1906–1999
Snowdonia 1950s
oil on canvas 14.3 x 19.5
1996.01

Galloway, Mary Gwendolyn 1906–1999
Winston Churchill (1874–1965) 1965
oil on canvas 51.1 x 41.1
1986.0126

Girardot, Mary Jane c.1855–1933
Evening Glow c.1900
oil on canvas 64 x 90
1976.1508

Facing page: Reni, Guido, 1575–1642, *Susanna and the Elders*, Glynn Vivian Art Gallery (p. 201)

Girardot, Mary Jane c.1855–1933
The Wanderers c.1900–1910
oil on canvas 64 x 90
1976.1436

Girardot, Mary Jane c.1855–1933
April
oil on canvas 40 x 55
1976.1502

Girardot, Mary Jane c.1855–1933
Mountain by Wales
oil on canvas 65 x 74
1976.1516

Goble, Anthony 1943–2007
Little Haven c.1998
acrylic on board
2000.0775

Goddard, Frank b.1927
Early Flight, Penclacwyd
oil on canvas 33 x 24
1997.1724

Hamill, Sybil C. b.1937
Summer Bouquet
acrylic on board 52 x 39.5
1997.1546

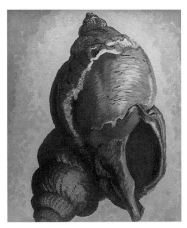

Hancock, Rhoda active c.1960–1980
Shells 1962
oil on board 75.1 x 67
1999.039

Hancock, Rhoda active c.1960–1980
Temple of Hera 1970s (?)
oil on panel 48 x 60
1997.1552

Harries, Sheila b.1934
Quiet Walk c.1988
oil on canvas 51 x 61
1988.011

Harries, Siloe
Sheltered 1985
oil on board 24.5 x 19.5
1997.1661

Havard (Mrs) (copy of)
Llanelli Church and Market, 1821 20th C
oil on card 66 x 101
1997.1482

Hector, M.
Captain James Buckley (1869–1924) 1909
oil on canvas 74 x 63
1976.1513

Herkomer, Hubert von 1849–1914
Der Bittgang (The Prayer Walk) 1877
oil on canvas 197 x 106
1997.0567

Holl, Frank 1845–1888
Connop Thirlwall (1797–1875), Bishop of St David's (1840–1874) c.1865
oil on canvas 136.3 x 113.5
1981.0411

Holland, Harry b.1941
Head of a Young Woman 1983
oil on canvas 24.5 x 23.5
1985.0045

Holland, Harry b.1941
Shadow 1988
oil on canvas 160 x 127
1995.0001

Hopkins, John Wynne b.1954
Siege of Carnwyllion 2003
oil on canvas 76 x 100
2003.2992

Hopson, Royston 1927–2003
Pembrokeshire Landscape
oil on board 11.5 x 17
1991.0162

Howard-Jones, Ray 1903–1996
Under Milk Wood, Homage to Dylan c.1965
oil on board 54 x 64
1997.0189

Howard-Jones, Ray 1903–1996
Gateholm and the Moon
oil on canvas 37 x 54.5
2002.0762

Hughes, Hugh 1790–1863
David Morley 1824
oil on paper on panel 18 x 14
1975.4629

Hughes, Hugh 1790–1863
*Mary Gwynne Hughes, born Mary Howell of
Danygraig (1830–1853)* c.1836–1842
oil on board 22.5 x 17.5
2000.058

Humphrey, Richard
Late Frost 1977
tempera on panel 94.2 x 76.5
2002.0766

Hunter, Robert 1920–1996
Carmarthenshire Landscape (Sunset) 1955
oil on board 79.5 x 54.5
2002.0757

Hunter, Robert 1920–1996
Celtic Image 1962
oil on board 51 x 91
2002.0751

Hunter, Robert 1920–1996
A Banner for Pwyll and Rhiannon 1974
oil & acrylic on canvas 120 x 123 (E)
2002.0737

Hurford, Vernon 1922–2001
Pentrepoeth to Carmarthen Bay Power Station
1955–1964
oil on board 49.3 x 64
1981.0065

Hurford, Vernon 1922–2001
Long Row 1963
oil on board 41.9 x 102.1
1986.0125

Hurford, Vernon 1922–2001
Falcon Bridge 1970
oil on board 44 x 55
1997.1479

Hurford, Vernon 1922–2001
Felinfoel 1972
oil on board 50 x 42
1997.1508

Hurford, Vernon 1922–2001
Water Street 1972
oil on canvas 45 x 55
1997.1584

Icke, Gillian Sybil 1925–1989
Laugharne – The Grist 1966
oil on canvas 53 x 78
2002.0768

Innes, James Dickson 1887–1914
View of Llanelli from the Furnace Quarry
c.1906
oil on canvas 45 x 60
1997.0568

James, Eunice 1892–1981
Landscape 1914
oil on canvas 59 x 28.7
1995.0474

James, Eunice 1892–1981
Seascape 1915
oil on board 21.9 x 29.5
1995.0472

James, Eunice 1892–1981
Rural Scene
oil on canvas 45.7 x 60
1995.047

James, Eunice 1892–1981
Seascape
oil on board 32 x 34
1995.0473

James, Eunice 1892–1981
Woodland Scene
oil on canvas 59.3 x 28.8
1995.0471

Jenkins, John Price
The Half Cut Field 1980
oil on board 58.4 x 70.6
1980.0374

Jenkins, John Price
View From Peniel 1980
oil on board 62.9 x 129.5
1980.0375

Jones, Betty H. active 1943–1965
Cei Caerfyrddin 1943
oil on board 50.7 x 40.6
1980.0187

Jones, Betty H. active 1943–1965
Cornel o'r Pwll 1965
oil on canvas board 19 x 27.7
1986.0119

Jones, Ernest Harold 1877–1911
Floral Pattern 1900
oil on canvas 76 x 18
1976.1532

Jones, Ernest Harold 1877–1911
Still Life: Chalice, Plate and Tankard c.1900
oil on canvas 107 x 92
1975.0701

Jones, Ernest Harold 1877–1911
Still Life: Pitcher, Globe and Statue c.1900
oil on canvas 107 x 92
1975.0702

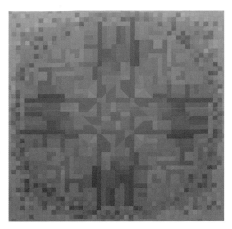

Jones, Mary Lloyd b.1934
Global Village 1972
acrylic on canvas 122 x 122
2002.0734

Kinsey, Christine
Llais Ymweled – Visit c.2004
oil on canvas 127 x 121
2007.0193

Kneller, Godfrey 1646–1723
*Lady Anne Vaughan, Duchess of Bolton
(d.1751)* c.1720
oil on canvas 126 x 98.4
1996.0079

Kneller, Godfrey (studio of) 1646–1723
*Lord John Vaughan, Baron of Emlyn (1639–
1713)* c.1710
oil on canvas 93 x 68
1996.0077

Lely, Peter (attributed to) 1618–1680
*Frances Vaughan, Countess of Carbery
(d.1650)* c.1650
oil on canvas 12.3 x 9.9
1996.0084

Lely, Peter (attributed to) 1618–1680
Lady Dorothy Spencer (?) c.1660
oil on canvas 96 x 67 (E)
1996.0078

Lely, Peter (attributed to) 1618–1680
John Vaughan c.1670
oil on canvas 124 x 97.5
1996.0083

Lewis, Benjamin Archibald 1857–1946
View of Carmarthen Quay 1893
oil on canvas 46.2 x 82.2
1976.1503

Lewis, Benjamin Archibald 1857–1946
Landscape 1910–1935
oil on panel 18.8 x 23.7
1980.0315

Lewis, Benjamin Archibald 1857–1946
View of a Coastline 1910–1935
oil on board 14.3 x 23.6
1980.0316

Lewis, Benjamin Archibald 1857–1946
Tenby Harbour c.1930–1935
oil on board 14.4 x 23.9
2007.1227

Lewis, Benjamin Archibald 1857–1946
View of Ferryside c.1930–1935
oil on board 22.6 x 33.8
2007.1155

Lewis, Benjamin Archibald 1857–1946
Island Wharf, Carmarthen 1935
oil on board 18 x 30.2
2007.1106

Lewis, Charles William Mansel 1845–1931
In the Golden Weather 1905
oil on canvas 100 x 149
1997.0573

Lewis, Charles William Mansel 1845–1931
Woodland Scene, Stradey Pond c.1905
oil on canvas 109 x 78
2003.2994

Lewis, Edward Morland 1903–1943
Scotch Quay, Waterford 1930
oil on card 29 x 37
1976.1448

Lewis, Edward Morland 1903–1943
Laugharne c.1930
oil on panel 190 x 270
2002.0545

Lewis, Edward Morland 1903–1943
Brass Band in a Bandstand c.1930–1933
oil on panel 19.5 x 27.2
1981.0271

Lewis, Edward Morland 1903–1943
Beach, Llanstephan c.1930–1935
oil on panel 20.7 x 27.1
1981.0279

Lewis, Edward Morland 1903–1943
Breakwater at Ferryside c.1930–1935
oil on board 20 x 27.2
1981.009

Lewis, Edward Morland 1903–1943
Dockside, Ireland c.1930–1935
oil on panel 20 x 25 (E)
2000.0535

Lewis, Edward Morland 1903–1943
Garden c.1930–1935
oil on board 20.5 x 31.4
1981.0287

Lewis, Edward Morland 1903–1943
Harbour at Low Tide c.1930–1935
oil on canvas 40.5 x 50.1
1981.0277

Lewis, Edward Morland 1903–1943
Harbour Scene c.1930–1935
oil on paper 25.6 x 41.6
1981.0265

Lewis, Edward Morland 1903–1943
Harbour Scene (recto) c.1930–1935
oil on board 29.8 x 35.6
1981.0283

Lewis, Edward Morland 1903–1943
Seascape with a Ship and a Jetty (verso)
c.1930–1935
oil on board 29.8 x 35.6
1981.0283

Lewis, Edward Morland 1903–1943
Harbour Scene c.1930–1935
oil on board 22.2 x 27.1
1981.0285

Lewis, Edward Morland 1903–1943
Harbour Scene c.1930–1935
oil on board 19.2 x 27.1
1981.0286

Lewis, Edward Morland 1903–1943
Harbour Scene c.1930–1935
oil on board 22.3 x 27
1981.031

Lewis, Edward Morland 1903–1943
Harbour Scene c.1930–1935
oil on board 40.2 x 55.5
1981.03.09

Lewis, Edward Morland 1903–1943
Landscape c.1930–1935
oil & pencil on paper 34 x 48.5
1981.0274

Lewis, Edward Morland 1903–1943
Landscape c.1930–1935
oil on panel 13.4 x 23.8
1981.029

Lewis, Edward Morland 1903–1943
Landscape c.1930–1935
oil, pen & ink on board 22.3 x 27.7
1981.0301

Lewis, Edward Morland 1903–1943
Landscape c.1930–1935
oil on panel 20.2 x 27
1981.0302

Lewis, Edward Morland 1903–1943
Landscape (recto) c.1930–1935
oil on panel 30.5 x 40.7
1981.0281a

Lewis, Edward Morland 1903–1943
Portrait of a Woman (verso) c.1930–1935
oil on panel 40.7 x 30.5
1981.0281b

Facing page: Gertler, Mark, 1891–1939, *The Artist's Mother*, 1913, Glynn Vivian Art Gallery (p. 177)

Lewis, Edward Morland 1903–1943
Landscape, Ferryside (?) c.1930–1935
oil on board 22.2 x 27.1
1981.0303

Lewis, Edward Morland 1903–1943
Landscape, Ferryside (?) c.1930–1935
oil on board 19.3 x 27
1981.0305

Lewis, Edward Morland 1903–1943
Lifeboat Station at Ferryside (?) c.1930–1935
oil on board 18.1 x 27.1
1981.0288

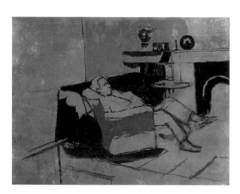

Lewis, Edward Morland 1903–1943
Man in an Armchair c.1930–1935
oil on board 48.5 x 63.2
1981.0278

Lewis, Edward Morland 1903–1943
Old Man Seated at a Table c.1930–1935
oil on panel 27.2 x 22.2
1981.0284

Lewis, Edward Morland 1903–1943
People Seated c.1930–1935
oil on board 63 x 46
1981.028

Lewis, Edward Morland 1903–1943
River Quayside c.1930–1935
oil on canvas 56 x 77
2002.0542

Lewis, Edward Morland 1903–1943
River Scene c.1930–1935
oil on board 22.2 x 27.1
1981.0298

Lewis, Edward Morland 1903–1943
Scotch Quay, Waterford c.1930–1935
oil on panel 23 x 27
2000.0534

Lewis, Edward Morland 1903–1943
Seated Figures c.1930–1935
oil on board 33.1 x 40.8
1981.0276

Lewis, Edward Morland 1903–1943
Still Life c.1930–1935
oil on board 56 x 38
1981.0275

Lewis, Edward Morland 1903–1943
Street Scene c.1930–1935
oil on panel 14.5 x 24.1
1981.0289

Lewis, Edward Morland 1903–1943
Street Scene c.1930–1935
oil on board 14.4 x 23.9
1981.0306

Lewis, Edward Morland 1903–1943
Street Scene, Carmarthen c.1930–1935
oil on board 19.2 x 25.3
1981.0297

Lewis, Edward Morland 1903–1943
The Beach and Estuary with Boats
c.1930–1935
oil on board 22.4 x 27.1
1981.0304

Lewis, Edward Morland 1903–1943
Three Figures in a Room c.1930–1935
oil on board 26 x 25 (E)
1981.0282

Lewis, Edward Morland 1903–1943
Townscape, Carmarthen Quay (?)
c.1930–1935
oil on board 19.1 x 27.3
1981.0308

Lewis, Edward Morland 1903–1943
Two Members of a Brass Band in a Bandstand
c.1930–1935
oil on panel 19.3 x 27.2
1981.0272

Lewis, Edward Morland 1903–1943
Two Members of a Brass Band in a Bandstand
c.1930–1935
oil on board 19 x 27.1
1981.0273

Lewis, Edward Morland 1903–1943
Village Scene with Gate, Ferryside (?)
c.1930–1935
oil on canvas 40.3 x 61
1981.0269

Lewis, Edward Morland 1903–1943
Village Scene, Houses and Grassy Bank
c.1930–1935
oil on board 14.4 x 23.8
1981.0307

Lewis, Edward Morland 1903–1943
Welsh Kitchen c.1930–1935
oil on board 21 x 27
1981.0091

Lewis, Edward Morland 1903–1943
The Bandstand c.1932
oil on panel 190 x 270
2002.0544

Lewis, Edward Morland 1903–1943
Three Profiles c.1932
oil on canvas 24 x 34 (E)
2002.0543

Lewis, Edward Morland 1903–1943
The Spanish Tutor c.1933–1936
oil on canvas 51 x 42
2002.054

Lewis, Edward Morland 1903–1943
General Sir William Nott (1782–1845) c.1935
oil on canvas 45.5 x 30.5
1995.0188

Lewis, Edward Morland 1903–1943
Quayside with Reflections c.1935
oil on canvas 47 x 62
2002.0541

Lewis, Edward Morland 1903–1943
Solva c.1935
oil on board 19 x 27
2003.2995

Lewis, Edward Morland 1903–1943
Backs of Houses, Wales c.1935–1938
oil on board 22.2 x 27.1
1981.03

Lewis, Edward Morland 1903–1943
Carmarthen Market and Clock Tower
c.1935–1938
oil on board 26.8 x 18.8
1981.0296

Lewis, Edward Morland 1903–1943
Snow at Undercliff c.1935–1938
oil on panel 27 x 19
1981.0294

Lewis, Edward Morland 1903–1943
St Ishmael's Sand Dunes c.1935–1938
oil on board 22.3 x 27.1
1981.0295

Lewis, Edward Morland 1903–1943
Townscape, South of France (?) c.1935–1938
oil on panel 18.7 x 27.1
1981.0291

Lewis, Edward Morland 1903–1943
Townscape, South of France (?) c.1935–1938
oil on panel 19.1 x 27.2
1981.0292

Lewis, Edward Morland 1903–1943
Townscape, South of France (?) c.1935–1938
oil on panel 18.8 x 27.1
1981.0293

Lewis, Edward Morland 1903–1943
Welsh Houses c.1935–1938
oil on board 22.2 x 26.3
1981.0299

Lewis, Edward Morland 1903–1943
Welsh Landscape c.1936
oil on board 24.8 x 33.7
1989.0236

Lewis, Edward Morland 1903–1943
Carmarthen Quay c.1940
oil on canvas 49.7 x 75.2
1983.0423

Lewis, Edward Morland 1903–1943
A Farm in the Tywi Valley 1942
oil on panel 29.5 x 33.6
1992.025

Lewis, John active 1736–1776
Elizabeth Eleanor Lloyd, Lady Stepney 1744
oil on canvas 124.5 x 97
1998.0013

Lewis, John active 1736–1776
Bridget Vaughan, Madam Bevan (1698–1779)
c.1744
oil on canvas 124.5 x 99
1998.0011

Lewis, John active 1736–1776
Landscape c.1768
oil on panel 30.5 x 125
1997.173

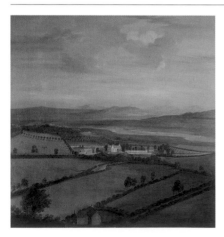

Lewis, John active 1736–1776
Buwchllaethwen late 1760s
oil on panel 143 x 139
1997.0566

Lewis, John (attributed to)
active 1736–1776
Mrs Lloyd of Laques, near Llanstephan
1740–1750
oil on canvas 124 x 95 (E)
1976.1433

Lewis, John (attributed to)
active 1736–1776
Arthur Bevan (1689–1743) (after John
Vanderbank) c.1744
oil on canvas 124.5 x 99
1998.0012

Lewis, Stanley Cornwall 1905–2009
Carmarthen Hill Farm, Cwmllyfri Farm 1955
oil on canvas 50.5 x 60
1981.0066

Lewis, Stanley Cornwall 1905–2009
Dylan Thomas' Cottage c.1960
oil on board 116.3 x 129.5
1980.0188

Lewis, Stanley Cornwall 1905–2009
Winter, Wauniago c.1960
oil on canvas 32 x 39
1995.0347

Lewis, Stanley Cornwall 1905–2009
Old Cockle Factory, Laugharne 1963
oil on board 46 x 51
1981.0088

Lewis, Stanley Cornwall 1905–2009
The Old Chapel
oil on canvas 51 x 61
1983.0002

Lewis, V. P.
Springtime at Carreg Cennen 1958
oil on board 44.5 x 59.5
1988.0093

Lloyd, A.
Portrait of an Unknown Gentleman 1895
oil on canvas 50 x 43
1976.1501

Lodwick, Edith Mary 1905–1993
Pontynys Wen, near Brechfa c.1950
oil on board 51 x 41
1981.0084

Lynn, Jenny active 1970s
Town Hall, Llanelli 1972
acrylic on board 60.4 x 75.5
1997.1726

Lynn, Jenny active 1970s
Station Road
oil on board 60 x 78.5
1997.1528

MacCallum, Andrew 1821–1902
Evening Glow 1863
oil on canvas 110 x 165
1997.0586

Malcolm, Victoria b.1957
Teifi III c.1996
acrylic on paper 29 x 41
1998.0025

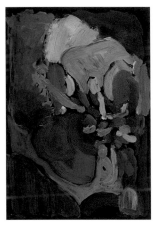

Malcolm, Victoria b.1957
Tulips on Black Card c.1996
acrylic on card 29.1 x 19.8
1998.0024

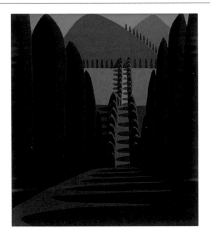

Markey, Peter b.1930
Cypress Trees 1990
oil on board 72 x 61 (E)
1991.0161

McCann, Susan
Old Quay and River Towy 1977
acrylic on paper 29.5 x 41
2002.0717

Meyler, Stephen b.1956
The Riots of 1911, a Reconstruction of the Event 1970s/1980s
oil on board 28 x 36
1997.1539

Meyler, Stephen b.1956
Dining Out c.1980
oil on canvas 44.5 x 92
1980.0676

Meyler, Stephen b.1956
Industrial Landscape c.1980
oil on canvas 43.2 x 57.6
1980.0677

Facing page: Petts, John, 1914–1991, *Red Structure*, 1958, Carmarthenshire Museums Service Collection (p. 40)

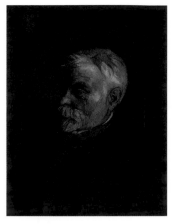

Midgley, J. C. active 1925–1930
Carmarthen Quay 1926
oil on canvas on board 21 x 30
1982.0851

Miers, Christopher b.1941
Lieutenant Colonel W. Kemmis Buckley 1950s
oil on board 68 x 57.5
1988.0119

Milner, Joseph 1880–1940
George Eyre Evans (1857–1939) 1911
oil on canvas 65 x 51
1976.1511

More, Guinevere
Carmarthen Bay Power Station 1955
oil on canvas 39.5 x 50
1983.0012

Morgan, Maldwyn active 1970s
Two Red Lorries
acrylic on board 50.3 x 75
2002.077

Morgan (Miss)
Bull Lane, Carmarthen c.1920
oil on canvas 53 x 42
1976.1531

Morris, Carey Boynes 1882–1968
Sir Lewis Morris (1833–1907) 1904
oil on canvas 145 x 99
1976.1432

Morris, Carey Boynes 1882–1968
Sir Lewis Morris (1833–1907) 1906
oil on canvas 61 x 51
1975.07

Morris, Carey Boynes 1882–1968
Colonel Delmé William Campbell Davies-Evans (1873–1953) c.1930
oil on canvas 93 x 71.5
1999.0309

Morris, Carey Boynes 1882–1968
Three Cliffs Bay Gower, Morning 1930s (?)
oil on board 32 x 36
2002.0643

Morse-Brown, Sam 1903–2001
Fog, Frost and Sunlight 1937
oil on board 32.8 x 40.9
1986.0124

Morse-Brown, Sam 1903–2001
*Sir Rhys Hopkins Morris (1888–1956), MBE,
QC, MP, LID, MP for Cardiganshire* 1950
oil on canvas 122 x 100
2005.0154

Moss, Sally b.1949
Relief: Green Shirt 1978
acrylic on canvas on board 52.7 x 25
1979.0553

Narbett, W. N. active c.1963–c.1967
Derwen Fawr Farm c.1963
oil on canvas 69 x 58
1988.009

Narbett, W. N. active c.1963–c.1967
Woodlands in May c.1967
oil on canvas 86.5 x 111.5
1988.0101

Nash, Thomas John b.1931
Llandybie Quarry 1955
oil on canvas 86.6 x 111.8
1983.0005

Nash, Thomas John b.1931
Coastal Wave 1960
oil on board 76 x 63
2002.073

Nash, Thomas John b.1931
Primordial Image 1976
oil on board 48 x 34.5
2002.0754

Oliver, William 1823–1901
Haymaking Scene late 19th C
oil on canvas 96 x 66
2003.1286

Patrick, David 1822–1899
John Williams 1850
oil on panel 28.5 x 22.5
1976.1445

Patrick, David 1822–1899
Mrs Mary and Miss Sarah Williams 1850
oil on panel 28.5 x 22.5
1976.1446

Petts, David b.1947
No Good Boyo 1982
acrylic, ink & paper on panel 40.6 x 45.7
1983.0401

Petts, David b.1947
A Window on the Hill 1983
acrylic, ink & paper on panel 26.7 x 22.9
1983.04

Petts, David b.1947
Ark No.6 1983
acrylic, ink & oil on panel 22.9 x 35.6
1983.0399

Petts, John 1914–1991
Red Structure 1958
oil on board 58 x 41
2004.0288

Petts, Kusha 1921–2003
Lieutenant Colonel W. Kemmis Buckley 1996
oil on canvas 56 x 45
2008.0231

Phillips, Ethne active after 1990
Raby's Furnace 2007
oil on canvas 51 x 61
2003.2972

Phillips, P.
Stac Fawr 1897
oil on canvas 67 x 50
2003.2993

Pratt, Derrick Edward Henry 1895–1979
Anne 1958
oil on canvas 129.5 x 101.6
1981.0048

Pratt, Derrick Edward Henry 1895–1979
Llwyn Farm, Llanelli c.1960
oil on canvas 30.5 x 40.6
1988.0078

Pratt, Derrick Edward Henry 1895–1979
Hydrangeas 1966
oil on canvas 54 x 65
2003.1262

Pratt, Derrick Edward Henry 1895–1979
Island Place 1969
oil on board 42 x 60
1997.1589

Pratt, Derrick Edward Henry 1895–1979
Llanelli Railway Station 1971
oil on panel 42 x 60
1997.093

Pryor, S. J. active 20th C
Llanelli Hospital 1960s (?)
oil on board 33 x 40
2003.1291

Prytherch, Thomas 1864–1926
Portrait of an Unknown Lady with a Lace Cap
1892
oil on canvas 65 x 55
1976.151

Prytherch, Thomas 1864–1926
Portrait of an Unknown Man with Full Beard
1893
oil on canvas 61.5 x 51
1976.1443

Ramsay, Frances Louisa Margaret
1858–1928
Charlotte Cookman née Johnes (1825–1911)
1900–1906
oil on canvas 69 x 52
2004.1269

Ramsay, Frances Louisa Margaret
1858–1928
Lady Elizabeth Hills Johnes of Dolaucothi (1834–1927) c.1906
oil on canvas 69 x 52
1981.0413

Ramsay, Isabelle
St Paul's Church 1985
oil on board 71 x 55.4
1997.1468

Ratcliffe, William Whitehead 1870–1955
Hertford Landscape c.1910–1920 (?)
oil on panel 31 x 61
2003.1268

Rayner, A. E.
Carreg Cennen Castle 1935
oil on board 32 x 42
1976.1504

Rees, Becky 1921–2010
Roses 1982
oil on board 48 x 31
1997.1471

Rees, John Bromfield Gay 1912–1965
Still Life with a Chianti Bottle 1953
oil on canvas 92 x 53
2002.0738

Reynolds, J.
A Scene in Kidwelly 1899
oil on board 30 x 38
1976.152

Richards, Frances 1903–1985
Nun 1968 (?)
tempera on wood 20 x 10
1986.0121

Roberts, Diana b.1941
The Scrap Metal Man 1971
oil on canvas 91.5 x 76
2002.0731

Roberts, Diana b.1941
Maliphant 1975
oil on board 80 x 93
2002.0736

Roberts, Dylan T. active 1960s
Industrial Lights c.1960
oil on board 38 x 49
1986.012

Roberts, Dylan T. active 1960s
High Tide, Amlwch c.1961
oil on board 24 x 31
1983_0800

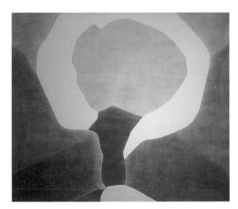

Roberts, Gwyn b.1953
Croth 1975
acrylic on canvas 138 x 162
2002.0735

Roberts, Jeremy active 1970s
Blodeuwedd 1974
acrylic on board 30.3 x 30.5
2002.0781

Roberts, Will 1907–2000
The Doubler 1970s
oil on board 90 x 120
1997.1529

Roe, John (attributed to)
active 1771–1811
Portrait of an Unknown Lady with a Velvet Choker c.1780
oil on canvas 76 x 62
1988.0122

Roos, William (attributed to)
1808–1878
Reverend David Lloyd (1805–1863), MA
1855–1863
oil on canvas 77 x 66
1976.1507

Rowan, Eric b.1931
Parable 1971
acrylic on canvas 47 x 47
2002.0742

Rowlands, Glenys active 1960–1967
The Melting Shop 1960
oil on canvas 50.5 x 77
1988.0099

Rowlands, Glenys active 1960–1967
Bonllwyn Bridge, Ammanford 1963
oil on board 61 x 100.1
1986.0127

Rowlands, Glenys active 1960–1967
Kidwelly Castle 1964
oil on canvas 50.8 x 61
1988.008

Rowlands, Glenys active 1960–1967
Talley Abbey and Lake 1967
oil on board 55 x 75
1988.0089

Saunders, B. A. active 20th C
'The Farriers'
acrylic on board 46 x 68
1997.1588

Scrutton, B. E. M. active 20th C
Still Life
oil on canvas 35 x 50
1997.1601

Scrutton, Ella
December Morning with Snow 1981
oil on board 30 x 39
1997.1547

Secco, L.
Townscape, Evening in Llanelli from Bigyn Hill
1970
oil on panel 75 x 148
2003. 1284

Selway, John b.1938
The Factory Inspector 1966
oil on canvas 83 x 83
2002.076

Shee, Martin Archer 1769–1850
*Lieutenant General Sir Thomas Picton
(1758–1815)* c.1815–1820
oil on canvas 245 x 150
1992.0033

Sirrell, Wilfred John 1901–1979
Capel Bethlehem, Coed Poeth
oil on canvas 35 x 45
1997.1517

Sirrell, Wilfred John 1901–1979
Llanerch Cottage, Llandindrod Wells
oil on canvas 46.2 x 56
1997.1033

Smith, Dudley active 1958–1983
Cothi near Abercothi House 1958
oil on board 51 x 60
1981.0063

Smith, Dudley active 1958–1983
Polperro Harbour 1978
oil on board 48.2 x 63.2
1997.1572

Smith, Dudley active 1958–1983
Mynydd Mawr Bridge, North Dock, Llanelli
1983
oil or acrylic on board 35 x 61
2003.1784

Smyth, Henry active c.1800–1873
A View of Kidwelly 1852
oil on canvas 31 x 42
1992.026

Spencer, Richard Barnett d.c.1890
The 'Carmarthenshire'
oil on canvas 56 x 92
1997.19

Steele-Morgan, Tony 1930–2009
Lord Elwyn Jones (1909–1989) 1990
oil on panel 82 x 77
2003.2997

Stephens, Brian active 1958–1970
Low Tide, New Dock (Llanelli) 1958
oil on board 49 x 64
1983.0006

Stephens, Brian active 1958–1970
Towards the Copperworks 1970
oil on board 50 x 40
2003.1271

Stuart, Gordon b.1924
The Beach 1980–1981
oil on board 37 x 55.6
1981.0445

Stuart, Gordon b.1924
The Flag, Gower c.1980
oil on canvas 47 x 54
2001.0951

Stuart, Gordon b.1924
Towy Farm c.1980
oil on board 127 x 159.4
1980.0146

Thatcher, C. F. active 1816–1846
Llangennech Park House 1832
oil on canvas 54 x 69
1991.0118

Thatcher, C. F. active 1816–1846
Llangennech Park House 1832
oil on canvas 54 x 69
1991.0119

Thomas, Bryn active 1980s
Jackson's Lane, Carmarthen 1987
oil on hardboard 61 x 45.8
1996.0095

Facing page: Frith, William Powell, 1819–1909, *Tenby Fisherwoman*, 1880, Pembrokeshire County Council's
Museums Service (p. 88)

Thomas, Bryn active 1980s
Capitol Bingo Hall, Carmarthen 1988
oil on wood 60.8 x 122.3
1996.0093

Thomas, Bryn active 1980s
Carmarthen from the Railway Station 1988
oil on canvas 35.4 x 60.8
1996.0096

Thomas, Bryn active 1980s
The Old Art School, Carmarthen 1988
oil on hardboard 63.5 x 87.4
1996.0094

Thomas, E. active 1970s
View of Tycroes 1976
oil on board 44 x 54
1997.1566

Thomas, Gareth b.1955
Abergwili Church in Mist 1980
oil on canvas 66 x 91.4
1981.0244

Thomas, Jefferson active c.1930–1983
Llandeilo Church 1959
oil on board 132.1 x 157.5
1978.0379

Thomas, Sid active 20th C
Llanelli Old Church
oil on board 51 x 61
1997.1535

unknown artist
John Vaughan (?) 1660s
oil on canvas 91.7 x 71.3
1996.0081

unknown artist
Francis, Lord Vaughan (1638–1667), MP
c.1665
oil on canvas 90 x 76.5
1996.0076

unknown artist
Richard Vaughan (1600–1686), 2nd Earl of Carbery (possibly after Adriaen Hanneman) c.1670
oil on canvas 126 x 101
1981.044

unknown artist
Sir John Altham Vaughan (1640–1713), 3rd Earl of Carbery c.1670
oil on canvas 126.5 x 103.5
1981.0431

unknown artist
Lady Frances Vaughan 1690–1700
oil on canvas 74 x 61.5
1996.0074

unknown artist
Portrait of an Unknown Gentleman c.1700
oil on canvas 76 x 63.8
1981.0437

unknown artist
Reverend George Bull (1634–1710), DD
1705–1710
oil on canvas 76.7 x 63.5
1981.0412

unknown artist
Richard Vaughan, Auditor of Wales c.1715
oil on canvas 73.6 x 61.8
1996.0075

unknown artist
Portrait of an Unknown Lady in Green c.1720
oil on canvas 127.2 x 103
1981.0432

unknown artist
Richard Vaughan, Esq. (1726–c.1780) c.1730
oil on canvas 127 x 102
1981.0433

unknown artist
Captain Ro(w)e 1760–1780
oil on canvas 89 x 76
2000.0561

unknown artist
Golden Grove c.1760
oil on canvas 50.3 x 63.1
1986.0002 (P)

unknown artist
Portrait of an Unknown Woman c.1780
oil on canvas 76.5 x 64.2
1988.0123

unknown artist
The Surrender of the French at Fishguard
1797
oil on panel 62.5 x 89.5
1975.1695

unknown artist
Vale of Towy 1800–1850
oil on card 15.5 x 23.5
1976.1526

unknown artist
Judge John Wilson (1785–1851) c.1800–1810
oil on canvas 76.5 x 63.5
1979.055

unknown artist
Portrait of an Unknown Gentleman c.1800–
1820
oil on panel 20.6 x 16.3
1976.1523

unknown artist
Ann Wilson, née Shutt (1796–1874) c.1810
oil on canvas 76.5 x 63.5
1979.0551

unknown artist
General Andrew Cowell (d.1821) c.1814
oil on canvas 83 x 67
1997.0578

unknown artist
Elizabeth Buckley, née Wedge c.1835
oil on canvas 63 x 52.6
1988.0124

unknown artist
Captain David Davies (1789–1873) c.1840
oil on canvas 76.5 x 63.7
1977.1272

unknown artist
James Buckley (1802–1883), JP, DL c.1840
oil on canvas 63 x 52
1988.0125

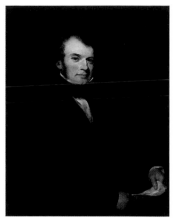

unknown artist
James Buckley (1802–1883), JP, DL c.1840
oil on canvas 63 x 52
1988.0126

unknown artist
Portrait of the Wife of Captain David Davies
c.1840
oil on canvas 77 x 67
1977.1273

unknown artist
*Portrait of an Unknown Gentleman with a
Checked Waistcoat* 1840s (?)
oil on canvas 70.6 x 63.5
1976.1441

unknown artist
*James Francis Hughes Buckley (b.1869), JP,
MA, FSA* c.1900
oil on canvas 122 x 102
1988.0127

unknown artist
Reverend Llewellyn Bevan c.1900
oil on canvas 184 x 120
1997.0584

unknown artist
Still Life – Red and Pink Roses c.1900–1910 (?)
oil on canvas 68 x 88
1976.1437

unknown artist
Portrait of an Unknown Girl c.1900–1920
oil on canvas 102 x 52
1996.0011

unknown artist
Portrait of an Unknown First World War Officer c.1916–1918
oil on canvas 49.5 x 35.5
1976.1505

unknown artist
William Joseph Buckley c.1920 (?)
oil on canvas 76 x 51
1997.1533

unknown artist
View of Llanelli Town Hall and Town Centre 1970s
oil or acrylic on panel 70 x 119
2006.0714

unknown artist
A View of Swiss Valley
oil on board 60 x 86
1997.0588

unknown artist
Haloed Figure
oil on cloth 96 x 36
1975.4208

unknown artist
Lady Anne, Countess of Carbery (1663–1669)
oil on canvas 12.5 x 10.2
1981.0438

unknown artist
Pembroke Castle
oil on canvas 20.3 x 30.8
1997.1611

unknown artist
Portrait of an Unknown Gentleman
oil on board 36 x 29
1976.1528

unknown artist
Portrait of an Unknown Gentleman (said to be called John Lewis)
oil on canvas 111 x 88
2007.1421

unknown artist
Portrait of an Unknown Gentleman with Glasses
oil on panel 38 x 29.5
1976.1527

unknown artist
Portrait of an Unknown Gentleman with Purple Flowers
oil on canvas 53 x 38
1976.1449

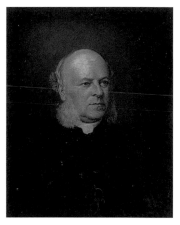

unknown artist
Portrait of an Unknown Man with Whiskers
oil on canvas 61 x 51
1976.1439

unknown artist
Portrait of Luke
oil on board 43.5 x 30.5
1976.1529

unknown artist
Reverend David Griffiths
oil on canvas 87 x 75
2000.0586

unknown artist
Richard, Lord Vaughan (1600–1686), 2nd Earl of Carbery
oil on canvas 75 x 62.7
1981.0439

unknown artist
Seascape
oil on canvas 41 x 32
1976.1444

unknown artist
Still Life
oil on board 30 x 25
1976.1518

unknown artist
Trinity College, Carmarthen
oil on paper 24.5 x 30.2
1976.1999

unknown artist
View of Laugharne Castle
oil on board   25 x 33.3
1976.1517

Walker, Christopher
Mount Gabriel 1990
acrylic on panel   26 x 30.5
1995.034

Walters, Evan 1893–1951
Eve c.1913–1920
oil on board   89 x 89 (E)
1980.0186

Walters, Evan 1893–1951
Still Life with Chrysanthemums c.1913–1920
oil on canvas   76.2 x 63.6
1980.0184

Walters, Evan 1893–1951
Winter Cherries c.1913–1920
oil on canvas   76.2 x 63.5
1980.0185

Walters, Evan 1893–1951
Rural District 1920–1929
oil on canvas   50 x 60.5
2003.1267

Walters, Evan 1893–1951
Daffodils c.1935
oil on canvas   61 x 51
2003.1266

Walters, Evan 1893–1951
Self Portrait c.1935
oil on canvas   34 x 44.5
2003.1264

Walters, Evan 1893–1951
The Artist's Mother Asleep c.1935
oil on canvas   41 x 51
2003.1265

Facing page: Evans, Tony, 1920–2001, *Triptych No.1 No.5 At the Bus Stop*, 1980s–1990s, Carmarthenshire Museums Service Collection (p. 17)

Walters, Evan 1893–1951
Artist's Father 1935–1942
oil on board 77.5 x 103.1
1981.0093

Walters, Evan 1893–1951
The Artist's Mother 1935–1945
oil on board 78.2 x 103.1
1981.0092

Walters, Evan 1893–1951
The Cockle Woman c.1940
oil on canvas 75 x 55
1997.0963

Walters, Evan 1893–1951
Bishop Havard c.1945
oil on canvas 16.2 x 12.5
1995.022

Walters, James Lewis active c.1900–1922
Llanboidy Mole Catcher c.1900
oil on canvas 142.2 x 111.8
1986.0129

Walters, James Lewis active c.1900–1922
The Artist's Mother c.1900
oil on canvas 127.5 x 102.5
2011_0022

Walters, James Lewis active c.1900–1922
John Hinds, Esq. (1862–1928), MP 1918–1922
oil on canvas 75 x 62 (E)
1976.1438

Walters, W. R.
The Cottage 1975
acrylic on panel 47 x 60.5
2002.0725

Westmacott, Phyllis active 1948–1972
Lieutenant Colonel William Howell Buckley, DL
oil on board 54.3 x 49.5
1988.0118

Williams, C. M. active c.1960–1967
Country Scene 1964
oil on board 52.5 x 61
1981.0064

Williams, C. M. active c.1960–1967
Cenarth Falls c.1967
oil on board 50.5 x 60.5
1988.0092

Williams, Christopher 1873–1934
Dryslwyn Castle c.1910
oil on canvas 124.5 x 218
1991.0004

Williams, Christopher 1873–1934
Barmouth Estuary 1910–1914
oil on canvas 82 x 141
1997.0589

Williams, Christopher 1873–1934
In the Alhambra c.1910–1914
oil on canvas 121 x 99
1997.1675

Williams, Christopher 1873–1934
John Hinds, Esq. (1862–1928)
oil on canvas 15.5 x 13.3
1990_162

Williams, D. H. active 1973–1974
Steel Works by Night 1973
oil on canvas 60.5 x 86
2003.1273

Williams, D. H. active 1973–1974
Dockland Scene 1974
oil on canvas 61 x 122
1997.1481

Williams, E. R. M. active 20th C
Court Farm 1908 – A Reconstruction
oil on board 46 x 55
1997.1536

Williams, Jacqueline b.1962
Still Life with Lamplight 1990
oil on board 122 x 58
2000.0772

Williams, Joel R.
Winter c.1964
oil on board 128.3 x 102.9
1981.0046

Williams, Kyffin 1918–2006
Tom Owen 1951
oil on canvas 83 x 74
2002.0733

Williams, Lauretta 1910–1993
A. W. Williams c.1960–1980
oil on board 45 x 30
1997.1679

Williams, Lauretta 1910–1993
Ann c.1960–1980
acrylic on board 74 x 50
1997.1715

Williams, Lauretta 1910–1993
Blodau Mawrth Cyntaf c.1960–1980
oil on board 60 x 45
1997.1701

Williams, Lauretta 1910–1993
Cactus c.1960–1980
oil on board 31 x 31
1997.1681

Williams, Lauretta 1910–1993
Castiau'r Haul I c.1960–1980
oil or acrylic on board 40.9 x 40
1997.1703

Williams, Lauretta 1910–1993
Castiau'r Haul II c.1960–1980
oil or acrylic on board 40.5 x 40.5
1997.1705

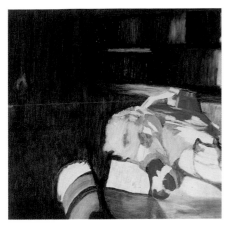

Williams, Lauretta 1910–1993
Castiau'r Haul III c.1960–1980
oil or acrylic on board 40.5 x 40.3
1997.1704

Williams, Lauretta 1910–1993
Cat c.1960–1980
oil on canvas 45 x 31
1997.1711

Williams, Lauretta 1910–1993
Catherine c.1960–1980
oil on board 45 x 31
1997.1682

Williams, Lauretta 1910–1993
Celyn y mor o Towyn Bach c.1960–1980
acrylic on board 35 x 28
1997.169

Williams, Lauretta 1910–1993
Cennin Pedr a Lorwg (recto) c.1960–1980
acrylic on board 38 x 30
1997.1694

Williams, Lauretta 1910–1993
Still Life (verso) c.1960–1980
acrylic on board 30 x 38
1998.1694

Williams, Lauretta 1910–1993
Cwm Lliedi c.1960–1980
acrylic on board 40.6 x 45.7
1997.1712

Williams, Lauretta 1910–1993
Cyfoesal c.1960–1980
acrylic on board 60.5 x 60.5
1997.1695

Williams, Lauretta 1910–1993
Er Cof am Smiw c.1960–1980
acrylic on board 60.5 x 51
1997.1696

Williams, Lauretta 1910–1993
Ffenestr Siop c.1960–1980
acrylic on canvas 69.5 x 60.5
1997.1699

Williams, Lauretta 1910–1993
Florie c.1960–1980
acrylic on board 43 x 36.1
1997.1721

Williams, Lauretta 1910–1993
G and Ruggeri c.1960–1980
oil on board 60 x 45.5
1997.1714

Williams, Lauretta 1910–1993
G. W. Williams c.1960–1980
acrylic on canvas 30.5 x 53.5
1997.1683

Williams, Lauretta 1910–1993
Garthychau c.1960–1980
oil on board 31 x 45
1997.1686

Williams, Lauretta 1910–1993
Glan y Fferi 1880 Hen Lun, Old Photograph
c.1960–1980
acrylic on canvas 51 x 61
1997.1706

Williams, Lauretta 1910–1993
Kidwelly Castle c.1960–1980
oil on board 36.5 x 46.8
1997.1702

Williams, Lauretta 1910–1993
Lafant y mor o Towyn Bach c.1960–1980
acrylic on board 38 x 28
1997.1691

Williams, Lauretta 1910–1993
M. Williams c.1960–1980
oil on board 45 x 31
1997.1688

Williams, Lauretta 1910–1993
Machlud Haul c.1960–1980
acrylic on board 30.4 x 30.4
1997.1693

Williams, Lauretta 1910–1993
Machlud Haul I c.1960–1980
acrylic on board 30.4 x 30.4
1997.1722

Williams, Lauretta 1910–1993
O Bydded I'r Hen iaith Barhau c.1960–1980
acrylic on board 72 x 85
1997.17

Williams, Lauretta 1910–1993
Poinsetta c.1960–1980
acrylic on board 53 x 38
1997.1719

Williams, Lauretta 1910–1993
Rhedeg c.1960–1980
acrylic on board 60 x 45.7
1997.1718

Williams, Lauretta 1910–1993
Roses c.1960–1980
oil on board 30.5 x 38
1997.1677

Williams, Lauretta 1910–1993
Self Portrait c.1960–1980
acrylic on board 46 x 31
1997.1687

Williams, Lauretta 1910–1993
W. H. Williams c.1960–1980
oil on board 45 x 30
1997. 1680

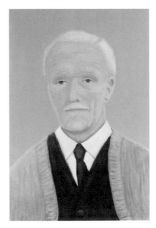

Williams, Lauretta 1910–1993
W. W. Williams c.1960–1980
oil on board 45 x 30
1997.1678

Williams, Lauretta 1910–1993
Y Diddiwedd c.1960–1980
acrylic on board 45 x 45
1997.1723

Williams, Lauretta 1910–1993
Y Llanc Glas c.1960–1980
acrylic on board 76.2 x 50.6
1997.1716

Williams, Lauretta 1910–1993
*Yr Hen Neuadd y Plwyf a'r Llys Ynadon
Newyd yn Llanelli* c.1960–1980
oil on board 50 x 75.5
1997.1697

Williams, Lauretta 1910–1993
Hickling Broad Gaeaf c.1965–1980
oil on board 45 x 51.1
1997.1676

Williams, Lauretta 1910–1993
Still Life with a Coffee Pot and Mug (recto)
c.1965–1980
oil on board 32 x 38
1997.1666

Williams, Lauretta 1910–1993
Autumn Scene (verso) c.1965–1980
oil on board 32 x 38
1998.1666

Williams, Lauretta 1910–1993
Village Scene c.1965–1980
oil on board 26 x 36
1997.1669

Williams, Lauretta 1910–1993
Cyfoesal 1972
acrylic on canvas 70 x 60
1997.1698

Williams, Lauretta 1910–1993
Cyfresol 1973 1973
acrylic & collage on board 51 x 61
1997.1713

Williams, Lauretta 1910–1993
Glan y Fferi 1944 Atgof, Recollects
oil on canvas 51 x 61
1997.1516

Williams, M. R.
Between Tides 1982 (?)
oil on board 40.6 x 50.9
1997.1662

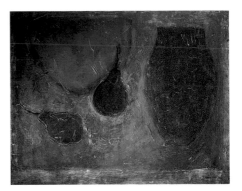

Williams, Vivienne b.1955
Still Life Fresco
acrylic on paper 40 x 51
2001.0952

Williams (Davies) (Mrs), E. R. M.
Sosban Fach 1977
oil on canvas 60.4 x 60.4
2002.0769

Winterhalter, Franz Xaver (possibly)
1805–1875
Lady Stepney c.1850
oil on canvas 54 x 44
1997.0582

Wissing, Willem (attributed to) 1656–1687
Portrait of an Unknown Man (either Sir
Edward Vaughan or George Savile, 1st
Marquis of Halifax) c.1660
oil on canvas 123 x 99
1996.0082

Woodland, S.
Our Freedom – Their Price c.2000
acrylic on panel 175 x 101
2002.0591

Wright, John b.1931
Rama c.1950
oil on board 81.8 x 106.7
1988.0075

Wright, John b.1931
Green Legend 1959
oil on board 50 x 38
2002.0712

Zobole, Ernest 1927–1999
Figure in a Chair 1954
oil on canvas 53 x 38
2002.0756

University of Wales Trinity Saint David

Alpin, H. L.
Christmas Tree
oil on board 36 x 27.6
113

Andrews, Janette
Still Life with Washing Vase and Basin 1989
oil on canvas 43.2 x 60.9
526

Beal, Nick 1885–1971
The Canterbury Building
acrylic on canvas board 50 x 74
TSD_PCF31

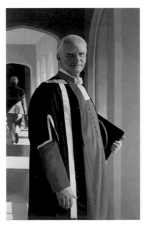

Brason, Paul b.1952
*Brian Robert Morris (1930–2001), Baron
Morris of Castle Morris, Principal of St David's
University College (1980–1991)* 1991
oil on board 120 x 80 (E)
TSD_PCF15

Brason, Paul b.1952
*Keith Gilbert Robbins (b.1940), Principal and
Vice-Chancellor of University of Wales
Lampeter (…)* 2003
oil on canvas 85 x 75 (E)
TSD_PCF18

Facing page: Devas, Anthony, 1911–1958, *Miss Farrant*, 1949, Tenby Museum & Art Gallery, (p. 129)

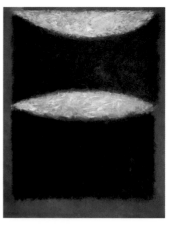

Brason, Paul b.1952
Brian Robert Morris (1930–2001) (triptych)
oil on board 58 x 130
TSD_PCF26

Chapman, George 1908–1993
Industrial Buildings at Blackburn c.1970
oil on canvas 59 x 89
TSD_PCF30

Davies, Adrian
Welsh Cauldron 1986
acrylic on canvas (?) 74 x 56
546

Davies, Adrian
Looking Through 1989
acrylic on canvas (?) 63.5 x 48.3
542

Davies, Adrian
Abstract*
acrylic on paper 56 x 74
544

Davies, Adrian
Abstract*
acrylic on paper 56 x 74
545

Edwards, Peter Douglas b.1955
John Elfed Jones (b.1933), President of University of Wales Lampeter, St David's University College (1992–1998) 1998
oil on board 120 x 80 (E)
TSD_PCF16

Foster, Ruth active 1919–1921
Hugh Walker (1855–1939), Professor of English at St David's College (1890–1939) 1919
oil on canvas 125 x 100
TSD_PCF9

Giaconia, Emmanuel
Thomas Price 'Carnhuanawc' (1748–1848) c.1826
oil on canvas
TSD_PCF7

Graves, J.
Edward Harold Browne (1811–1891),
Vice-Principal of St David's College (1843–
1850) 1851
oil on canvas
TSD_PCF4

Griffiths, David b.1939
Eric Sunderland (1930–2010), President of the
University of Wales Lampeter (1998–2002)
2002
oil on canvas 120 x 80
TSD_PCF17

Griffiths, David b.1939
Alfred Cosier Morris (b.1941), Vice-Chancellor
of the University of Wales Lampeter (2003–
2008) 2009
oil on canvas (?)
TSD_PCF25

Hayter, George 1792–1871
Sir Charles Cockerell (1755–1837), Bt 1819
oil on canvas 134 x 109
TSD_PCF2

Hunter, Hoi May
Still Life (recto) 1959
oil on board 63 x 33
84

Hunter, Hoi May
Portrait Studies (verso) 1959
oil on board 33 x 63
84

Lawrence, Thomas (after) 1769–1830
John Scandrett Harford II (1785–1866), Donor
of the Site for St David's College, Benefactor
and Sub Visitor 1857
oil on canvas
TSD_PCF6

Mason, Arnold 1885–1963
Henry Kingsley Archdall (1866–1976),
Principal of St David's College (1938–1953)
1952
oil on canvas 110 x 90
TSD_PCF10

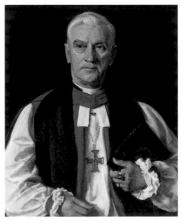

Mason, Arnold 1885–1963
Alfred Edwin Morris (1894–1971), Bishop of
Monmouth (1945–1967), Archbishop of Wales
(1957–1967) 1959
oil on canvas 75 x 65
TSD_PCF21

Mason, Arnold 1885–1963
John Roland Lloyd Thomas (1908–1984),
Principal of St David's College/St David's
University College (1953–1975) 1961
oil on canvas 120 x 80 (E)
TSD_PCF11

Owen, William 1769–1825
Bishop Thomas Burgess (1756–1837), Bishop of
St David's (1803–1825), Bishop of Salisbury
(1825–1837) (…) c.1825
oil on canvas
TSD_PCF1

Pickersgill, Henry William 1782–1875
Llewelyn Llewellin (1827–1878), First Principal
of St David's College
oil on canvas
TSD_PCF3

Rathmell, Thomas Roland 1912–1990
John Richards (1901–1990), Bishop of St
David's University College (1971–1977) 1977
oil on canvas 80 x 70
TSD_PCF12

Robertson, James
Rowland Williams (1817–1870), Vice-Principal
of St David's College (1843–1850) 1863
oil on canvas 96 x 80
TSD_PCF5

Todd, Daphne b.1947
Evan Roderic Bowen (1913–2001), President of
St David's University College (1977–1992)
1992
oil on canvas
TSD_PCF13

unknown artist
*Abstract Composition**
acrylic on board 117 x 117
PCF84

unknown artist
*Abstract Flower Forms on Black**
acrylic on canvas 100 x 77
178

unknown artist
*Abstract Forms on Lemon Yellow**
acrylic on canvas 100 x 78
176

unknown artist
*Abstract Pastel Forms on Black**
acrylic on canvas 100 x 77
177

unknown artist
*Analytical Cubist Style Abstract Landscape**
acrylic on canvas 59 x 100
414

unknown artist
*Assembled Composition**
acrylic on canvas 111.8 x 81.3
530

unknown artist
Canon Evan Thomas Davies (1847–1927) (?)
oil on canvas 60 x 50
TSD_PCF22

unknown artist
*Composition with Figure, Building and Other Scenes**
acrylic on canvas 55.9 x 172.7
533

unknown artist
*Figure Looking through Archway**
acrylic on board with material 117 x 77
281

unknown artist
*Green, Yellow and Blue Geometric Forms**
acrylic on board 36 x 96.5
537

unknown artist
*Mary**
acrylic on board 28.3 x 21
304

unknown artist
*Mary**
acrylic on board 27.9 x 30.5
309

unknown artist
*Mixed Composition with Figures in Various Locations**
acrylic on canvas 86.4 x 147.3
531

unknown artist
*Mixed Composition, Stripes, Figures and Cartoon Character**
acrylic on canvas 116.8 x 228.6
532

unknown artist
*Mother and Son and Other Scenes**
acrylic on canvas 91.4 x 101.6
534

unknown artist
Personal Icon
oil, copper wire & metallic paint on canvas
91 x 70
74

unknown artist
*Still Life, Green Vessels**
acrylic on board 61 x 92
536

unknown artist
*Triptych: Figure with Hat and Other Themes**
acrylic on board 86.3 x 56
528

unknown artist
*Triptych: Figure with Hat and Other Themes**
acrylic on board 56 x 55.5
528

unknown artist
*Triptych: Figure with Hat and Other Themes**
acrylic on board 86 x 55
528

unknown artist
*Woman in Mirror**
oil on canvas 46 x 36
PCF83

Walters, Evan 1893–1951
Maurice Jones (1863–1957), Principal of St David's College (1923–1938) 1934
oil on canvas 120 x 90
TSD_PCF8

Ware, Margaret
Anthony Bedford Steel (1900–1973), Principal of University College Cardiff (…) 1961
oil on canvas 90 x 80
TSD_PCF19

Ware, Margaret
Sir David John James (1887–1967), Benefactor 1961
oil on canvas 90 x 70
TSD_PCF20

Williams, Ivor 1908–1982
Brinley Roderick Rees (1919–2004), Principal of St David's University College (1975–1980) 1982
oil on canvas 60 x 50
TSD_PCF14

Wright, John b.1931
Magic Land 1960
oil on board 76 x 122
11

Zebole, E.
Red Sunset over Sea
oil on canvas 91.3 x 123
21

Llandovery Town Council

Chapman, Ronald A. 1928–1982
Vicar Prichard and the Goat 1981
oil on canvas 49 x 63
PCF2

Hall, Graham 1937–2001
A Scene of the Upper Towy Valley, near Rhandirmwyn c.1997
acrylic on canvas 64 x 90 (E)
PCF4

Harvey-Thomas
Pantycelyn Farmhouse, Home of William Williams and His Descendants 1937
oil on board 30 x 50
PCF1

Williams, Peter
Self Portrait
oil on canvas 43 x 33
PCF3

Neath Antiquarian Society

Hill, C.
The River Neath with the Ship 'Viola'
oil on canvas 59 x 71.5
PCF1

Neath Port Talbot College

Harris, Jade b.1990
Aberafon Beach in a Storm 2008
modelling medium, acrylic & oil on canvas 49 x 69.5
PCF6

Howells, Neale b.1965
Industrial Scene at Night
poster paint & acrylic on paper 53 x 79
PCF13

Facing page: Brangwyn, Frank, 1867–1956, *Caernarvon Castle*, Glynn Vivian Art Gallery (p. 165)

Harris, Jade b.1990
Aberafon Beach in a Storm 2008
modelling medium, acrylic & oil on
canvas 49 x 69.5
PCF6

Howells, Neale b.1965
Industrial Scene at Night
poster paint & acrylic on paper 53 x 79
PCF13

Rees, Paul b.1971
Pontrhydyfen 1989
acrylic (?) on paper 51.5 x 64
PCF15

Rinaldi, Jason G. b.1970
Swansea Docklands 1989
acrylic on paper 50.7 x 76
PCF16

Woodford, Paul
Pebbles 1999
acrylic & mixed media on paper 27.8 x 39.8
PCF1

Neath Port Talbot County Borough Council

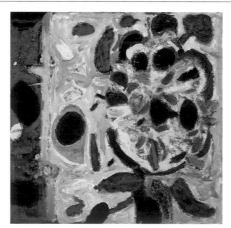

Bevan, Graham 1935–2006
Bouquet
oil on board 122 x 122
NEA_PCF13

Bevan, Graham 1935–2006
Landscape
oil on hardboard 183 x 122.5
NEA_PCF8

Burrow, G.
Drymma Hall 1971
oil on board 58.5 x 79.1
1995.P.2

Carlson, Ron 1936–2002
Daffodil Bulbs
oil on canvas 89 x 120
NEA_PCF9

Chapman, George 1908–1993
Blaengwynfi
oil on canvas 120 x 85
NEA2_PCF23

Cort, Hendrik Frans de 1742–1810
The Gnoll and Castle, Neath
oil on panel 43.3 x 59
NEA2_PCF1

Curry, T. H.
Miner Feeding a Pit Pony 1959
oil on board 167.6 x 134.6
PCF1

Davies, Gwyn active c.1950–c.1960
Cadoxton Church
oil on board 91 x 121
NEA2_PCF2

Davies, Gwyn active c.1950–c.1960
Crynant Street Scene
oil on board 48.7 x 73.7
1995.P.9

Deane, Charles 1794–1874
Vale of Neath
oil on canvas 118 x 174
NEA2_PCF3

Eynon, William Arthur
The Crossroads 1957
oil on board 50.5 x 82.5
NEA_PCF10

Flanagan, John 1895–1964
Harry Parr Davies (1914–1955) 1935
oil on canvas 49.5 x 39
NEA_PCF2

Gleaves, Percy 1882–1944
*Lloyd George Receiving the Freedom of the
Borough of Neath, c.1920*
oil on canvas 152.5 x 304.8
NEA2_PCF9

Hump (possibly)
River Scene
oil on canvas 38 x 50.5
NEA_PCF3

James, Douglas
Companions
oil on board 122 x 67.3
NEA_PCF11

Jones, Harry
*Alderman M. G. Roberts, Mayor of Neath
(1922–1923)*
oil on canvas 110 x 85 (E)
NEA2_PCF26

Jones, V. A.
Neath Abbey 1916
oil on canvas 61 x 91.5
NEA_PCF4

Kennington, Thomas Benjamin 1856–1916
*Alderman Pendrill Charles, Mayor of Neath
(1864–1865)*
oil on canvas 122 x 99 (E)
NEA2_PCF28

Kennington, Thomas Benjamin 1856–1916
*Henry Pendrill Charles III, Mayor of Neath
(1864, 1878, 1899, 1901 & 1916)*
oil on canvas 122 x 99
NEA2_PCF12

Kennington, Thomas Benjamin 1856–1916
Howel Cuthbertson, Mayor of Neath (1867)
oil on canvas 122 x 99
NEA2_PCF11

Kennington, Thomas Benjamin 1856–1916
J. H. Rowland, Mayor of Neath (1865, 1871, 1879, 1880 & 1886)
oil on canvas 122 x 99
NEA2_PCF10

Parminter, Agnes Vye c.1836–1915
Howel Gwyn, Mayor of Neath (1842 & 1844)
oil on canvas 122 x 91.5
NEA2_PCF14

Phillips, C.
Neath Abbey 1912
oil on canvas 60 x 90
1994.P.1

Pyne, James Baker 1800–1870
Vale of Neath
oil on canvas 129 x 180
NEA2_PCF4

Riley, J.
Harry Parr and Guests 1998
acrylic on board 50 x 75.4
NEA_PCF7

Roberts, Will 1907–2000
Cae Rhys Ddu Cimla 1952
oil on board 72.5 x 98
NEA2_PCF5

Roberts, Will 1907–2000
The Gallery
oil on board 59.3 x 74.5
NEA_PCF12

Smith, James Burrell 1822–1897
The Falls of Dulais, c.1870
oil on canvas 89.5 x 68.5
NEA2_PCF6

Stuart, Gordon b.1924
Port Talbot Steelworks
oil on canvas 73.3 x 98.3
NEA2_PCF25

Tennant, Dorothy 1855–1926
Tom Harri(e)s as a Boy 1883
oil on canvas 36 x 26.5
NEA_PCF1

Thomas, Dilys
Victoria Gardens, Neath, 1901 1991
acrylic on board 63.6 x 89.3
NEA_PCF5

unknown artist
*Alderman David Davies, Mayor of Neath
(1931–1932)*
oil on canvas 110 x 85 (E)
NEA2_PCF27

unknown artist
Portrait of an Unknown Mayor of Neath
oil on canvas 122 x 99 (E)
NEA2_PCF29

unknown artist
Richard Burton
oil on woven rag or wool 163 x 113.5
NEA2_PCF7

Williams, Margaret Lindsay 1888–1960
*Hopkin Morgan, Mayor of Neath (1894, 1911,
1917 & 1921)*
oil on canvas 122 x 99
NEA2_PCF15

South Wales Miners' Museum

Duncan, C. active 1970–1978
Miner Drilling at the Coalface 1970
acrylic or emulsion on board 102 x 83.5
PCF1

Duncan, C. active 1970–1978
Miner Drilling at the Coalface 1978
acrylic or emulsion on board 113 x 113
PCF2

Haverford Town Museum

Lindley, David b.1930
Town Houses 1955
oil on canvas 54.1 x 72
TOW.FA.OP.001

Lindley, David b.1930
View of Haverfordwest 1955
oil on canvas 49 x 64
TOW.FA.OP.002

Lindley, David b.1930
Haverfordwest Square 1956
oil on canvas 54.2 x 70.2
TOW.FA.OP.004

Lindley, David b.1930
St Martin's Church, Haverfordwest 1956
oil on canvas 54.1 x 72.1
TOW.FA.OP.003

Pitt, William c.1818–c.1900
Haverfordwest Castle 1872
oil on canvas 30 x 21.5
PCF100

unknown artist
William Walters 1866
oil on canvas 127 x 103
TOW.FA.OP. 001A

unknown artist
Sir John Perrot (1528–1592) 1998
oil on canvas 56 x 46
TOW.FA.OP.999

Pembrokeshire County Council's Museums Service

Pembrokeshire is noted amongst artists as having excellent light qualities. The county boasts a very large artistic community, although it has not yet developed a 'School', as other regions have in the past. Since the nineteenth century artists have moved to Pembrokeshire to find inspiration. And the county has not lacked for home-grown talent, including Gwen and Augustus John and Ray Howard-Jones.

The Pembrokeshire County Collection has always striven to collect fine art by local artists of note as well as works by amateurs. The contemporary collection has been built up through collaboration with the Contemporary Arts Society for Wales and the Welsh Arts Council.

The main base for the County Collection is the County Museum – Scolton Manor. Paintings are displayed in the County Hall and the Registry Office in Haverfordwest. Other paintings are loaned to the Haverfordwest Town Museum. The collection contains an eclectic selection of portraiture, from local dignitaries and heroes to highly personal family portraits of the Higgon family who lived at Scolton Manor from the 1850s to the 1970s.

Pembrokeshire not only has excellent light but also has stunning views, which for many years have been painted by artists from the county and outside. The county collection reflects the beauty of the countryside. The contemporary collection is mostly made up of artwork by local people artistically inspired by living in Pembrokeshire, with some additions from outside artists also inspired by the county to create art.

The Collection boasts over 30 works by the little-known artist Edgar Herbert Thomas. Narberth-born Thomas, who deserves greater recognition, was active in south west Wales during the early decades of the twentieth century. Most of the Thomas collection was purchased for the princely sum of £12 15s from Tenby estate agent Frank B. Mason in 1955. Most of Thomas's works show clever use of light and dark, and are as delicate as any watercolour.

Local landscapes feature heavily in the David Lindley collection. Lindley was a local schoolmaster who specialised in painting views of Haverfordwest town centre during the 1950s and 1960s. Also included are two charming views of Pembrokeshire beaches, Solva and Marloes Sands.

In collaboration with the Welsh Arts Council, the Collection obtained an extensive collection of naïve paintings by self-taught Pembroke artist Olive Rogers.

The Collection also holds a series of works of local industrial views by noted railway and industry artist Stella Whatley. We also have a good selection of charming surrealist works by the late Tony Steele-Morgan.

The County Museum runs a number of galleries based in libraries across Pembrokeshire, which display exhibitions of works from local artists, art groups and from the Collection.

The *Tenby Fisherwoman* by William Powell Frith is the jewel of the Collection and is on display at Scolton Manor. It actually portrays a Llangwm oyster seller who has tramped more than 12 miles to sell oysters fished in the River Cleddau to Tenby ladies. As the painting is of considerable local importance it is occasionally displayed at other institutions.

Artworks from other institutions also adorn the walls of Scolton Manor, including a painting showing the 1797 Invasion of Fishguard, which is on display in the Master Bedroom. This painting is part of the Carmarthen Museum collection.

The County Museum is planning to exhibit works from the collection in other local public spaces such as the local hospitals. The Museum is keen to increase the use and exhibition of the County Art collection as a whole. After all, the Collection belongs to the people of Pembrokeshire and should occasionally be seen by its owners.

Catriona Hilditch, Collections Manager

Adcock, Doris
Church, Castle and Bay, Manorbier c.1961
oil on hardboard 28 x 46.7
SCO.FA.Op.017

Allen, H. C. G.
J. H. V. Higgon, Esq. 1945
oil on canvas 64.5 x 49.5
SCO.FA.Op.178 (P)

Allen
Sandy Haven 1947
oil on canvas 63.5 x 76.5
SCO.FA.Op.207

Arnold, Victor b.1944
Scolton Manor: Rhododendron Time 1990
oil on board 37.5 x 49.5
SCO.FA.Op.115

B., S. J.
Modern Harvesting Scene 1983
acrylic on board 30.2 x 40.2
SCO.FA.Ap.021

Bendtsen, Axel 1893–c.1952
Portrait of a Gentleman in Regimental Uniform
oil on canvas 105.5 x 75
SCO.FA.Op.165

Bright, Beatrice 1861–1940
Major John Arthur Higgon early 20th C
oil on canvas 141 x 90
SCO.FA.Op.179 (P)

Bright, Beatrice 1861–1940
Mrs Lurline May Higgon early 20th C
oil on canvas 141 x 90
SCO.FA.Op.180 (P)

Brown, Gordon active 1957–1958
Beggar's Reach 1957
oil on canvas board 30 x 40
SCO.FA.Op.081

Brown, Gordon active 1957–1958
Cleddau, Benton Woods, Winter Sunrise 1957
oil on canvas board 50.8 x 41.3
SCO.FA.Op.023

Brown, Gordon active 1957–1958
Winter – Pembrokeshire Lane
oil on hardboard 35.6 x 45.2
SCO.FA.Op.153

Burne-Jones, Philip Edward 1861–1926
Edward Lucas Jenks Ridsdale (1833–1901)
1892
oil on canvas 59.2 x 39
SCO.FA.Op.185 (P)

Burne-Jones, Philip Edward 1861–1926
Sir Edward Aurelian Ridsdale (1864–1923)
1893
oil on canvas 59.2 x 39
SCO.FA.Op.186 (P)

Burne-Jones, Philip Edward 1861–1926
Mrs Esther Lucy J. Ridsdale (1840–1909) 1906
oil on canvas 59.2 x 39
SCO.FA.Op.184 (P)

Burne-Jones, Philip Edward 1861–1926
Lady Susan Stirling Ridsdale 1908
oil on canvas 102 x 76
SCO.FA.Op.187 (P)

Facing page: Herman, Josef, 1911–2000, *Mother and Child*, 1945–1950, Glynn Vivian Art Gallery (p. 182)

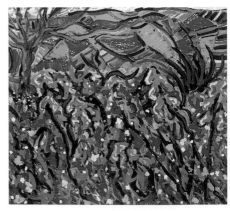

Burton-Richardson, David b.1961
Preseli Fields and Wild Flowers 1998
acrylic on canvas 100 x 110
SCO.FA.Ap.001

Burton-Richardson, David b.1961
Landscape: Rainy Day 1999
oil on linen 23 x 29
SCO.FA.Op.027

Burton-Richardson, David b.1961
Twisted Trees, Efailwen 1999
oil on board 46.5 x 30
SCO.FA.Op.090

Burton-Richardson, David b.1961
Dark Autumn 2000
oil on linen 137 x 152
SCO.FA.Ap.002

Burton-Richardson, David b.1961
Landscape: Setting Sun 2000
oil on linen 151.6 x 152
SCO.FA.Ap.003

Burton-Richardson, David b.1961
The Clown 2000
oil on linen 152.3 x 136.6
SCO.FA.Ap.008

Burton-Richardson, David b.1961
Under the Cherry Moon 2000
acrylic on board 126 x 122
SCO.FA.Ap.011

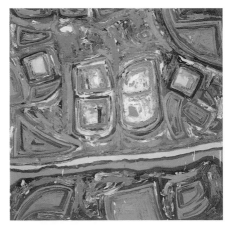

Burton-Richardson, David b.1961
Valley 2000
oil on linen 153 x 151.5
SCO.FA.Ap.005

Burton-Richardson, David b.1961
The Window 2002
oil on linen 127 x 122.4
SCO.FA.Ap.007

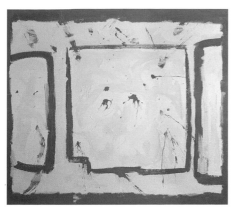

Burton-Richardson, David b.1961
The Window Study (in Blue and Yellow) 2002
acrylic on canvas 137.4 x 153
SCO.FA.Ap.010

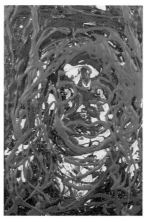

Burton-Richardson, David b.1961
Julie 2003
acrylic on board 38 x 25
SCO.FA.Ap.013

Burton-Richardson, David b.1961
Landscape with Castle 2005
acrylic & mixed media on canvas 64 x 67.4
SCO.FA.Mm.001

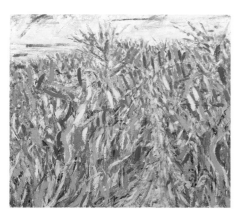

Burton-Richardson, David b.1961
Skrinkle
acrylic on canvas 106 x 120.7
SCO.FA.Ap.019

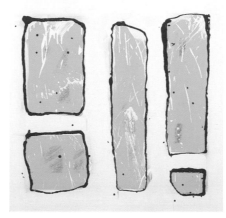

Burton-Richardson, David b.1961
The Room
acrylic on canvas 122 x 126.5
SCO.FA.Ap.004

Christopherson, John 1921–1996
Hill Farm 1965
oil on cardboard 27 x 23
SCO.FA.Op.091

Cole, Ethel 1892–1934
Landscape with Trees
oil on board 45.3 x 32.5
SCO.FA.Op.183

Cole, Ethel 1892–1934
Trees and Lakeside
oil on board 45.3 x 32.5
SCO.FA.Op.182

Colley, Cyril
Flower Piece 1961
oil on hardboard 75 x 61.5
SCO.FA.Op.230

Cramp, Jonathan D. b.1930
Standing Stones (recto) 1960
oil on hardboard 92.8 x 121.7
SCO.FA.Op.020a

Cramp, Jonathan D. b.1930
Gnarly Tree (verso) 1960 (?)
oil on hardboard 121.7 x 92.8
SCO.FA.Op.020b

Cramp, Jonathan D. b.1930
Pembrokeshire Landscape
oil on board 47.8 x 71
SCO.FA.Op.032

Cramp, Jonathan D. b.1930
Still Life with Geraniums
oil on board 82 x 44
SCO.FA.Op.016

Crawford, David
Oil Refinery
acrylic on canvas 186.3 x 186.3
SCO.FA.Ap.024

Crome, Vivian 1842–c.1926
View of Castle Pill and Castle Hall 1881
oil on canvas 60.7 x 91.2
SCO.FA.Op.194

Cross, Tom 1931–2009
Light Catch 1970
acrylic on canvas 146.4 x 206.7
SCO.FA.Ap.023

Davies, M. J. active 1896–1913
Picton Castle 1896
oil on canvas 25.5 x 40.5
SCO.FA.Op.100

Dorrington, Barbara
Blue and Green Abstract Shapes
oil on board 50.5 x 74.4
SCO.FA.Op.151a

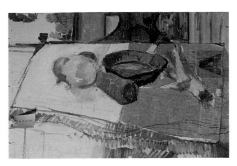

Dorrington, Barbara (attributed to)
Still Life with Vegetables (unfinished)
oil on board 50.5 x 74.4
SCO.FA.Op.151b

Edmunds, Michael
The Fishtrap 1956
oil on canvas board 76 x 55.2
SCO.FA.Op.029

Ellis, Lawrence Martin 1905–1981
Bosherston Lily Pond
oil on canvas 127 x 163
SCO.FA.Op.209

Ellis, Lawrence Martin 1905–1981
Main Road, near Redberth
oil on canvas 50.7 x 60.9
SCO.FA.Op.144

Ellis, Lawrence Martin 1905–1981
Stackpole Woods
oil on board 37 x 50
SCO.FA.Op.138

Ellis, Lawrence Martin 1905–1981
Treffgarne Quarry Workings
oil on canvas 41.5 x 50.5
SCO.FA.Op.131

Elwyn, John 1916–1997
Landscape 1956
oil on board 27.8 x 38
SCO.FA.Op.018

Evans, J.
Fishing Boats
oil on board 54.5 x 89
SCO.FA.Op.099

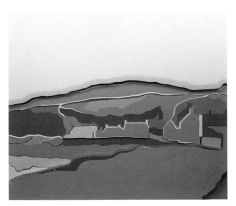

Evans-Thomas, Martin
The Front at Dale
emulsion & mixed media relief 44.1 x 50.7
SCO.FA.Mm.003

Fisher, Mark 1841–1923
Still Life 1912
oil on canvas 42 x 60
SCO.FA.Op.189

Fisher, Samuel Melton 1859–1939
*Mabel Carlisle, Wife of Hugh Edwardes, 6th
Baron Kensington* 1919
oil on canvas 152.5 x 91.3
SCO.FA.Op.046

Fisher, Samuel Melton 1859–1939
*Hugh Edwardes (1873–1938), 6th Baron
Kensington* 1919 (?)
oil on canvas 153.2 x 92
SCO.FA.Op.203

Ford, Harry E. active 1892–1956
Beach Scene 1956
oil on canvas 56 x 82
SCO.FA.Op.214

Frith, William Powell 1819–1909
Tenby Fisherwoman 1880
oil on canvas 82 x 60
SCO.FA.Op.193

G., S.
Church near Weir 1898
oil on board 24 x 34
SCO.FA.Op.148

Game, Aaron (attributed to) c.1791–1842
Portrait of a Military Gentleman
oil on canvas 62 x 48
SCO.FA.Op.030

Green, T. W.
'Margaret' 1982
oil on hardboard 50 x 61.2
SCO.FA.Op.152

H., M.
Waiting for the Music to Start 1988
oil on canvas 54 x 39.1
SCO.FA.Op.038

Hoare, William 1707–1792
William Edwardes (c.1711–1801), 1st Lord Kensington
oil on canvas 61.8 x 58.5
SCO.FA.Op.011

Hock, G. (attributed to)
F. C. Meyrick, CB c.1878
oil on canvas 141.5 x 97
SCO.FA.Op.082

Holland, Harry b.1941
The Breadwinner 1978
oil on canvas 111 x 130
SCO.FA.Op.122

Hopson, Royston 1927–2003
Fishguard Invasion
oil on board 64.9 x 92
SCO.FA.Op.154

Howard-Jones, Ray 1903–1996
Island of Scalmeye, Welshway 1970
oil on paper 54.5 x 74
SCO.FA.Op.210

Icke, Gillian Sybil 1925–1989
St Martin's, Haverfordwest
oil on canvas 49.5 x 75
SCO.FA.Op.097

Jones, Clifford active 1936–1982
New Bridge, Haverfordwest 1936
oil on board 49 x 59.5
SCO.FA.Op.219

Jones, Selwyn 1928–1998
Two Labourers 1960
oil on canvas 64 x 76.5
SCO.FA.Op.051

Kay, Bernard b.1927
Brantome 1955
oil on plywood 63.7 x 76.5
SCO.FA.Op.021

Knapp-Fisher, John b.1931
House and Shed, North Pembrokeshire 1998
acrylic on paper 38 x 57.4
SCO.FA.Ap.012

Könekamp, Frederick 1897–1977
Canadian Forest 1942–1943
oil on sacking 50 x 70
SCO.FA.Op.026

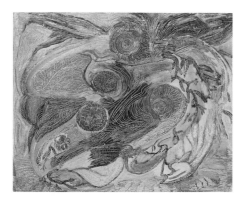

Könekamp, Frederick 1897–1977
Abstract 1946
oil on canvas 25.5 x 31
SCO.FA.Op.039

Könekamp, Frederick 1897–1977
Nucleus 1953
oil on canvas 55.5 x 42.3
SCO.FA.Op.037

Könekamp, Frederick 1897–1977
Low Tide at Newport 1953/1954
oil on plywood 93.8 x 94.2
SCO.FA.Op.036

Könekamp, Frederick 1897–1977
Jetsam on the beach 1959
oil on board 120.2 x 180
SCO.FA.Op.083

Könekamp, Frederick 1897–1977
Fire on the Mountain 1962
oil on plywood 92.3 x 122
SCO.FA.Op.035

Landseer, Edwin Henry (after) 1802–1873
Blacksmith and Forge
oil on canvas 60.5 x 51.5
SCO.FA.Op.084

Lely, Peter (attributed to) 1618–1680
Lucy Walter (c.1630–1658)
oil on board 34.5 x 27.5
SCO.FA.Op.188

Facing page: John, Gwen, 1876–1939, *Winifred John*, c.1900, Tenby Museum and Art Gallery (p. 132)

Lewis, S. G.
Pembroke Castle 2005
oil on canvas board 49.5 x 75
SCO.FA.Op.220

Lindley, David b.1930
Haverfordwest Castle 1954–1955
oil on canvas 51 x 61
SCO.FA.Op.096

Lindley, David b.1930
Barn Street 1955
oil on canvas 49.6 x 59
SCO.FA.Op.195

Lindley, David b.1930
Haverfordwest River, Quay and Castle 1955
oil on canvas 50.5 x 60.8
SCO.FA.Op.196

Lindley, David b.1930
Marloes Sands 1957
oil on hardboard 50.5 x 61
SCO.FA.Op.098

Lindley, David b.1930
Solva 1957
oil on canvas 46 x 61
SCO.FA.Op.121

Lindley, David b.1930
Haverfordwest, Looking North from Foley House 1958
oil on hardboard 50.5 x 68.7
SCO.FA.Op.120

Lloyd, M.
Pwllgwaelod 1830
oil on board 30.5 x 50
SCO.FA.Op.033

Lloyd, M. E.
Cwm-yr-Eglwys 1830
oil on board 30.5 x 50
SCO.FA.Op.034

Lowe, Ronald 1932–1985
Flood Tide off St Bride's 1960
oil on hardboard 52.7 x 95.5
SCO.FA.Op.204

Lowe, Ronald 1932–1985
Across the Estuary 1968
acrylic & mixed media on canvas 76 x 101.5
SCO.FA.Mm.002

Lowe, Ronald 1932–1985
Reflected 1
polymer on board 59 x 73
SCO.FA.Ap.025

Macklin, Thomas Eyre 1867–1943
Colonel R. F. Hill 1890
oil on canvas 71 x 58.4
SCO.FA.Op.113

Marks, Barnett Samuel 1827–1916
Reverend Dr Thomas Davies 1889
oil on canvas 127 x 101.5
SCO.FA.Op.181

Mayou, Helen active 1960–1977
Abstract of Acrobats and Blue Horses 1960
oil on board 60.2 x 121
SCO.FA.Op.222

Mayou, Helen active 1960–1977
Abstract of Four Acrobats and Two Blue Horses
1960
oil on board 121 x 60
SCO_FA_Op_218

Mayou, Helen active 1960–1977
Bearing the Cross 1977
oil on board 119 x 58
SCO.FA.Op.217 (P)

Mayou, Helen active 1960–1977
Abstract of Flowers
oil on board 81 x 60
SCO.FA.Op.211b

Mayou, Helen active 1960–1977
Abstract of Man and Dragons
oil on board 60 x 108
SCO.FA.Op.213

Mayou, Helen active 1960–1977
Abstract of Man with Dove
oil on board 59.4 x 121
SCO.FA.Op.218

Mayou, Helen active 1960–1977
Abstract of People
oil on board 60.5 x 121
SCO.FA.Op.221

Mayou, Helen active 1960–1977
Abstract of People
oil on board 81 x 60
SCO_FA_Op_211a

Mayou, Helen active 1960–1977
Grey Abstract
oil on board 60.2 x 121
SCO.FA.Op.223

Mayou, Helen active 1960–1977
Red Abstract of Man with Sword
oil on board 119 x 60.4
SCO.FA.Op.224

McLaren, Duncan
Child Fantasy (slightly damaged) c.1978
oil on canvas 90 x 75
SCO.FA.Op.119

Morris, Carey Boynes 1882–1968
Quayside
oil on canvas 22.5 x 28
SCO.FA.Op.094

Morris, Carey Boynes 1882–1968
Ships
oil on canvas 28.3 x 23
SCO.FA.Op.013

Murray Whatley, Margaret Stella b.1942
Panoramic View of Rosebush with Railway
1986 (?)
oil on canvas 55 x 104
SCO.FA.Op.198

Murray Whatley, Margaret Stella b.1942
Grove Colliery
oil on canvas 65.6 x 105.6
SCO.FA.Op.197

Murray Whatley, Margaret Stella b.1942
'Margaret'
oil on canvas (?) 36.6 x 42.9 (E)
SCO.FA.Op.136

Murray Whatley, Margaret Stella b.1942
Prendergast Paper Mill
oil on canvas 66.3 x 102
SCO.FA.Op.042

Murray Whatley, Margaret Stella b.1942
Sarnau Signal Box
oil on canvas 60 x 100
SCO.FA.Op.201

Musk, Will
The Milford Fishing Fleet 1896
oil on board 60.7 x 122
SCO.FA.Op.167

Nash, Thomas John b.1931
From Blue 1967
oil on board 22.5 x 47
SCO.FA.Op.048

Newton, Francis Milner
Thomas Meyrick of Bush 1833
oil on canvas 71 x 55
SCO.FA.Op.159

Oakley, Herbert Colborne 1869–1944
John 1928
oil on board 58.5 x 49
SCO.FA.Op.086

Oakley, Herbert Colborne 1869–1944
John Gregg 1928
oil on board 48.4 x 43.3
SCO.FA.Op.087

Parsons, Christine b.c.1912/1914
Three Russet Apples 1972
oil on wood 17.5 x 15
SCO.FA.Op.015

Parsons, Christine b.c.1912/1914
Two Russet Apples 1972
oil on wood 17.5 x 15
SCO.FA.Op.014

Pitt, William c.1818–c.1900
Haverfordwest Castle, South Wales
oil on canvas (?) 41.3 x 33.6
SCO.FA.Op.200

Preiss, Fritz 1882–1943
Street Market
oil on canvas 53.5 x 64.5
SCO.FA.Op.164

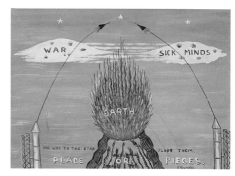

Reynolds, Ernie active 1969–1982
Peace or Pieces: Nuclear War 1969
oil on hardboard 23 x 31
SCO.FA.Op.107

Reynolds, Ernie active 1969–1982
Mirror Painted with Two Birds on Branches
1979
oil on glass 38.1 x 29.3
SCO.FA.Op.110

Reynolds, Ernie active 1969–1982
Milford Haven Welcomes Good Drivers 1982
oil on board 47.3 x 30.5
SCO.FA.Op.108

Reynolds, Ernie active 1969–1982
Milford Haven Welcomes Good Drivers 1982
oil on board 47.3 x 30.9
SCO.FA.Op.109

Reynolds, Ernie active 1969–1982
'When drink is in wit is out'
oil on board 36 x 68.3
SCO.FA.Op.089

Reynolds, Ernie active 1969–1982
'When drink is in wit is out'
oil on board 37.3 x 47.3
SCO.FA.Op.116

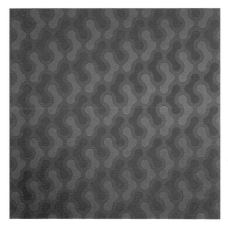

Richardson II, Anne
Composition
acrylic on canvas 150.6 x 152.3
SCO.FA.Ap.020

Rogers, Olive
A Rest by the Way, Manorbier Church
oil, watercolour & Plasticine on cardboard
50.5 x 57.1
SCO.FA.Mm.005

Rogers, Olive
Abstract (Fantasy Cliffs and Sea View)
oil on canvas 76 x 51
SCO.FA.Op.140

Rogers, Olive
Amy Rogers at the Piano
oil & mixed media on board 61.4 x 29
SCO.FA.Op.146

Rogers, Olive
Cliff with Boat
oil, Plasticine & mixed media on cardboard
43.4 x 38
SCO.FA.Mm.004

Rogers, Olive
Pembrokeshire Coast
oil & mixed media on board 52.9 x 34.4
SCO.FA.Op.145

Rogers, Olive
Sea between Rocks
oil on board 26 x 20.2
SCO.FA.Op.149

Rogers, Olive
Warship in Milford Haven
oil on board 18.3 x 46.7 (E)
SCO.FA.Op.150

Rogers, Olive
Warship, Milford Haven
oil on board 33 x 43.5
SCO.FA.Op.147

Round, Janie
Autumn, Monkhaven 1962
oil on board 31 x 25.5
SCO.FA.Op.128

Round, Janie
Cliffs 1962
oil on board 35.7 x 45.6
SCO.FA.Op.134

Round, Janie
Pembrokeshire View 1962
oil on board 31 x 40.4
SCO.FA.Op.129

Round, Janie
Farm Outbuilding
oil on board 40.7 x 60.8
SCO.FA.Op.142

Round, Janie
Goldtop
oil on board 31.8 x 35.4
SCO.FA.Op.135

Round, Janie
Haverfordwest Castle
oil on board 40.2 x 50.8
SCO.FA.Op.141

Round, Janie
Llwyngwair
oil on board 40.4 x 61
SCO.FA.Op.139

Round, Janie
Outbuildings, Llwyngwair
oil on board 40.7 x 59.8
SCO.FA.Op.143

Round, Janie
Penally
oil on board 35.5 x 55.2
SCO.FA.Op.133

Scurlock, Grace d.2005
Bird's Eye View
oil on board 60 x 122
SCO.FA.Op.019

Sheppard, Maurice Raymond b.1947
At the Edge of the Wood 1974–1975
oil on board 46 x 61
SCO.FA.Op.157 🐝

Sheppard, Maurice Raymond b.1947
Evening: Rhoose Ferry 1975–1976
oil on board 46.5 x 61
SCO.FA.Op.158 🐝

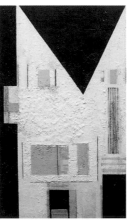

Shore, Jack b.1922
Theme from Barry Harbour 1961
oil, PVA & distemper on board 122 x 74
SCO.FA.Op.205

Solomon, Leopold active 1940s
Spanish Girl 1938
oil on canvas 50.6 x 40.7
SCO.FA.Op.040

Solomon, Leopold active 1940s
Girl in a Green Dress
oil on canvas 45.7 x 36
SCO.FA.Op.166

Solomon, Leopold active 1940s
Russian Girl
oil on canvas 51 x 41
SCO.FA.Op.137

Solomon, Leopold active 1940s
Self Portrait
oil on canvas 43.2 x 34
SCO.FA.Op.045

Steele-Morgan, Tony 1930–2009
'To whom it may concern' 1973
acrylic on canvas 74.5 x 61.3
SCO.FA.Ap.016

Steele-Morgan, Tony 1930–2009
Vanessa atalanta 1974–1978
acrylic on canvas 74.2 x 61.3
SCO.FA.Ap.018

Steele-Morgan, Tony 1930–2009
The Daydream 1975
acrylic on canvas 61.6 x 61.8
SCO.FA.Ap.006

Steele-Morgan, Tony 1930–2009
An Origin Viewing a Source 1976
acrylic on canvas 93 x 62.3
SCO.FA.Ap.015

Steele-Morgan, Tony 1930–2009
St Malo 1979
acrylic on canvas 74.5 x 74.5
SCO.FA.Ap.017

Steele-Morgan, Tony 1930–2009
Time Cage 1989
acrylic on canvas 61.2 x 44.1
SCO.FA.Ap.014

Steele-Morgan, Tony 1930–2009
Gwen John, Aged 10 1997
oil on canvas board 48 x 36.5
SCO.FA.Op.202

Steele-Morgan, Tony 1930–2009
Sir John Perrot (1527–1592) 2003
oil on board 61 x 60
SCO.FA.Op.022

Facing page: Povey, Edward, b.1951, *The Herb of the Field (Self Portrait)*, 1999–2000, Glynn Vivian Art Gallery (p. 198)

Stubbing, Tony 1921–1983
Gower Shapes 1975
oil on canvas 150 x 150
SCO.FA.Op.199

Taggert, E. M.
Haverfordwest Castle
oil on canvas 49.7 x 70.6
SCO.FA.Op.130

Thomas, Edgar Herbert 1862–1936
Canal 1893
oil on canvas 50.4 x 30.8
SCO.FA.Op.063

Thomas, Edgar Herbert 1862–1936
Teresa 1903/1905
oil on cardboard 22.5 x 15
SCO.FA.Op.059

Thomas, Edgar Herbert 1862–1936
The Flush of Youth 1908
oil on cardboard 30 x 22
SCO.FA.Op.065

Thomas, Edgar Herbert 1862–1936
Winter Sunlight on Glamorgan Canal, Cardiff
1908
oil on cardboard 30 x 22
SCO.FA.Op.069

Thomas, Edgar Herbert 1862–1936
Canal 1909
oil on cardboard 30 x 22
SCO.FA.Op.058

Thomas, Edgar Herbert 1862–1936
Storm Tossed 1909
oil on cardboard 31 x 23 (E)
SCO.FA.Op.075

Thomas, Edgar Herbert 1862–1936
Flowers in a Globe Vase 1919
oil on cardboard 60.5 x 45.2
SCO.FA.Op.053

Thomas, Edgar Herbert 1862–1936
Sweet Peas in a Blue Glass Vase 1919
oil on cardboard 61.6 x 46.6
SCO.FA.Op.079

Thomas, Edgar Herbert 1862–1936
Landscape 1921
oil on cardboard 50.4 x 30.8
SCO.FA.Op.080

Thomas, Edgar Herbert 1862–1936
Rhododendrons in a Blue Vase 1927
oil on canvas 50.4 x 30.8
SCO.FA.Op.055

Thomas, Edgar Herbert 1862–1936
Flowers in a Dark Vase 1929
oil on canvas 57 x 43.5
SCO.FA.Op.054

Thomas, Edgar Herbert 1862–1936
A Child
oil on cardboard 23 x 15.3
SCO.FA.Op.072

Thomas, Edgar Herbert 1862–1936
Canal
oil on cardboard 30 x 22
SCO.FA.Op.071

Thomas, Edgar Herbert 1862–1936
Daffodils
oil on canvas 60.8 x 50.7
SCO.FA.Op.052

Thomas, Edgar Herbert 1862–1936
Ever Fresh
oil on cardboard 31 x 23 (E)
SCO.FA.Op.074

Thomas, Edgar Herbert 1862–1936
Flowering Shrubs and Stream
oil on cardboard 60 x 45
SCO.FA.Op.077

Thomas, Edgar Herbert 1862–1936
Foliage, Water and Bird
oil on canvas 40.8 x 50.8
SCO.FA.Op.070

Thomas, Edgar Herbert 1862–1936
Head of a Child
oil on cardboard 28.4 x 22 (E)
SCO.FA.Op.067

Thomas, Edgar Herbert 1862–1936
Llawrenny Pond
oil on cardboard 23 x 30
SCO.FA.Op.064

Thomas, Edgar Herbert 1862–1936
Morn Glamorgan Canal
oil on canvas 22 x 30
SCO.FA.Op.061

Thomas, Edgar Herbert 1862–1936
Morning Reflections
oil on cardboard 22 x 30
SCO.FA.Op.066

Thomas, Edgar Herbert 1862–1936
Nude Figure
oil on canvas 143.3 x 75
SCO.FA.Op.076

Thomas, Edgar Herbert 1862–1936
Pink Roses in a Glass Bud Vase
oil on cardboard 38 x 23
SCO.FA.Op.060

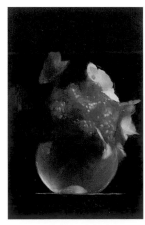

Thomas, Edgar Herbert 1862–1936
Red Berries and Flowers in a Gold Vase
oil on cardboard 50.1 x 30.8
SCO.FA.Op.057

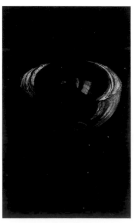

Thomas, Edgar Herbert 1862–1936
Reflecting Bowl
oil on cardboard 50.5 x 30.9
SCO.FA.Op.062

Thomas, Edgar Herbert 1862–1936
Sorrowful Day
oil on cardboard 22 x 30
SCO.FA.Op.073

Thomas, Edgar Herbert 1862–1936
Still Life
oil on canvas 61 x 49.5
SCO.FA.Op.078

Thomas, Edgar Herbert 1862–1936
The Autumn of Roses
oil on cardboard 30 x 22
SCO.FA.Op.068

Thomas, Edgar Herbert 1862–1936
Young Girl Reading
oil on wood 40 x 50.1
SCO.FA.Op.056

unknown artist
Colonel Charles E. G. Phillips, Bt 1903 (?)
oil on canvas 149.5 x 103
SCO.FA.Op.004

unknown artist
A Country Man with a Dog
oil on wood 30.5 x 27.8
SCO.FA.Op.102

unknown artist
A Winter Scene (Thunn)
oil on board 39.9 x 53
SCO.FA.Op.163

unknown artist
Abstract
oil on canvas 65 x 45
SCO.FA.Op.212

unknown artist
Carl Linnaeus (1707–1778)
oil on canvas 88.5 x 66.5
SCO.FA.Op.176

unknown artist
Cattle and Landscape
oil on hardboard 29 x 33.4
SCO.FA.Op.092

unknown artist
Colonel the Honourable Robert Fulke Greville of Castle Hall (1800–1867)
oil on canvas 77.5 x 64
SCO.FA.Op.012

unknown artist
Cows in Ford
oil on canvas 97 x 147
SCO.FA.Op.174

unknown artist
Dr George Griffith (1838–1912)
oil on canvas 127 x 102
SCO.FA.Op.002

unknown artist
Farmhouse and Haystacks
oil on canvas 63.5 x 76
SCO.FA.Op.171

unknown artist
Farmhouse with Cows
oil on canvas 63.3 x 76
SCO.FA.Op.170

unknown artist
Foreign Beach Scene with Cattle
oil on canvas 76 x 103
SCO.FA.Op.215

unknown artist
Frederick (1847–1911), 3rd Lord Cawdor
oil on canvas 126 x 100
SCO.FA.Op.008

unknown artist
General Sir Thomas Picton (1758–1815)
oil on canvas 247 x 165
SCO.FA.Op.009

unknown artist
Honestas optima politia
oil on canvas   138.4 x 157.5
SCO.FA.Op.024

unknown artist
Industrial Scene
acrylic on board   122 x 244
SCO.FA.Ap.022

unknown artist
John Meyrick
oil on canvas   74 x 60.5
SCO.FA.Op.112

unknown artist
Lady Riding a Horse
oil on wood   24 x 22.5
SCO.FA.Op.104

unknown artist
Landscape of a Cottage and Lake
oil on cardboard   25.2 x 46
SCO.FA.Op.175

unknown artist
Landscape of a River and Cottage
oil on cardboard   25.4 x 46.2
SCO.FA.Op.190

unknown artist
*Landscape with a Church and a Figure with a
Boat*
oil on canvas   15.2 x 35.7
SCO.FA.Op.132

unknown artist
Landscape with a Mountain
oil on cardboard   29.9 x 40.4
SCO.FA.Op.125

unknown artist
Laurence Hugh Higgon
oil on canvas   102.7 x 81.5
SCO.FA.Op.123

unknown artist
Life Drawing Class
oil on canvas 71.5 x 91.5
SCO.FA.Op.192

unknown artist
Mediterranean View
oil on board 25 x 35.7
SCO.FA.Op.093

unknown artist
Neda Kathleen Cecil Higgon, née Rennick
oil on canvas 100 x 80
SCO.FA.Op.124

unknown artist
Pembrokeshire View
oil on canvas 97 x 147
SCO.FA.Op.172

unknown artist
Pier Scene
oil on board 12.6 x 26.2
SCO.FA.Op.047

unknown artist
Portrait of a Baroque Lady
oil on canvas 80 x 64
SCO.FA.Op.177

unknown artist
Portrait of a Gentleman in Regency Dress
oil on canvas 90 x 70
SCO.FA.Op.031

unknown artist
Portrait of a Georgian Gentleman
oil on canvas 75.5 x 63.2
SCO.FA.Op.162

unknown artist
Portrait of a Georgian Gentleman
oil on canvas 74 x 62
SCO.FA.Op.231

Facing page: Collier, John, 1850–1934, *Souvenir of Chu Chin Chow*, Glynn Vivian Art Gallery (p. 169)

unknown artist
Portrait of a Georgian Man in a Decorative Waistcoat
oil on canvas 75.4 x 63
SCO.FA.Op.161

unknown artist
Portrait of a Lady in a Ballgown and Tiara
oil on canvas 148 x 100
SCO.FA.Op.005

unknown artist
Portrait of a Man
oil on canvas 75 x 62.5
SCO.FA.Op.227

unknown artist
Portrait of a Man in a Clerical Collar
oil on glass 56 x 40.6
SCO.FA.Op.127

unknown artist
Portrait of a Man in a White Shirt
oil on canvas 30 x 27
SCO.FA.Op.191

unknown artist
Portrait of a Man Wearing a Tie
oil & pastels on board 49.6 x 39.4
SCO.FA.Op.041

unknown artist
Portrait of a Man with a Beard
oil on paper 56.1 x 45.2
SCO.FA.Op.156

unknown artist
Portrait of a Naval Cadet
oil on paper 41.9 x 34.2
SCO.FA.Op.155

unknown artist
Portrait of a Victorian Gentleman
oil on canvas 91 x 70.4
SCO.FA.Op.043

unknown artist
Portrait of a Victorian Lady in a Frilly Bonnet
oil on canvas 75 x 61.5
SCO.FA.Op.229

unknown artist
Portrait of a Victorian Man
oil on canvas 51 x 37.6
SCO.FA.Op.225

unknown artist
Portrait of a Victorian Man
oil on canvas 75 x 63
SCO.FA.Op.228

unknown artist
Portrait of a Victorian Woman in a Bonnet
oil on canvas 91 x 70.4
SCO.FA.Op.044

unknown artist
Portrait of a Victorian Woman in a Bonnet
oil on canvas 75 x 62.5
SCO.FA.Op.226

unknown artist
Portrait of a Woman with a Bonnet
oil on canvas 51.2 x 45
SCO.FA.Op.117

unknown artist
Portrait of a Woman with a Veil
oil on canvas 61.2 x 50.7
SCO.FA.Op.206

unknown artist
Portrait of a Young Woman
oil on canvas 53.5 x 42
SCO.FA.Op.126

unknown artist
Portrait of an Elizabethan Man
oil on board 48 x 38
SCO.FA.Op.010

unknown artist
Primitive Cattle
oil & enamel on oilboard 13 x 20.9
SCO.FA.Op.101

unknown artist
Primitive Horse
oil on hardboard 21.6 x 24.2
SCO.FA.Op.106

unknown artist
Primitive Horses
oil on wood 14.5 x 15.8
SCO.FA.Op.105

unknown artist
Primitive Landscape of Sea and Buildings
oil on wood 33 x 33
SCO.FA.Op.103

unknown artist
Richard Fenton (1747–1821), KC, FAS
oil on canvas 127 x 101.4
SCO.FA.Op.003

unknown artist
Road near St David's
oil on canvas 97.5 x 148
SCO.FA.Op.173

unknown artist
Robert Anstice
oil on canvas 48.1 x 38.8
SCO.FA.Op.111

unknown artist
*Sir John Henry Philipps Scourfield (1808–
1876), Bt, MP*
oil on canvas 228 x 141
SCO.FA.Op.001

unknown artist
Sir John Meyrick
oil on canvas 75.2 x 63.2
SCO.FA.Op.160

unknown artist
Sir John Owen (d.1861), Bt
oil on canvas 76.5 x 63
SCO.FA.Op.007

unknown artist
Standing Man
oil on canvas 138.5 x 105
SCO.FA.Op.238

unknown artist
The Dream of George Stephenson
oil on canvas 101.5 x 125.7
SCO.FA.Op.208

unknown artist
'The Duke of Sussex'
oil on board 23.5 x 46
SCO.FA.Op.025

unknown artist
Thomas James, Mayor of Haverfordwest (1887, 1896 & 1897)
oil on canvas 73 x 60.5
SCO.FA.Op.232

unknown artist
Three Tree Stumps
oil on white glass 23.7 x 29
SCO.FA.Op.114

unknown artist
Two Soldiers
oil on wood 33 x 24.7
SCO.FA.Op.028

unknown artist
View of Haverfordwest from (…)
oil on circular table top inlaid with mother of pearl 45.5 x 50.3
SCO.FA.Op.118

unknown artist
William Edwardes (1835–1896), 4th Baron Kensington
oil on canvas 150 x 102
SCO.FA.Op.006

Vale, Edith
Bormes-les-Mimosas 1939
oil on board 37 x 38.5
SCO.FA.Op.095

Wells, Arthur
Female Field, Smile Please
acrylic on canvas 133.5 x 101
SCO.FA.Ap.009

Williams, Elizabeth
Little Haven c.1960
oil on hardboard 35.5 x 62
SCO.FA.Op.085

Williams, Margaret Lindsay 1888–1960
Lady Gwilym Lloyd George (d.1971), Lady Tenby 1945
oil on canvas 124.5 x 99.5
SCO.FA.Op.050a

Williams, Margaret Lindsay 1888–1960
Lord Gwilym Lloyd George (1894–1967), Lord Tenby
oil on canvas 110.5 x 85.5
SCO.FA.Op.049a

Milford Haven Heritage and Maritime Museum

Allen, Elsie
'Sybil' 1996
acrylic on board 40 x 60.2
PCF10

Bell, John H.
Off Landshipping in Milford Haven
oil on canvas 51 x 76
PCF9

Brett, Oswald Longfield b.1921
A View of Milford Haven, Wales, 1798
oil on canvas 60 x 93
1993.0364

Cadme, Christabel
Vessels in Castle Pill
oil on canvas 49 x 75
2011.0019

Clayton, Tommy F.
The Trawler 'David Ogilvie'
oil on canvas 41 x 60
2000.0074

Clayton, Tommy F.
The Trawler 'The Merit' LO56 Passing the
Trawler 'Pheneas Beard' LO283
oil on board 56 x 79
PCF1

Clayton, Tommy F.
Tug 'Turmoil' and Cargo Ship 'Flying
Enterprise'
oil on canvas 45 x 60
2000.0072

Harrison
HMS 'Ardent'
oil on canvas 62 x 75.3
1993.0488

McIntosh
Milford Docks
oil on board 24 x 75
2001_0040

McIntosh
Milford Docks
oil on board 24 x 75
M203

Murray, G.
Side Trawler 'Notts County' GY 643
acrylic on board 41 x 62
PCF6

Rickard, Robert
'Esso', Pembrokeshire 1996
acrylic on board 33 x 62
PCF5

Rickard, Robert
*German Minelaying Aircraft Dropping
Parachute Mines near the Entrance to Milford
Haven*
oil on canvas board 50 x 73
1996.0514

S., R. M.
Milford Haven, 1979
acrylic on canvas board 37.5 x 52.1
PCF13

T., D. T.
Passenger Liner 'Aquitania'
acrylic on board 45.5 x 61
2001_0041

unknown artist
Cardiff Vessel 1913
oil on canvas 41 x 56
PCF7

unknown artist
'Alert' H264
oil on canvas 41.5 x 59.5
2011.0051

unknown artist
Cliffs with Vessel in the Background
oil on canvas 30 x 40
PCF8

unknown artist
'Kinellen' Leaving Dock
oil on board 46 x 50
PCF4

unknown artist
'Norrard Star' on the Slip
oil on board 60 x 59
PCF2

unknown artist
Padstow, Cornwall
oil on board 83 x 121.5
PCF11

unknown artist
Schooner 'Gypsy'
oil on board 41 x 52
2001_0029

unknown artist
Steam Trawler 'Yezo' LO74
oil on canvas 30 x 45.5
2011.0021

unknown artist
Stokeholdof Trawler
oil on board 57.3 x 44
PCF3

unknown artist
'Tamura' LOG3
oil on board 28 x 39
PCF12

unknown artist
Trawler 'Lephreto' LO458
oil on board 30 x 46
1993.0604

Vaughan, Richard
'Kandahar' GY123
acrylic on board 45.3 x 60
2001_0038

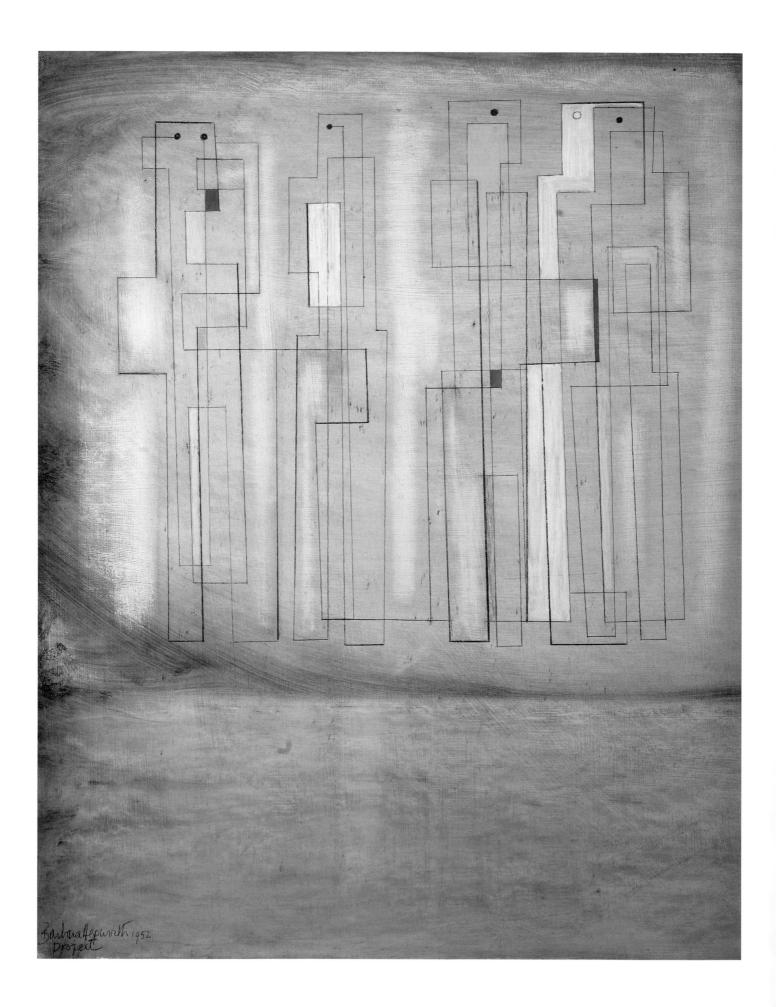

Pembroke Dock
Sunderland Trust

Banks, Arthur active 1984–1990
X/210 P. D. 1944 (To John Evans, the
inspiration for this theme) 1984
acrylic on board 36.6 x 50.5
AC2011.A.0029

Banks, Arthur active 1984–1990
*The New Sunderlands, Dar-es-salaam,
Catalina and Sunderlands* 1985
oil on canvas 50.6 x 76.2
AC2011.A.0019 (P)

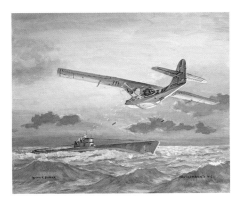

Banks, Arthur active 1984–1990
*Study for 'Canadian Homecoming' (422
Squadron RCAF)* 1987
oil on board 50 x 60
AC2011.A.0020

Banks, Arthur active 1984–1990
Cruikshank's VC
acrylic on canvas board 46 x 56
AC2011.A.0031

Banks, Arthur active 1984–1990
*Sunderland ML814 'Islander' at Lord Howe
Island* (acknowledgments to Angela Smith)
acrylic on board 38.7 x 49.5
AC2011.A.0028

Bearman, Robert D. b.1927
Seaplane 201 A over White Cliffs
acrylic on canvas 39.5 x 50
AC2011.A.0021

Curtis, Ian J.
Royal Dockyard, Pembroke Dock (one of two)
1993
oil on canvas board 45.5 x 56
AC2011.A.0011

Curtis, Ian J.
Royal Dockyard, Pembroke Dock (two of two)
1993
oil on canvas board 36 x 55.6
AC2011.A.0012

Facing page: Hepworth, Barbara, 1903–1975, *Project*, 1952, Glynn Vivian Art Gallery (p. 182)

Griffiths, A. T. active c.1980–1990s
'AOZ'
acrylic on board 45.5 x 60
AC2011.A.0015

Griffiths, A. T. active c.1980–1990s
Sunderland Flying Boat
acrylic on board 35.7 x 55
AC2011.A.0027

Hughes, G. S.
Sea Plane at Traitors Gate, Tower of London
1988
oil on canvas 40.5 x 51
AC2011.A.0026

Hughes, S. S.
Aircraft RN303 with Crane 1981
oil on canvas 40.5 x 51
AC2011.A.0024

Jarvis, Robin
Another Sortie Over 1998
acrylic on board 51 x 76.5
AC2011.A.0016

Martin, T. J.
Sea Plane over Headland
acrylic on board 34.3 x 44.5
AC2011.A.0018

Palmer, D.
Seaship 2661 1981
oil on canvas 40.5 x 60.5
AC2011.A.0023

Rickard, Robert
'AOB' and 'AOC' 2009
oil on panel 58.6 x 73.3
AC2011.A.0014

Rickard, Robert
Sea Plane with Purple Sky
oil (?) on canvas 61 x 76
AC2011.A.0022

Roberts, K.
Sea Plane and Tender 1985
acrylic on board 46 x 56.3
AC2011.A.0017

Robin, E.
RAF Hamworthy 1983
oil on board 33.8 x 40.4
AC2011.A.0032

Spencer, Kenneth
Return to Pembroke Dock (…) 1985
oil on panel 50 x 75
AC2011.A.0013

Tee, Jonny active c.1980–1990s
Short Sunderland, 'On Patrol'
acrylic on canvas 27.5 x 43
AC2011.A.0030

unknown artist
*Champion Gibraltar Bound F7 304, 'Depicting
a Catalina of 270 Squadron'*
oil on canvas board 29.8 x 40
AC2011.A.0009

unknown artist
Police Station
oil on canvas 67.7 x 45.7
AC2011.A.0025

unknown artist
'VA715'
oil on canvas 20 x 30
AC2011.A.0010

unknown artist
'Z' W4004, 10 Squadron RAAF Drake's Island
oil on board 35 x 45
AC2011.A.0033

Puncheston School

Cooper, Ken
Puncheston
acrylic on canvas board 29.8 x 39.5
PCF4

Curry, Denis b.1918
Sheep and Rain
oil on board 35.8 x 42.5
PCF2

Gwyn, Elis
Beardsey
oil on board 22.3 x 33.5
PCF7

Heal, Katrina
Colour of Coal
oil on canvas 38.6 x 49
PCF9

Howard-Jones, Ray 1903–1996
Rock Pool
acrylic on board 31 x 41.5
PCF11

Lloyd, Ben b.1973
Eggshell Brewery
acrylic on canvas 95 x 73
PCF5

MacKeown, James b.1961
The Classroom
oil on canvas 180 x 212
PCF6

Owens, Wyn
Trych Mynachbyddu
oil on canvas 75.7 x 90.5
PCF8

Prichard, Gwilym b.1931
Big Bala/Byrnau Mawr
oil on canvas 36.6 x 44.5
PCF13

Robinson, Beth b.1959
The Sea
acrylic on board 23.6 x 43.3
PCF3

Rosenthal, Stan b.1933
Black Cows
oil on canvas 74.3 x 60
PCF1

Williams, Claudia b.1933
Mother and Child
oil on canvas 44.3 x 36.3
PCF12

Young, Sarah b.1971
Pilgrims Road
acrylic on paper 63 x 44.3
PCF15

Young, Sarah b.1971
Porthgain
acrylic on paper 39.4 x 49.2
PCF14

Tenby Museum & Art Gallery

Artist Graham Sutherland once stated, 'the quality of light here (Pembrokeshire) is magical and transforming.' When one examines the sheer volume of artists who have been drawn to the area it becomes obvious that Sutherland's observation was not an idle one. Tantalisingly changing with every opportunistic whim of nature, the locality presents itself as something new with every passing moment, all four seasons presented often in one day, and it is the good fortune of both the locality and Tenby Museum that so many artists have been tempted to come to the county to paint and that so many high quality works have found their way into the care of the museum's collection.

The earliest oil painting in the collection is *Tenby from North Cliff* by William Golding, which dates from around 1799. This large and stylistically quite naïvely executed oil on panel depicts a panoramic view of Georgian

Tenby and its sprawling North Bay and eagle-eyed observers will note nude bathers on the beach before the laws of modesty were imposed upon the town during its period of regeneration in the early nineteenth century.

No mention can be made of the museum's art collection without reference to two of its most well-known artists, siblings Augustus and Gwen John. Both had close connections with the town. Augustus was born in Tenby in 1878 and the family moved to Tenby when he was young, following the death of his mother. Both Augustus and Gwen went off to further their artistic skills at the Slade School of Fine Art in London. Augustus became renowned as a portrait painter and three oils in the museum's collection illustrate his talent for portraiture. The first, of friend Richard Hughes, author of *A High Wind in Jamaica*, was bequeathed to the museum by the artist. The second is a large portrait of Augustus's eldest son, David John, painted c.1937 when David was in his thirties. This picture was purchased by the museum in 1997 with assistance from the Victoria and Albert Museum Purchase Grant Fund. The third is a self-portrait, c.1940, donated to the museum in 2011.

Gwen John's portrait of her younger sister, Winifred, is a beautifully executed oil. Gwen and Winifred had an especially close relationship and this is evident in the warmth of the painting. Winifred often appears as a model in Gwen's earlier work. This portrait highlights Gwen's 'fine sense of tone' as Whistler described her talent. Perhaps of more interest is the early oil by Gwen entitled *Landscape at Tenby with Figures* dated c.1896. This picture is rare not only in its age but also in the fact that it depicts the town of her childhood. It is not a typical Gwen John painting and in its subject matter, as far as the museum is aware, is unique in her oeuvre.

As a registered charity and the oldest independent museum in Wales, having been established in 1878, the museum is fortunate to have been the beneficiary of the generosity of both organisational and individual donors in the acquisition of works of art. Donors have included the Contemporary Art Society for Wales (Elizabeth Haines' *Streetscape, Candes*) and works donated by individuals include paintings by John Uzzell Edwards (*Barges*) who had a studio in Tenby in the 1960s and Philip Sutton (*Tenby Harbour*), whose exhibition in 1995 was the first in the museum's New Art Gallery.

One of the most popular oil paintings with visitors in the collection is *The Domino Players* painted by Edward Joseph Head in 1910, donated to the museum in 1985, which depicts two Tenby fishermen enjoying a game of dominoes with St Catherine's Island in the background. Head had taught a young Augustus John in his Tenby Art Classes at the end of the nineteenth century and it was on his recommendation that John's father Edwin permitted Augustus to attend the Slade. Another popular work by Head, entitled *Frank B. Mason and Family on the Beach*, is on loan from descendants of the family in the picture. Frank B. Mason was proprietor of the local newspaper the *Tenby Observer* and was responsible for the passing of the Parliamentary Bill, 'The Admission of the Press Bill' in 1908, the same year the large portrait was painted.

Artists have also donated their work and recently the museum has benefitted from donations of oil paintings by Gwilym Prichard (*Snow – South Beach*), Claudia Williams (*Boxing Day Plunge, 2001*) and Grahame Hurd-Wood (*View of St David's*). The museum continues to receive financial support from The Friends of Tenby Museum and in the past has successfully obtained grant aid from MLA and the Art Fund which, under their previous titles of the Museums and Galleries Commission and the National Art Collections Fund, facilitated acquisition of the two important works by Gwen John previously discussed and illustrated in this catalogue.

Mark Lewis, Collections Manager

Adams, K. D.
Brother Thomas's Garden 1973
oil on board 28 x 22
TENBM:2009:0077

Adlam, Hank b.1922
*Trawler out of Tenby in a South West Wind,
c.1895* 2001
oil on canvas 34 x 48
TENBM:2005:0013

Allen, Herbert Charles Goodeve Allen
1878–1965
Tenby from Waterwynch 1944
oil on canvas 28 x 38
TENBM:1983:1477

Allen, Herbert Charles Goodeve Allen
1878–1965
Louis Kingdom (owner and skipper of 'The Hermes') 1945
oil on canvas 66 x 75
TENBM:1983:1365

Allen, Herbert Charles Goodeve Allen
1878–1965
Tenby Lifeboat 'J. R. Webb II' and Coxswain Benjamin Richards 1952
oil on board 100.5 x 87
TENBM:1994:0108

Allen, Herbert Charles Goodeve Allen
1878–1965
Preselly's 1953
oil on board 78 x 88
TENBM:2009:0003(3)

Allen, Herbert Charles Goodeve Allen
1878–1965
St Julian's Church 1956
oil on board 78 x 80
TENBM:2009:0003(2)

Artz active 20th C
Portrait of a Mother and Children
oil on porcelain 37.5 x 25.5
TENBM:1983:1436

Blake-Reed, John 1882–1966
Tenby Five Arches 1965
oil on board 16.5 x 10.5
TENBM:2009:0003(10a)

Bowen, Augusta M. 1869–1944
Cottage near the Sluice 1895
oil on canvas 70 x 60
TENBM:1983:1411

Bowen, Augusta M. 1869–1944
Quay Hill 1895
oil on canvas 30.5 x 46
TENBM:1983:1473

Bowen, Augusta M. 1869–1944
Tenby Harbour 1895
oil on canvas 60.5 x 70.5
TENBM:1983:1413

Bowen, Augusta M. 1869–1944
The Sluice, Tenby c.1900
oil on canvas 42 x 37
TENBM:1983:1482

Bradforth, Eric b.1920
Pembrokeshire Corner, Hodgeston 1969
oil on board 52 x 70
TENBM:1983:1442

Bradforth, Eric b.1920
The Mayor's Slip 1995
oil on board 59 x 68
TENBM:1996:0025

Facing page: Jones, Selwyn, 1928–1998, *Two Labourers*, 1960, Pembrokeshire County Council's Museums Service (p. 89)

Bradforth, Eric b.1920
Tenby in 1586
acrylic on board 127 x 97.5
TENBM:1993:0053

Buckley, Elizabeth Anne Kershaw
1854–1920
St Mary's Church Interior
oil on canvas 35.5 x 45.5
TENBM:1996:0164

Burton-Richardson, David b.1961
Landscape: Snowfall 1999
oil on linen 90 x 105
TENBM:2004:0006

Burton-Richardson, David b.1961
Preseli Hills: Evening Sunset 2004
acrylic on linen 103 x 113
TENBM:2004:0007

Cook, Eric Trayler 1893–1978
Hotels on the Front at Tenby 1955
oil on board 21.5 x 26.6
TENBM:1984:0001(2)

Cook, Eric Trayler 1893–1978
St Florence Church near Tenby 1955
oil on board 21.5 x 26.5
TENBM:1984:0001(3)

Cook, Eric Trayler 1893–1978
St Lawrence, Gumfreston near Tenby 1955
oil on board 35.7 x 26
TENBM:1984:0001(1)

Cook, Eric Trayler 1893–1978
Tenby Castle and Castle Hill 1955
oil on board 38 x 28.5
TENBM:1984:0001(4)

Coulson, Jerry
Robin Crockford c.1966
oil on canvas 59 x 44.5
TENBM:2007:0006

Devas, Anthony 1911–1958
Miss Farrant 1949
oil on canvas 96 x 73
TENBM:1997:0012

Duncan, James Robert b.1939
Shed on Caldey Island 2006
oil on canvas 25 x 35
TENBM:2007:0012

Edwards, John Uzzell b.1937
Barges 1964
oil on canvas 93.5 x 88
TENBM:2009:0003(1)

Edwards, John Uzzell b.1937
Bride and Groom, Tenby 1968
tempera on board 101 x 101
TENBM:2002:0103

Edwards, P. D.
HMS 'Tenby' (1941–1946) 2002
oil on board 45 x 62
TENBM:2010:0012(1)

Felder, J. H. L. (attributed to)
Interior of St Mary's Church 1904
oil on canvas 55.5 x 40.5
TENBM:1983:1435

Fisher-Hoch, Nesta Donne 1903–1997
Landscape 1972
oil on paper 21 x 29.6
TENBM:2006:0213(1)

Fishley, Reginald
'Edith of Milford' (Captain Clark) 1909
oil on canvas 60 x 80
TENBM:1983:1504

Gere, Charles March 1869–1957
Caldey from Sunny Mead
oil on board 38 x 51
TENBM:1983:1415

Golding, William c.1771–1845
Tenby from North Cliff 1799
oil on wood 77 x 107
TENBM:1983:1361

Gregson, Anne b.1936
Magic Symbols, 2010 2010
acrylic on board 108 x 81
TENBM:2010:0064

Grupton
Family Life 1921
oil on porcelain 37.5 x 25.5
TENBM:1983:1437

Guy, Roy b.1944
Chiaroscuro 2005
oil on canvas 146 x 122
TENBM:2005:0049

Haines, Elizabeth b.1945
Streetscape, Candes 1999
oil on board 79 x 69
TENBM:2012:0023

Hammersley, Doreen b.1926
Miss Jessie Allen 1960s
oil on board 52 x 45
TENBM:1983:1445

Hammersley, Doreen b.1926
Nurse Marjorie Knowling 1960s
oil on canvas 51 x 46
TENBM:1983:1410

Hammersley, Doreen b.1926
Harry Billing late 1960s
oil on canvas 68 x 57
TENBM:2006:0028

Head, Edward Joseph 1863–1937
White Roses c.1890
oil on canvas 61 x 51.5
TENBM:1983:1502

Head, Edward Joseph 1863–1937
A Tenby Fisherman c.1900
oil on canvas 89 x 77
TENBM:1983:3875

Head, Edward Joseph 1863–1937
Manorbier Castle 1905
oil on canvas 70 x 105
TENBM:1997:0013

Head, Edward Joseph 1863–1937
Frank B. Mason and Family on the Beach
1908
oil on canvas 165 x 140
TENBM:1987:0073 (P)

Head, Edward Joseph 1863–1937
The Domino Players 1910
oil on canvas 95.5 x 117.5
TENBM:1985:0095

Head, Edward Joseph 1863–1937
Joseph (Currie) Davies 1911
oil on canvas 59 x 49
TENBM:1985:0055 (P)

Head, Edward Joseph 1863–1937
Eira Rosetta Thomas (Dolly and I) c.1929
oil on canvas 103 x 82
TENBM:1997:0014

Head, Edward Joseph 1863–1937
Nancy Flynn 1935–1936
oil on board 68 x 59.5
TENBM:2012:0024

Head, Edward Joseph 1863–1937
A Bowl of Roses
oil on canvas 61 x 52
TENBM:2009:0003(113)

Head, Edward Joseph 1863–1937
Waggoners Well
oil on board 46 x 37
TENBM:1991:0055

Head, Edward Joseph (attributed to)
1863–1937
Mother Hen and Chicks
oil on paper on canvas 35.5 x 50
TENBM:2011:0002

Howard-Jones, Ray 1903–1996
Mary Constance 1925
oil on canvas 73.5 x 63
TENBM:2003:0022

Howard-Jones, Ray 1903–1996
Moment of Perception 1967
oil on canvas 65.5 x 91
TENBM:2003:0023

Hurd-Wood, Grahame Fergus b.1956
View of St David's c.2009
oil on canvas 58 x 109
TENBM:2011:0001

John, Augustus Edwin 1878–1961
Richard Hughes 1937
oil on canvas 61 x 51.5
TENBM:1983:1412

John, Augustus Edwin 1878–1961
David John c.1937
oil on canvas 95 x 80
TENBM:1988:0117

John, Augustus Edwin 1878–1961
Self Portrait c.1940
oil on panel 37.5 x 32.5
TENBM:2011:0304

John, Gwen 1876–1939
Landscape at Tenby with Figures c.1896/1897
oil on board 46 x 57
TENBM:1996:0030

John, Gwen 1876–1939
Winifred John c.1900
oil on canvas 25 x 20
TENBM:1983:1385

Jones, Ida (attributed to) 1883–1966
Fisherman and Wife c.1918
oil on canvas 57 x 36.5
TENBM:1983:1461

Knapp-Fisher, John b.1931
Cresswell Street, Tenby 1998
oil on paper 90 x 83
TENBM:2009:0008

Llywelyn Hall, Dan b.1980
Tenby Harbour 2006
oil on canvas 57 x 81
TENBM:2008:0018

Marquis
Fisherman's Cottage (Tenby Harbour) 1850
oil on board 57.5 x 71
TENBM:1983:3872

Morgan, Oliver
Jubilee Oak, 1889 1970
oil on canvas 32 x 44.5
TENBM:1983:4882

Morris, Dorothy b.1953
Dŵr
acrylic on canvas 65 x 65
TENBM:2008:0029

Morris, Reginald 1883–1941
Gypsy c.1920
oil on canvas 40.5 x 51
TENBM:1983:1476

Morris, Reginald 1883–1941
The 'Gwendoline'
oil on board 68 x 86.5
TENBM:1983:3885

Morse-Brown, Sam 1903–2001
Viaduct and the Green, Tenby 1939
oil on board 59 x 69
TENBM:1983:1416

Nash, Eustace P. E. 1886–1969
Manorbier Bay
oil on board 34 x 39
TENBM:1983:1430

Noble, W. F.
Fisherman's Wife
oil on board 42.5 x 34.5
TENBM:1983:5299

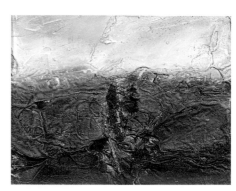

Organ, Michael b.1939
Landscape Study: Craig y Cilau 2002
oil on board 33 x 38
TENBM:2004:0008

Pearse, Margaretta b.c.1883
Altar Steps, St Mary's Church
oil on canvas 45 x 51
TENBM:1996:0163

Perry, Douglas William b.1926
Caldey from Castle Hill 2000
oil on board 13 x 13
TENBM:2006:0021

Plunkett, Brendan S.
Green Bridge (Stack Rocks)
oil on board 53.5 x 80
TENBM:1996:0012(2)

Powis Evans, Nellie 1875–1948
Old Friends 1901
oil on canvas 57 x 92
TENBM:1983:1505

Powis Evans, Nellie 1875–1948
Tommy Parcell c.1910
oil on canvas 43 x 32.5
TENBM:1983:1453

Powis Evans, Nellie 1875–1948
Flowers in a Vase
oil on canvas 46 x 32.5
TENBM:2009:0003(114)

Powis Evans, Nellie 1875–1948
Monkstone
oil on board 10 x 14
TENBM:2009:0003(9)

Price-Gwynne, Fanny 1819–1901
St Catherine's Isle before 1868
oil on board 21.9 x 30
TENBM:1983:2349

Prichard, Gwilym b.1931
Snow – South Beach, 2010 2010
oil on canvas 27 x 34.5
TENBM:2010:0062

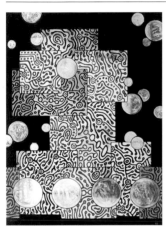

Pritchard, Ceri b.1954
Divide or Multiply 2010
oil & pigment on canvas 134 x 100
TENBM:2010:0063

Rhys-Jones, D. C. active 1975–1977
Christmas 1975, High Street at Midnight 1975
oil on board 31 x 26.6
TENBM:1983:1426

Rhys-Jones, D. C. active 1975–1977
Tenby 11am Any Day 1977
oil on board 48.5 x 35.5
TENBM:1983:2371

Rixon, William Augustus 1858–1948
Cenarth Falls, River Teifi 1931
oil on board 64 x 73
TENBM:1983:1401

Rixon, William Augustus 1858–1948
Manorbier Church 1931
oil on canvas 49.5 x 42.5
TENBM:1983:1380

Rixon, William Augustus 1858–1948
Pembroke Castle 1931
oil on board 50 x 60
TENBM:1983:1390

Rosenthal, Stan b.1933
St David's 1994
oil & gouache on canvas 67 x 57
TENBM:1994:0178

Salisbury, Frank O. 1874–1962
Mrs Margaret Perry 1947
oil on canvas 115 x 94
TENBM:1985:0011

Salisbury, Frank O. 1874–1962
W. Harold Perry, Esq. 1947
oil on canvas 134 x 108
TENBM:2002:0003

Sivell, Marcia
Ivor Crockford (1911–1990) 1991
oil on board 67 x 57
TENBM:1998:0285

Sutton, Philip b.1928
Tenby Harbour, 1989 1989
oil on canvas 100 x 100
TENBM:1996:0120

Thompson, Linda b.1950
'On no account…' 2008
acrylic, oil, ink & photograph on board
75.5 x 51
TENBM:2011:0335

unknown artist
Tenby Harbour c.1850
oil on board 34 x 42
TENBM:1983:3871

unknown artist
South Gate, Five Arches 1853
oil on board 32 x 43
TENBM:1983:4090

unknown artist
Steamship 'Éclair' c.1869
oil on board 25 x 44
TENBM:1983:3882

Facing page: Lewis, Edward Morland, 1903–1943, *People Seated*, c.1930–1935, Carmarthenshire Museums Service
Collection (p. 30)

unknown artist
Quay Hill, Tenby c.1880
oil on canvas 42.5 x 33
TENBM:1987:0036

unknown artist
Portrait of a Boy in a Sailor's Suit c.1893
oil on canvas 46 x 36
TENBM:1983:1429

unknown artist
North Bay c.1909
oil on board 10 x 18
TENBM:1983:5313

unknown artist
Caldey from South Beach with Donkey
oil on canvas 24 x 35
TENBM:1983:1483

unknown artist
Landscape
oil on paper 32.5 x 46
TENBM:1983:1443

unknown artist
M. Thierry, the Past Owner of 'Imperial Hotel'
oil on canvas 60.5 x 45
TENBM:1983:1506

unknown artist
Portrait of a Monk
oil on canvas 55 x 44.5
TENBM:1983:1432

unknown artist
St Mary's College, Tenby, Looking South
oil on canvas 23 x 32
TENBM:1996:0132

unknown artist
Tenby Harbour
oil on canvas 33 x 43
TENBM:2009:0018

unknown artist
Thomas Kynaston of Caldy Island
oil on canvas 64 x 54
TENBM:1987:0052

Williams, Claudia b.1933
Boxing Day Plunge, 2001 (at Tenby) 2002
oil on canvas 89 x 107
TENBM:2005:0075

Tenby Town Council

Allen
View of Tenby 1948
oil on canvas 65 x 110
PCF7

Dunbar, J. active 2003–2004
John Thomas, Tenby Town Crier 2003
oil on board 55 x 44
PCF5

Dunbar, J. active 2003–2004
Mayoral Group 2004
oil on board 54.5 x 70
PCF1

Franck, Ellen
Alderman Clement Williams, JP, Mayor of Tenby (1891–1893 & 1898–1901) 1906
oil on canvas 112 x 87
PCF4

unknown artist
Portrait of a Gentleman with a Flute
c.1750–1830
oil on canvas 128 x 104
PCF6

unknown artist
Portrait of an Unknown Lady in a Red Dress
c.1750–1830
oil on canvas 128 x 104
PCF3

unknown artist
George White, Mayor of Tenby (1862–1864),
Descendant of the White Family
oil on canvas 180 x 75
PCF2

Abertawe Bro Morgannwg University Health Board

In the nineteenth century, Florence Nightingale wrote:

> *'The effect on sickness of beautiful objects, of variety of objects and especially of brilliancy of colour is hardly at all appreciated. People say the effect is only on the mind. It is no such thing. The effect is on the body, too. Little as we know about the way in which we are affected by form, by colour and light, we do know this, they have an actual physical effect. Variety of form and brilliancy of colour in the objects presented to patients are actual means of recovery.'* (1860)

It seems incredible that it is a relatively recent recognition that the environment within a healthcare setting has a major impact on a person's well being and road to recovery, when Florence Nightingale acknowledged its effects over a century and a half ago. The arts enrich the built environment, enhancing care and healing, a springboard for new relationships and a catalyst for cultural change.

There are very few historical artworks in South Wales Hospitals, mostly portraits of the industrialists who became benefactors of the early health provision in deprived areas. It appears that the most popular and noticeable method of donation was to buy a bed.

Since 2005, and gathering momentum every year, Abertawe Bro Morgannwg University Health Board has taken up the initiative, ensuring that Capital Building Schemes earmark a percentage for artworks. This is reflected in the current Collection. The spirit of each body of work commissioned for a scheme, as well as enhancing the general environment for patients, visitors and staff, must evoke the role or effect it should have on that specialty's patients e.g. distracting, calming, enlivening, practical, questioning, therapeutic, reminiscence. Experience has proved that interpretations of Swansea locales are a must!

Fiona M. Edwards, Property Manager (Arts in Health)

Atkins, S. A.
A Plate with Two Pears and an Apple
poster paint on paper 41 x 57
PCF118

Atkins, S. A.
Blue and White Bowl with an Apple
poster paint & charcoal on paper 29.5 x 38
PCF117

Atkins, S. A.
Jug and Plate with Apples
poster paint on paper 49 x 69.5
PCF109

Atkins, S. A.
Jug and Two Bowls with Fruit
acrylic on canvas 60 x 45.5
PCF115

Atkins, S. A.
Two Bowls, Two Apples, a Pear and a Place Mat
poster paint & charcoal on paper 34.5 x 49.5
PCF116

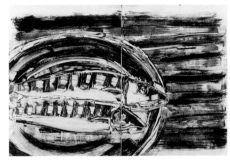

Atkins, S. A.
Two Fish on a Plate
poster paint on paper 40 x 60
PCF108

Bannon, Ian
Breaking Wave 2010
acrylic on canvas 91.5 x 112
PCF99

Cresswell, Rebecca b.1980
Lady from the Lake (tale from the Mabinogion) 2008
acrylic (?) & mixed media on canvas 180 x 200
PCF39

Cresswell, Rebecca b.1980
Lady from the Lake; Shepherd (tale from the Mabinogion) 2008
acrylic (?) & mixed media on canvas 180 x 200
PCF38

Davies, Alexandra Jane b.1980
*Bird of Prey and Hot Air Balloon in the Black
Mountains* 2006
acrylic on board 59.5 x 69
PCF94

Davies, Alexandra Jane b.1980
Sea to Garden Journey 2006
acrylic on board 60 x 123
PCF20

Davies, Alexandra Jane b.1980
Sea to Garden Journey 2006
acrylic on board 60 x 176
PCF21_D1

Davies, Alexandra Jane b.1980
Sea to Garden Journey 2006
acrylic on board 60 x 22.5
PCF21_D2

Davies, Alexandra Jane b.1980
Sea to Garden Journey 2006
acrylic on board 60 x 140
PCF22

Davies, Alexandra Jane b.1980
Sea to Garden Journey 2006
acrylic on board 60 x 103.5
PCF23

Davies, Alexandra Jane b.1980
Sea to Garden Journey 2006
acrylic on board 60 x 189
PCF24

Davies, Alexandra Jane b.1980
Sea to Garden Journey 2006
acrylic on board 60 x 189
PCF25

Davies, Alexandra Jane b.1980
Sea to Garden Journey 2006
acrylic on board 59 x 199
PCF26

Davies, Alexandra Jane b.1980
Sea to Garden Journey 2006
acrylic on board 60 x 243.5
PCF27_1

Davies, Alexandra Jane b.1980
Sea to Garden Journey 2006
acrylic on board 59 x 149
PCF27_2

Davies, Alexandra Jane b.1980
South West Wales Landscapes 2006
acrylic on board 59.5 x 147.5
PCF62

Davies, Alexandra Jane b.1980
South West Wales Landscapes 2006
acrylic on board 59.5 x 147.5
PCF63

Davies, Alexandra Jane b.1980
Window View (triptych, left wing) 2007
acrylic on board 78 x 65
PCF64_T1

Davies, Alexandra Jane b.1980
Window View (triptych, centre panel) 2007
acrylic on board 78 x 65
PCF64_T2

Davies, Alexandra Jane b.1980
Window View (triptych, right wing) 2007
acrylic on board 78 x 65
PCF64_T3

Davies, Alexandra Jane b.1980
Tropical Bird Frieze: Leopard 2008
acrylic on board 45 x 93.5
PCF92

Davies, Alexandra Jane b.1980
Distraction Panels: Fairy Woodland
acrylic on board 99 x 99
PCF41

Davies, Alexandra Jane b.1980
Distraction Panels: Mermaids and Underwater Creatures
acrylic on board 99 x 99
PCF40

Davies, Alexandra Jane b.1980
Potting Shed Shelf
acrylic on board 58 x 198
PCF93

Davies, Alexandra Jane b.1980
Tropical Bird Frieze
acrylic on board 44 x 122
PCF61_T1

Davies, Alexandra Jane b.1980
Tropical Bird Frieze
acrylic on board 44 x 140
PCF61_T2

Davies, Alexandra Jane b.1980
Tropical Bird Frieze
acrylic on board 44 x 140
PCF61_T3

Davies, Alexandra Jane b.1980
Window View of Sea
acrylic on board 140.5 x 120
PCF19

Donovan, James b.1974
Boxer 1998
oil on canvas 59 x 68.3
PCF87

Donovan, James b.1974
Gulliver 1998
oil on canvas 129.5 x 159.5
PCF89

Donovan, James b.1974
King 1998
oil on canvas 117 x 178.5
PCF90

Facing page: Brangwyn, Frank, 1867–1956, *Self Portrait with Miners*, 1907, Glynn Vivian Art Gallery (p. 162)

Donovan, James b.1974
Man in Fez 1998
oil on canvas 127.5 x 103.5
PCF91

Donovan, James b.1974
Man on Tower with Net 1998
oil on canvas 177 x 150
PCF88

Hawkins, David
Swansea Bay 1979
acrylic on board 58.8 x 120
PCF95

Iles, James
Beach Huts 2005
acrylic on canvas 95 x 122
PCF85

Iles, James
Cranes Triptych (left wing) 2005
acrylic on board 95 x 122
PCF86_T1

Iles, James
Cranes Triptych (centre panel) 2005
acrylic on board 95 x 122
PCF86_T2

Iles, James
Cranes Triptych (right wing) 2005
acrylic on board 95 x 122
PCF86_T3

Iles, James
Steps to the Beach 2005
acrylic on canvas 95.5 x 122
PCF97

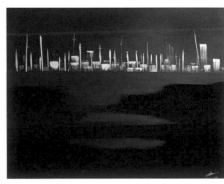

Iles, James
Waterfront in Red and Blue 2005
acrylic on canvas 95 x 122
PCF98

J., S.
Winter Scene
oil on paper 16.6 x 11.5
PCF122

Jenkins, Glyn
Mountain Scene
acrylic on canvas 48.5 x 39
PCF123

Le Grice, Kathryn b.1972
All Saints Church, Mumbles 2008
acrylic (?) & mixed media on paper 30 x 39
PCF45

Le Grice, Kathryn b.1972
Maritime Quarter, Swansea 2008
acrylic (?) & mixed media on paper 30 x 39
PCF44

Le Grice, Kathryn b.1972
'Morgans Hotel', Swansea 2008
acrylic (?) & mixed media on paper 39 x 30
PCF42

Le Grice, Kathryn b.1972
Mumbles Road Methodist Church 2008
acrylic (?) & mixed media on paper 39 x 30
PCF52

Le Grice, Kathryn b.1972
Newton Road, Mumbles, No.1 2008
acrylic (?) & mixed media on paper 39 x 30
PCF49

Le Grice, Kathryn b.1972
Newton Road, Mumbles, No.2 2008
acrylic (?) & mixed media on paper 39 x 30
PCF51

Le Grice, Kathryn b.1972
Patti Pavilion, Swansea 2008
acrylic (?) & mixed media on paper 39 x 30
PCF43

Le Grice, Kathryn b.1972
Picton Arcade 2008
acrylic (?) & mixed media on paper 39 x 30
PCF48

Le Grice, Kathryn b.1972
Southend, Mumbles, No.1 2008
acrylic (?) & mixed media on paper 30 x 39
PCF50

Le Grice, Kathryn b.1972
Southend, Mumbles, No.2 2008
acrylic (?) & mixed media on paper 30 x 39
PCF53

Le Grice, Kathryn b.1972
Swansea Market 2008
acrylic (?) & mixed media on paper 39 x 30
PCF47

Le Grice, Kathryn b.1972
Wind Street, Swansea 2008
acrylic (?) & mixed media on paper 39 x 30
PCF46

Oliveri
Rainy French Street Scene
oil on board 49.4 x 75
PCF96

Potter, Andrew
Boats 2005
acrylic on board 30 x 90
PCF69_1

Potter, Andrew
Boats 2005
acrylic on board 30 x 90
PCF69_2

Potter, Andrew
Boats 2005
acrylic on board 30 x 90
PCF70_1

Potter, Andrew
Boats 2005
acrylic on board 30 x 90
PCF70_2

Potter, Andrew
Float Painting I 2005
acrylic on board 30 x 30
PCF75

Potter, Andrew
Float Painting II 2005
acrylic on board 30 x 30
PCF76

Potter, Andrew
Float Painting III 2005
acrylic on board 30 x 30
PCF77

Potter, Andrew
Float Painting IV 2005
acrylic on board 30 x 30
PCF78

Potter, Andrew
Float Painting V 2005
acrylic on board 30 x 30
PCF79

Potter, Andrew
Seascape Triptych (left wing) 2005
acrylic on board 44.5 x 35
PCF81_T1

Potter, Andrew
Seascape Triptych (centre panel) 2005
acrylic on board 44.5 x 35
PCF81_T2

Potter, Andrew
Seascape Triptych (right wing) 2005
acrylic on board 44.5 x 35
PCF81_T3

Potter, Andrew
Single Boat 2005
acrylic on board 30 x 90
PCF82

Potter, Andrew
Stepping Stones 2005
acrylic on board 68.5 x 24.5
PCF83

Potter, Andrew
Beach Huts
acrylic on board 35 x 70.5
PCF68

Richards, Helen active 2003–2004
Floral V 2003
acrylic on board 120 x 243
PCF104

Richards, Helen active 2003–2004
Butterfly 2004
household paint on board 121 x 120
PCF72

Richards, Helen active 2003–2004
Floral VI 2004
household paint on board 121 x 181
PCF80

Richards, Helen active 2003–2004
Brynmill Park
household paint on board 121 x 243
PCF71

Richards, Helen active 2003–2004
Clyne Gardens
household paint on board 121 x 243
PCF73

Richards, Helen active 2003–2004
Cwmdonkin Park
household paint on board 121 x 243
PCF74

Richards, Helen active 2003–2004
Floral I
acrylic on board 150 x 90
PCF100

Richards, Helen active 2003–2004
Floral II
acrylic on board 176 x 29
PCF101

Richards, Helen active 2003–2004
Floral III
acrylic on board 150 x 90
PCF102

Richards, Helen active 2003–2004
Floral IV
acrylic on board 166 x 29.6
PCF103

Richards, Helen active 2003–2004
Victoria Park
household paint on board 121 x 243
PCF84

Taylor, Sean b.1951
Fishing Trip 2008
acrylic on canvas 40 x 40
PCF54

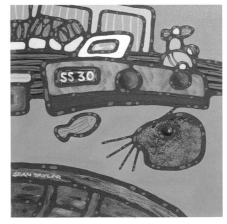

Taylor, Sean b.1951
Harbour Boats 2008
acrylic on canvas 30 x 30
PCF55

Taylor, Sean b.1951
Harbour Window 2008
acrylic on canvas 30 x 30
PCF56

Taylor, Sean b.1951
Seal 2008
acrylic on canvas 30 x 30
PCF57

Taylor, Sean b.1951
St Ives Gull 2008
acrylic on canvas 30 x 30
PCF58

Taylor, Sean b.1951
St Ives Harbour 2008
acrylic on canvas 30 x 30
PCF59

Taylor, Sean b.1951
Two Gulls and Three Yachts 2008
acrylic on canvas 30 x 30
PCF60

Thomas, Hilda
A Dog and Slipper
oil on canvas (?)
PCF105

Trust, Peter 1936–2008
Dragon Express
acrylic on canvas 91.5 x 61
PCF111

Trust, Peter 1936–2008
Laser Appointment Today
acrylic on canvas 91.5 x 61
PCF112

Trust, Peter 1936–2008
Welcome to Bridgend Laserland
acrylic on canvas 91.5 x 61
PCF110

Turley, Jessica
Beside the Seaside (panel 1 of 5) 2010
acrylic on board 129.5 x 67
PCF28_P1

Turley, Jessica
Beside the Seaside (panel 2 of 5) 2010
acrylic on board 130 x 67
PCF28_P2

Turley, Jessica
Beside the Seaside (panel 3 of 5) 2010
acrylic on board   130 x 67
PCF28_P3

Turley, Jessica
Beside the Seaside (panel 4 of 5) 2010
acrylic on board   130 x 67
PCF28_P4

Turley, Jessica
Beside the Seaside (panel 5 of 5) 2010
acrylic on board   130 x 67
PCF28_P5

unknown artist
Alpine Scene
oil on canvas   47 x 98
PCF121

unknown artist
Apples and Plums on a Plate
acrylic on canvas   37.3 x 32
PCF113

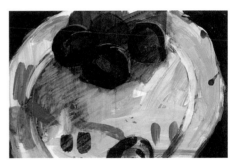

unknown artist
Cherries (?) on a Plate
poster paint on paper   20.8 x 31.3
PCF131

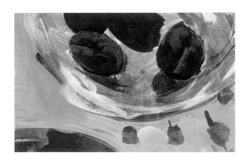

unknown artist
Cherries (?) on a Plate (detail)
poster paint on paper   22 x 35
PCF132

unknown artist
Eygptian Scene
acrylic on canvas   50.5 x 76
PCF124

unknown artist
Lighthouse with Boat and Left-Hand Wing Mirror
poster paint on paper   122 x 91
PCF125

unknown artist
Lighthouse with Boat and Right-Hand Wing Mirror
poster paint on paper 121 x 92
PCF126

unknown artist
One Fish on a Plate
poster paint, pastel & charcoal on paper 15 x 29.7
PCF130

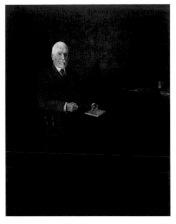

unknown artist
Portrait of a Benefactor of Swansea General Hospital
oil on canvas 200.5 x 156.5
PCF65

unknown artist
Portrait of a Benefactor of Swansea General Hospital
oil on canvas 141 x 94.5
PCF66

unknown artist
Portrait of a Benefactor of Swansea General Hospital
oil on canvas 141 x 94.5
PCF67

unknown artist
Steamboat with Windshelter in the Foreground
poster paint on paper 90 x 64
PCF127

unknown artist
Tulips in a Vase
poster paint collage on paper 83.3 x 58.7
PCF119

unknown artist
Tulips in a Vase with a Boat and a Lighthouse
poster paint on paper 74.5 x 50.7
PCF120

unknown artist
View of a Lighthouse, Boat and Balloon with Tulips in a Vase in the Foreground
poster paint on paper 47.6 x 74
PCF129

Facing page: Walters, Evan, 1893–1951, *Abstract Figures Smoking*, Glynn Vivian Art Gallery (p. 218)

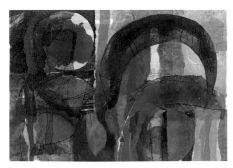

Waite, Trevor
Abstract in Blue, Orange, Peach and Green
1996
poster paint & charcoal on paper 34.5 x 49.5
PCF107

Waite, Trevor
Abstract in Blue, Tan, Pink and Red 1996
poster paint & charcoal on paper 41.3 x 56.5
PCF134

Waite, Trevor
Abstract in Blue, White, Black and Dark Red
1996
poster paint & charcoal on paper 28 x 37.3
PCF137

Waite, Trevor
Abstract in Tan, Orange and Blue 1996
poster paint & charcoal on paper 47 x 35.3
PCF135

Waite, Trevor
Abstract in White, Red and Orange 1996
poster paint & charcoal on paper 53.3 x 74.5
PCF133

Waite, Trevor
*Abstract with a Dark Blue Container in the
Foreground* 1996
poster paint & charcoal on paper 36 x 52
PCF136

Waite, Trevor
Openings V
poster paint on paper 43.2 x 31.8
PCF106

Ward, Amy
Orientation Panel; Flowers 2008
acrylic on board 100 x 17.8
PCF7

Ward, Amy
Orientation Panel; Flowers 2008
acrylic on board 84.7 x 54
PCF8.D1

Ward, Amy
Orientation Panel; Flowers 2008
acrylic on board 85 x 39
PCF8.D2

Ward, Amy
Orientation Panel; Flowers 2008
acrylic on board 100 x 17.8
PCF9

Ward, Amy
Orientation Panel; Birds 2008
acrylic on board 100 x 17.8
PCF1

Ward, Amy
Orientation Panel; Birds 2008
acrylic on board 100 x 17.8
PCF2

Ward, Amy
Orientation Panel; Lighthouse 2008
acrylic on board 100 x 17.8
PCF4

Ward, Amy
Orientation Panel; Lighthouse 2008
acrylic on board 100 x 17.8
PCF5

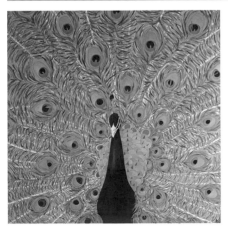

Ward, Amy
Orientation Panel; Peacock 2008
acrylic on board 115 x 115
PCF3

Ward, Amy
Orientation Panel; Ponds 2008
acrylic on board 100 x 17.8
PCF10

Ward, Amy
Orientation Panel; Ponds 2008
acrylic on board 100 x 17.8
PCF11

Ward, Amy
Orientation Panel; Ponds 2008
acrylic on board 115 x 115
PCF12

Ward, Amy
Orientation Panel; Schooner 2008
acrylic on board 115 x 115
PCF6

Ward, Amy
Orientation Panel; Trees 2008
acrylic on board 100 x 17.8
PCF13

Ward, Amy
Orientation Panel; Trees 2008
acrylic on board 100 x 17.8
PCF14

Ward, Amy
Orientation Panel; Trees 2008
acrylic on board 115 x 115
PCF15

Ward, Amy
Orientation Panel; Welsh Dresser 2008
acrylic on board 100 x 17.8
PCF16

Ward, Amy
Orientation Panel; Welsh Dresser 2008
acrylic on board 100 x 17.8
PCF17

Ward, Amy
Orientation Panel; Welsh Dresser 2008
acrylic on board 115 x 115
PCF18

Wood, Charlotte
Wild Savannah 2010
acrylic on board 130 x 67
PCF33_P1

Wood, Charlotte
Wild Savannah 2010
acrylic on board 130 x 67
PCF33_P2

Wood, Charlotte
Wild Savannah 2010
acrylic on board 130 x 67
PCF33_P3

Wood, Charlotte
Wild Savannah 2010
acrylic on board 130 x 67
PCF33_P4

Wood, Charlotte
Wild Savannah 2010
acrylic on board 130 x 67
PCF33_P5

Glynn Vivian Art Gallery

Founded in 1911, this handsome Edwardian gallery offers a broad range of visual arts from the original bequest of Richard Glynn Vivian (1835–1910) to art of the twenty-first century.

In 1855, Richard Glynn Vivian inherited his share in the family's famous Hafod copper works. He travelled the world, and collected art throughout his life. In his old age, he decided to gift his collection to the people of Swansea for their enjoyment, ensuring that the Gallery was built to house the artworks. The City & County of Swansea is proud to inherit this unique legacy, and the Gallery continues to thrive today.

Richard Glynn Vivian's bequest comprises British and European old masters, with notable Welsh artists such as Richard Wilson (1713–1782) and Penry Williams (1798–1885), whose paintings were produced at a time when very few Welsh artists were working in Italy. European oil paintings date from the sixteenth to the nineteenth century, and many of these will be redisplayed when the Gallery re-opens in 2014 following the refurbishment. These include R. E. Pfeninger's portrait of Richard Glynn Vivian, religious paintings such as *Ecce Homo* attributed to Correggio (c.1489–1534), as well as works by Gustave Doré (1832–1883), purchased from the artist's studio sale in Paris in 1885. These and other works in the bequest are currently being researched for the new displays, with support from the Heritage Lottery Fund and Welsh Government.

Whilst Richard Glynn Vivian's paintings generally reflect traditional classical taste, his travels and philanthropy are offering fresh insights into our local heritage. The bequest inspired many other philanthropists to make gifts to the Gallery, including François Depeaux (1853–1920), who was a major collector of Impressionist paintings and patron of Alfred Sisley (1839–1899), who also visited the city in the summer of 1897. François Depeaux loved Swansea, where he had established his business in coal-mining, and he donated an important group of Impressionist paintings by artists from Rouen, where he lived. Other major gifts have since followed, and more recently, architect, Sir Alex Gordon (1917–1999), bequeathed his very fine personal collection to the Gallery, with paintings by Ben Nicholson, Barbara Hepworth, John Piper and Kyffin Williams, amongst others.

The twentieth century is particularly well-represented with modern painting acquired by William Grant Murray (1877–1950), the Gallery's first Curator and Principal of Swansea School of Art. He received considerable encouragement from local art patron, Winifred Coombe Tennant (1874–1956), and so the Gallery soon established a tradition of supporting contemporary art practice. The collection includes significant paintings by local Welsh artists, such as Evan Walters, as well as Gwen John, Augustus John and J. D. Innes; works were later acquired by Paul Nash, Ivon Hitchens and Stanley Spencer, alongside Cedric Morris, Alfred Janes and Ceri Richards. The 1930s also brought to Swansea the British Empire Panels by Sir Frank Brangwyn, which can be seen at the city's Guildhall. The Gallery continues to be supported by the Contemporary Art Society in London and Wales who, together with the Friends of the Gallery, have donated many important paintings by artists such as Mark Gertler, Wyndham Lewis and Josef Herman. Welsh artists are well-represented with late twentieth-century paintings by Terry Setch, Harry Holland, Glyn Jones and Sue Williams, and more recent work by Shani Rhys-James, Richard Monahan, Brendan Stuart Burns and Merlin James. A major gift from the Arts Council of Wales and Welsh Government, who generously support the Gallery, was received in 2002, and the annual Wakelin Award continues to add steadily to the collection of contemporary Welsh art.

The collection lives deep in the memory of our local communities, and continues to play an active part in our culture and heritage today. These artworks complement the exhibitions programme in the modern wing, which brings the work of today's artists alive with its sharp, contemporary overview of the arts. The Gallery also has a lively learning programme with an open, engaging and transformative approach to participation in the visual arts.

Jenni Spencer-Davies, Curator

Allen, Colin Gard 1926–1987
Landscape with Snow 1953
oil on board 59.8 x 79.8 (E)
GV 1957.1339

Allen, Harry Epworth 1894–1958
Summer 1940
tempera on canvas 50.4 x 60.8
GV 1943.926

Babić, Ljubo 1890–1974
The Black Flag
oil on canvas 62 x 51
GV 1930.498

Baker, Joan b.1922
Miss Cotton 1949
oil on board 53.8 x 39.2
GV 1949.1076

Barker, Thomas 1769–1847
Landscape with Sheep
oil on canvas 29.8 x 40.4
18

Bassano the elder, Jacopo (attributed to)
c.1510–1592
Virgin and Infant Saviour
oil on copper 38 x 19.4
GV 1920.329

Baynes, Keith 1887–1977
Port Meirion, North Wales
oil on canvas 31.5 x 39.5
GV 1932.576

Bell, David 1915–1959
Clyne Common 1957
oil on hardboard 50.5 x 60.9
GV 1961.1439

Belleroche, Albert de 1864–1944
Berthe
oil on canvas 69 x 56
GV 1955.1317

Birchall, Thomas
Seascape to Cliffs 1863
oil on canvas 25.6 x 38.2
GV 1932.562

Birchall, Thomas
Shipping in the Channel
oil on canvas 48.2 x 76.2
GV 1932.561

Bonnor, Rose Dempster 1875–1967
Herbert Eccles, High Sheriff 1909
oil on canvas 161.5 x 121
GV 1994.180

Brangwyn, Frank 1867–1956
Self Portrait with Miners 1907
oil on canvas 124.5 x 127
GV 1985.41

Brangwyn, Frank 1867–1956
British Empire Panel (1) England c.1930
oil on canvas 365.7 x 396
GV 1934.646.1.1

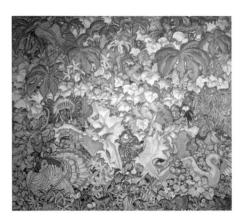

Brangwyn, Frank 1867–1956
British Empire Panel (2) Canada c.1930
oil on canvas 365.7 x 396
GV 1934.646.1.2

Brangwyn, Frank 1867–1956
British Empire Panel (3) Canada c.1930
oil on canvas 609 x 396
GV 1934.646.1.3

Brangwyn, Frank 1867–1956
British Empire Panel (4) Canada c.1930
oil on canvas 609 x 396
GV 1934.646.1.4

Brangwyn, Frank 1867–1956
British Empire Panel (5) Canada c.1930
oil on canva 609 x 396
GV 1934.646.1.5

Facing page: Correggio, c.1489–1534, *Ecce Homo*, Glynn Vivian Art Gallery (p. 169)

Brangwyn, Frank 1867–1956
British Empire Panel (6) West Africa c.1930
oil on canvas 365.7 x 396
GV 1934.646.1.6

Brangwyn, Frank 1867–1956
British Empire Panel (7) West Indies c.1930
oil on canvas 365.7 x 396
GV 1934.646.1.7

Brangwyn, Frank 1867–1956
British Empire Panel (8) Siam c.1930
oil on canvas 365.7 x 396
GV 1934.646.1.8

Brangwyn, Frank 1867–1956
British Empire Panel (9) Burma c.1930
oil on canvas 365.7 x 396
GV 1934.646.1.9

Brangwyn, Frank 1867–1956
British Empire Panel (10) India c.1930
oil on canvas 609 x 396
GV 1934.646.1.10

Brangwyn, Frank 1867–1956
British Empire Panel (11) India c.1930
oil on canvas 609 x 396
GV 1934.646.1.11

Brangwyn, Frank 1867–1956
British Empire Panel (12) India c.1930
oil on canvas 609 x 396
GV 1934.646.1.12

Brangwyn, Frank 1867–1956
British Empire Panel (13) East Africa c.1930
oil on canvas 365.7 x 396
GV 1934.646.1.13

Brangwyn, Frank 1867–1956
British Empire Panel (14) Australia c.1930
oil on canvas 365.7 x 396
GV 1934.646.1.14

Brangwyn, Frank 1867–1956
British Empire Panel (15) East Indies c.1930
oil on canvas 365.7 x 396
GV 1934.646.1.15 ✳

Brangwyn, Frank 1867–1956
British Empire Panel (16) Decorative Panel
c.1930
oil on canvas 213.5 x 264.2
GV 1934.646.1.16 ✳

Brangwyn, Frank 1867–1956
British Empire Panel (17) North Africa c.1930
oil on canvas 365.7 x 396
GV 1934.646.1.17 ✳

Brangwyn, Frank 1867–1956
Caernarvon Castle
oil board 62.2 x 75.6
GV 1995.110 ✳

Brangwyn, Frank 1867–1956
Venetian Boats
oil on card 76.5 x 62.3
GV 1943.930 ✳

Bratby, John Randall 1928–1992
Janet and Lilies 1961
oil on canvas 116 x 85.4
GV 1962.1467 ✳

Breun, John Ernest 1862–1921
William Thomas of Lan, JP, Mayor of Swansea
1877
oil on canvas 99.2 x 69
GV 1994.182

Breun, John Ernest 1862–1921
Portrait of a Mayoress of Swansea 1884
oil on canvas 140.4 x 111.5
GV 1994.183

Breun, John Ernest 1862–1921
William Williams, JP, MP, Mayor of Swansea
(1884) 1884
oil on canvas 140.5 x 112
GV 1994.181

Breun, John Ernest 1862–1921
Mayor of Swansea 1899
oil on canvas 39.3 x 29
GV 1994.190

Briscoe, Mike b.1960
Coast Combinations
acrylic on canvas 121.2 x 182.7
GV 1985.2

British (English) School
Landscape with Figures
oil on canvas 36 x 45.2
19

British (English) School
Portrait of a French Gentleman
oil on canvas 76.5 x 63.7
23

Brooker, William 1918–1983
The Green Divan 1957
oil on canvas 63.5 x 76.2
GV 1958.1383

Burns, Brendan Stuart b.1963
Study for 'Petrol Bomb Attack' 1987
oil on board 41.2 x 39.4
GV 2007.43

Burns, Brendan Stuart b.1963
Taste of Sight Series, 2005 (July 5th) 2005
oil, wax & graphite on board 60 x 72
GV 2007.40

Butler, William 1824–1870
Swansea Bay 1865
oil on canvas 63.1 x 98.3
GV 1989.24

Cadogan, Herbert
Still Life 1932
oil on canvas 41.5 x 61
GV 1932.574

Cirel, Ferdinand 1884–1968
Lobster Study 1920
oil on canvas 29 x 48.6
GV 1953.1218

Cirel, Ferdinand 1884–1968
Light and Dark Grapes
oil on board 34.7 x 42.7
GV 1958.1385

Coats, John F.
Coal Hoist 1948
oil & wax on paper & asbestos 79.2 x 69.3
GV 1948.1055

Collier, John 1850–1934
Souvenir of Chu Chin Chow
oil on canvas 218.2 x 114.5
GV 1936.697

Collins, W. J.
Lake and Cattle
oil on canvas 50.8 x 61
GV 1913.45

Constable, John 1776–1837
Foxgloves
oil on paper 36.7 x 19.6
GV 1994.131

Cooper, John F. b.1929
*Tirlun Dwydianol yn y Nos, Port Talbot
(Industrial Landscape at Night)*
acrylic on canvas 12 x 18
GV 2007.37

Correggio c.1489–1534
Ecce Homo (detail)
oil on canvas 29.4 x 22.3
54

Cortona, Pietro da 1596–1669
Diana and Endymion
oil on canvas 99 x 127.8
35

Cour, Glenys b.1924
Industrial Scene 1961
oil on board 75.7 x 90.2
GV 1967.1724

Cour, Glenys b.1924
The Pool, Cefn Bryn 1963
oil on canvas 87.5 x 106
GV 2002.15

Cour, Glenys b.1924
Cliff Path 1984
oil on canvas 101.5 x 102
GV 1984.8

Cox the elder, David 1783–1859 or **Cox the younger, David** 1809–1885
Landscape with Shepherd
oil on paper 32.4 x 38.2
GV R 137

Crabtree, Jack b.1938
Save This Pit
oil on plyboard 99 x 99
GV 1982.11

Daborn, Erica b.1951
Waiting Room 1 1979
egg tempera on board 127 x 89
GV 1985.3

Davies, Hanlyn b.1942
Mr D. Gwynfor Thomas
oil on canvas 91.5 x 45.6
GV 1998.43

Davies, Margaret Sidney 1884–1963
A Cornfield
oil on canvas 35.7 x 45.8
GV 1953.1138

Delattre, Joseph 1858–1912
The Seine above Rouen
oil on canvas 46.8 x 65.7
GV 1911.6

Delattre, Joseph 1858–1912
The Seine below Rouen
oil on canvas 52.6 x 71.1
GV 1911.5

Delattre, Joseph 1858–1912
Vieilles maisons
oil on canvas 54.9 x 69.7
GV 1919.318

Donaubauer, Wilhelm 1866–1949
The Mill
oil on canvas 23.1 x 33.8
GV 1937.799

Donovan, James b.1974
Ironman Grandpa 1998
acrylic on paper 12 x 7
GV 2007.33

Donovan, James b.1974
The Connoisseur c.1998
acrylic on calico 80 x 70
GV 1999.2

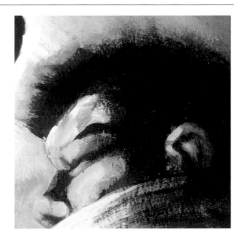

Donovan, James b.1974
Sleeper 2000
acrylic on paper 12 x 12
GV 2007.32

Doré, Gustave 1832–1883
Christ Leaving the Praetorium
oil on canvas 73.1 x 48
38

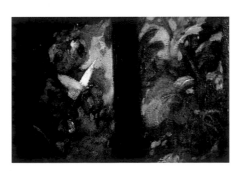

Doré, Gustave 1832–1883
Coin de cellier
oil on canvas 73 x 93
GV 1994.169

Doré, Gustave 1832–1883
Ecce Homo
oil on canvas 138.2 x 88.3
36

Doré, Gustave 1832–1883
Genius Kindled by Fame
oil on canvas 72.5 x 41
33

Doré, Gustave 1832–1883
Judith with the Head of Holofernes
oil on canvas 301 x 208
GV 1990.32

Doré, Gustave 1832–1883
La baigneuse
oil on canvas 191.4 x 128
45

Doré, Gustave 1832–1883
La folie
oil on canvas 170.5 x 120.5
42

Doré, Gustave 1832–1883
La Sainte Trinité
oil on board 63.4 x 50.8
39

Doré, Gustave 1832–1883
Madame Adelina Patti
oil & charcoal on canvas 52.5 x 37
34

Dutch School
The Shepherd c.1790
oil on panel 48.1 x 55.5
GV 1920.327

Edwards, Paul b.1954
Yellow Table/Saxophone 1987
oil on canvas 181.7 x 146
GV 1987.13

Elwyn, John 1916–1997
In the Valley 1940
oil on canvas 23 x 30.5
GV 1948.1051

Facing page: Carracci, Ludovico (attributed to), 1555–1619, *Virgin and Infant Saviour*, Glynn Vivian
Art Gallery (p. 167)

Elwyn, John 1916–1997
Miners Returning over Waste Ground 1951
oil on panel 33.5 x 53.7
GV 2002.16

Elwyn, John 1916–1997
Dark Shapes in the Rain 1952
oil on board 23 x 29.5
GV 1998.8

Elwyn, John 1916–1997
Tree Architecture 1953
oil on canvas 51 x 61
GV 1954.1268

Elwyn, John 1916–1997
Ydlan Yn Sir Aberteifi 1954
oil on canvas 59.5 x 74.4
GV 1954.1267

Evans, Nicholas 1907–2004
Untitled (Pithead Scene) 1976
oil on board 122 x 81
GV 2002.17

Evans, Nicholas 1907–2004
Aberfan 1979
oil on board 122 x 122
GV 1986.87

Evans, Nicholas 1907–2004
Coming to the Surface 1983
oil on board 187.5 x 127.4
GV 1986.65

Evans, Olive E.
Mount Pleasant 1976
oil on paper on card 59.5 x 48.6
GV 2002.18

Evans, Vincent 1896–1976
A Snack 1935
oil on canvas 29.5 x 39.5
GV 1936.708

Evans, Vincent 1896–1976
Family Life c.1935
oil on board 141.5 x 321.2
GV 1983.2

Evans, Vincent 1896–1976
At the Coalface
oil on canvas 46.4 x 56.2
GV 1983.3

Evans, Vincent 1896–1976
Mr Stanley Williams
oil on canvas 68.8 x 58.4
GV 1985.46

Evans, Will 1888–1957
Ploughing 1926
oil on canvas 102.4 x 128.2
GV 1980.16

Evans, Will 1888–1957
Street Scene 1927
oil on canvas board 33 x 28.4
GV 1984.19

Evans, Will 1888–1957
Snow in Swansea 1931
oil 61.5 x 45.9
GV 1932.568

Evans, Will 1888–1957
Entrance to Swansea Market, 1941 1941
oil on panel 41 x 51.2
GV 1994.103

Evans, Will 1888–1957
Llanberis Pass, North Wales
oil on canvas 61.2 x 66
GV 1937.807

Evans, Will 1888–1957
Nant Ffrancon Pass, North Wales
oil on board 54 x 79
GV 1977.57

Evans, Will 1888–1957
Snow, 1945, St Mary's Church, Swansea
oil on canvas 44.7 x 60.1
GV 1994.93

Evans, Will 1888–1957
Wesley Chapel, Swansea, 1941
oil on canvas 58.1 x 63.6
GV 1994.92

Fairley, George 1920–2003
Little Lyric
oil on hardboard 60.3 x 63.2
GV 1961.1447

Flemish School
Sleeping Angel with Emblems of Death
oil on panel 28.3 x 20.4
48

Forbes, Andrew Douglas
Breakfast Eggs
oil on canvas 34.5 x 42.5
GV 1993.11

Ford, Mabs d.2011
Daniel Jones
oil on board 28.7 x 23.6
GV 1995.4

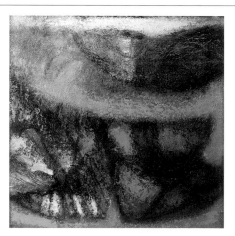

Frechon, Charles 1856–1929
View of Rouen through an Apple Tree
oil on canvas 49.5 x 68
GV 1911.8

Freeman, Michael John b.1936
Angel Visiting a Shipwreck 1990
oil on board 38 x 38
GV 1991.41

French School
Portrait of a Lady with an Ermine Cloak
oil on canvas 90 x 73.5
60

Ganz, Valerie b.1936
Coaling In G8 1986
oil on canvas 84.4 x 206.2
GV 1987.32

Garner, David b.1958
Politics Eclipsed by Economics 1997
oil on tarpaulin 200 x 306
GV 2004.2

German School
Chess Players
oil on glass 56 x 67.9
773

German School
Lady in a Blue Dress
oil on glass 36 x 25.5
776

German School
Untitled (a mythological subject)
oil on glass 32 x 45
777

German School
Untitled (a mythological subject)
oil on glass 32.8 x 45.1
779

Gertler, Mark 1891–1939
The Artist's Mother 1913
oil on canvas 45 x 42.5
GV 1954.1275

Ginner, Charles 1878–1952
Penally Hill
oil on canvas 61 x 50.7
GV 1923.352

Giulio Romano (school of) c.1499–1546
Two Wrestlers
oil on canvas on board 25 x 18.3
53

Goble, Anthony 1943–2007
Water Crossing
oil on board 79.5 x 65.1
GV 1995.14

Goodall, Frederick 1822–1904
The Artist's Daughter
oil on canvas 52 x 44
GV 1911.1

Govier, James Henry 1910–1974
Landscape near Brill
oil on canvas 47.5 x 57.2
GV 1935.687

Grant, Duncan 1885–1978
View in Venice
oil on canvas 48.7 x 67.4
GV 1951.1100

Griffiths, Gwenny b.1867
*Mrs Octavia Howell, Founder of the Swansea
Orphan Home*
oil on canvas 69.2 x 57
GV 1972.7

Guilbert, Narcisse 1878–1942
Banks of the Seine at Croisset
oil on canvas 54.5 x 73
GV 1911.3

Gwynne-Jones, Allan 1892–1982
Emmy as a Bridesmaid 1958
oil on canvas 39.3 x 29.1
GV 1983.38

Gwynne-Jones, Allan 1892–1982
August morning, Suffolk
oil on canvas 48.8 x 66.7
GV 1947.1016

Haddon, Arthur Trevor 1864–1941
Lord Glantawe 1905
oil on canvas 177 x 102
GV 1960.1435

Hagers, Albert Clarence b.1915
Two Fishermen of Ostend 1941
oil on canvas 61.2 x 53.5
GV 1942.911

Hall, Oliver 1869–1957
Welsh Mountains
oil on canvas 59.6 x 75
GV 1995.108

Hancock, Kenneth W. 1911–1978
Ben Davies
oil on canvas 64.2 x 51.9
GV 1935.672

Hancock, Kenneth W. 1911–1978
Mr Sydney Heath
oil on canvas 59.5 x 49.3
GV 1990.35

Hancock, Kenneth W. 1911–1978
Two Figures in a Landscape
oil on board 27 x 44.5
GV 1951.1093

Handley-Read, Edward Henry 1870–1935
Mametz Wood 1916
oil on canvas 121 x 151.6
GV 1942.908

Harlow, George Henry 1787–1819
Portrait of a Gentleman (said to be Burns)
oil on canvas 61.2 x 51.9
25

Harris, Annie
Grandfather's Darling 1890
oil on canvas 91.9 x 61
GV 1980.19

Harris Senior, James 1810–1887
Shipping off Messina 1851
oil on canvas 61 x 91.6
GV 1985.40

Harris Senior, James 1810–1887
Picking up the Pilot 1869
oil on canvas 64 x 107.8
GV 1955.1278

Harris Senior, James 1810–1887
Seascape with Three Barques 1882
oil on canvas 45.8 x 76.4
GV 1921.339

Harris Senior, James 1810–1887
From Paviland to the Worm
oil on canvas 59.5 x 105.5
GV 1996.10

Harris Senior, James 1810–1887
Hafod Copper Works, River Tawy, Swansea
oil on canvas 88.7 x 139.6
GV 1956.1324

Harris Senior, James 1810–1887
Ship in Distress, Hove To
oil on canvas 20.3 x 35.3
GV 1986.52

Haughton, Benjamin 1865–1924
Spring Evening
oil on panel 34.4 x 39.5
GV 1937.804

Haughton, Benjamin 1865–1924
Spring Wheat
oil on panel 33.5 x 43
GV 1937.803

Hayter, George 1792–1871
Lady Belgrave
oil on canvas 61.5 x 51.1
56

Helst, Bartholomeus van der 1613–1670
Portrait of a Young Lady c.1640–1645
oil on canvas 161.6 x 128.6
GV 1974.63

Facing page: Morris, Cedric Lockwood, 1889–1982, *Llanmadoc Hill, Gower*, 1928, Glynn Vivian
Art Gallery (p. 193)

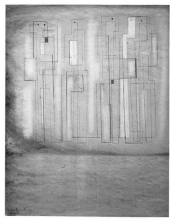

Hepworth, Barbara 1903–1975
Project (group of figures for sculpture) 1952
oil & pencil on board 45 x 34.5
GV 1998.23

Herman, Josef 1911–2000
Miners 1951
oil on board 132.4 x 281.6
GV 1988.1.1

Herman, Josef 1911–2000
Mother and Child 1945–1950
oil on canvas 103 x 87.3
GV 1952.1118

Hickin, George Arthur 1821–1885
Untitled (Landscape)
oil on canvas 30.2 x 45.8
GV 1994.113

Hillier, Tristram Paul 1905–1983
Flooded Meadow 1949
tempera on canvas 60.2 x 80.7
GV 1974.83 ✖

Hitchens, Ivon 1893–1979
Essex River and Greenhill 1946
oil on canvas 68.1 x 117
GV 1955.1277

Hitchens, Ivon 1893–1979
Blue vase
oil on canvas 72.6 x 77.1
GV 1960.1431

Holl, Frank 1845–1888
John Jones Watkins, Lord Glantawe, Mayor of Swansea (1869 & 1879–1880)
oil on canvas 80.2 x 75.2
GV 1994.189

Holland, Harry b.1941
Preparatory Study for 'Corridor' 1982
oil on plyboard 25.4 x 28.2
GV 1982.3

Holland, Harry b.1941
The Corridor 1982
oil on canvas 159.8 x 178
GV 1982.2

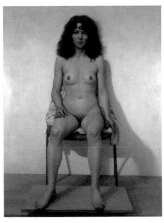

Holland, Harry b.1941
Phil, Ess and Sue (Ess)
oil on canvas 122.2 x 91.2
GV 1986.27

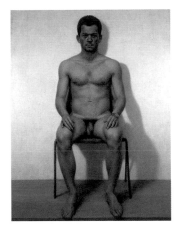

Holland, Harry b.1941
Phil, Ess and Sue (Phil)
oil on canvas 121.7 x 91.2
GV 1986.28

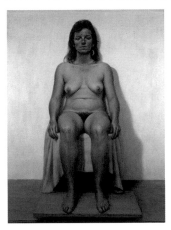

Holland, Harry b.1941
Phil, Ess and Sue (Sue)
oil on canvas 121.6 x 91.2
GV 1986.26

Howard, Henry 1769–1847
Charles Kemble
oil on canvas 155.8 x 114.2
24

Howard-Jones, Ray 1903–1996
Seascape from Mumbles 1959
oil on board
GV 2009.9

Hubbard, Eric Hesketh 1892–1957
Harlech Castle
oil on canvas 61.8 x 71.3
GV 1995.112

Ibbetson, Julius Caesar 1759–1817
Scene in the Taff Valley
oil on panel 31.5 x 38
GV 1961.1445

Ifold, Cyril 1922–1986
Welsh Village
oil on hardboard 58 x 98
GV 1986.66

Innes, James Dickson 1887–1914
Arenig Mountain c.1912
oil on canvas 25.5 x 35.4
GV 1953.1145

Innes, James Dickson 1887–1914
Garn Lake 1913
oil on canvas 76.8 x 127.1
GV 1982.1

Innes, James Dickson 1887–1914
View in Wales
oil on panel 24.2 x 32.2
GV 1951.1085

Italian (Venetian) School
The Holy Family
oil on canvas 90.2 x 72.3
GV 1920.328

Italian School
Bacchanals
oil on panel 18.8 x 15.7
30

Italian School
Bacchanals
oil on canvas 80.2 x 89.1
66

Italian School
Boy and Viper
oil on canvas 71 x 56
46

Italian School
Daedalus Fastening Wings on Icarus
oil on canvas 40.5 x 32.2
68

Jackson, John 1778–1831
Mr John Deffett
oil on canvas 54 x 43.2
GV 1928.459

James, Merlin b.1960
Way Up 1995
acrylic & mixed media on canvas 69 x 87
GV 2011.7

Jamieson, Alexander 1873–1937
Wedding at St Cloude
oil on canvas 75.8 x 126.9
GV 1939.892

Janes, Alfred 1911–1999
D. Pugsley Gwynne 1929
oil on canvas 51 x 61
GV 1989.28

Janes, Alfred 1911–1999
Still Life – Fruit 1930
oil on canvas 49.6 x 57.9
GV 1931.556

Janes, Alfred 1911–1999
Untitled (Portrait of a Man) 1931
oil on canvas 89.1 x 69.5
GV 1994.176

Janes, Alfred 1911–1999
Mervyn Levy 1935
oil on canvas 54.1 x 44.2
GV 1935.685

Janes, Alfred 1911–1999
Hyacinths 1937
oil on canvas
GV 1949.1070

Janes, Alfred 1911–1999
Study for a Portrait of Daniel Jones 1947
oil on card 58.6 x 46.4
GV 1996.11

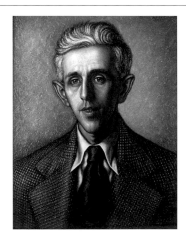

Janes, Alfred 1911–1999
Vernon Watkins 1949
oil on canvas 50 x 39.5
GV 1950.1080

Janes, Alfred 1911–1999
Blodeuwydd 1957
oil on hardboard 105.8 x 88
GV 2004.3

Janes, Alfred 1911–1999
Chirrup and Fruit 1959
oil on board 110.6 x 94.4
GV 1990.27

Janes, Alfred 1911–1999
Still Life – Benedictine Bottle
oil on canvas 54.4 x 64.8
GV 1935.684

Janes, Alfred 1911–1999
Still Life – Fruit
oil on board 55.9 x 76
GV 1937.800

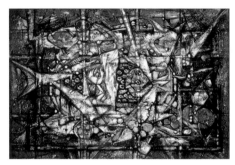

Janes, Alfred 1911–1999
Still Life with a Fish
tempera on board 27 x 37
GV 2002.24

Jenkins, Percy Pickard b.1908
Morning (Swansea Landscape)
acrylic on paper 43.8 x 59.6
GV 1995.10

John, Augustus Edwin 1878–1961
The Tutor c.1911
oil on panel 52.9 x 41.6
GV 1948.1049

John, Augustus Edwin 1878–1961
Caitlin c.1936
oil on canvas 66.2 x 58.2
GV 1981.4

John, Augustus Edwin 1878–1961
Arenig Mountain
oil on canvas 46 x 76.8
GV 1953.1256

John, Augustus Edwin 1878–1961
Irish Coast
oil on panel 51.8 x 59.6
GV 1948.1054 🐝

John, Augustus Edwin 1878–1961
L'Hermitage Martigues
oil on canvas 90.8 x 78.2
GV 1949.1063 🐝

John, Gwen 1876–1939
The Nun late 1910s
oil on canvas 56 x 35.2
GV 1949.1069

John, Gwen 1876–1939
Woman with a Coral Necklace late 1910s–
early 1920s
oil on canvas 39.5 x 31.5
GV 2002.25

Johns, John White
Jesus and Martha at the Sepulchre of Lazarus
oil on canvas 91.7 x 70.8
GV 1922.347

Johnstone, E.
Alexandra Road, Swansea c.1900
oil on canvas 61 x 51
GV 1981.6

Jones, Calvert Richard 1804–1877
Sheep Dog 1855
oil on board 24.7 x 30.2
GV 1976.3

Jones, Colin 1928–1967
Funeral, Merthyr
oil on board 126.1 x 101.3
GV 1965.1712

Jones, Glyn b.1936
For Macsen 1980
acrylic on canvas 170.9 x 170.9
GV 1982.9

Jones, Jack 1922–1993
Jack Jones 1979
oil on canvas 47.6 x 37.5
GV 1994.207

Jones, Jack 1922–1993
Zoar, Horeb and the Villiers 1988
oil on canvas 43 x 58.3
GV 1998.44

Jones, Jack 1922–1993
Landore Viaduct 1991
oil on board 19.6 x 24.7
GV 1992.2

Jones, Thomas 1742–1803
Ruins in Naples 1782
oil on paper 24.4 x 39.7
GV 1954.1273

Jones, Thomas 1742–1803
On the Road from Albano to Rome
oil on canvas 29.1 x 43.6
GV 1985.39

Jordaens, Jacob 1593–1678
Pan and Pipes
oil on canvas 95 x 80.5
63

Keith, Alexander active 1808–1874
The Late John Williams
oil on canvas 89 x 78.9
GV 1915.85

Knell, William Adolphus 1802–1875
Shipping off Oystermouth
oil on canvas 43.3 x 73.8
GV 1971.9

Knell, William Calcott 1830–1880
Fishing Boats Hauling Nets near Lowestoft
1872
oil on canvas 30.7 x 61
GV 1921.340

Lady Malet
Lady with Roses
oil on canvas 62 x 49.4
59

Lairesse, Gerard de 1640–1711
Floral Tributes to Venus
oil on canvas 63 x 76
32

Landseer, Edwin Henry 1802–1873
Lord Ellesmere, and His Pony, 'Jack'
oil on canvas on board 47.3 x 39.7
15

Lanyon, Peter 1918–1964
Ilfracombe 1960
oil on canvas 152.3 x 76.2
GV 1961.1444

Lawrence, Thomas 1769–1830
Sir Robert Peel
oil on canvas 75 x 62
GV 1935.649

Lebourg, Albert 1849–1928
A Wharf on the Seine at Dieppedalle
oil on canvas 48 x 75.5
GV 1911.7

Lees, Derwent 1885–1931
Welsh Landscape in Winter 1912–1913
oil on panel 25.2 x 35.5
GV 1951.1086

Leighton, Frederic 1830–1896
A Spanish View 1866
oil on canvas 14.7 x 27
71

Leighton, Frederic 1830–1896
A Temple on the Nile 1868
oil on canvas 15.5 x 25.5
70

Leighton, Frederic 1830–1896
Head of a Girl
oil on canvas on board 17.5 x 14.2
69

Lely, Peter 1618–1680
Countess of Bedford
oil on canvas 77 x 63.8
22

Lewis, Benjamin Archibald 1857–1946
A Carmarthenshire Farm c.1937
oil on board 22.7 x 32.9
GV 1938.812

Lewis, Edward Morland 1903–1943
Distant View of Laugharne
oil 51.1 x 76.1
GV 1932.566

Lewis, Edward Morland 1903–1943
'Lion Hotel' and Castle, Pembroke
oil on canvas 51 x 61
GV 1935.651

Lewis, Edward Morland 1903–1943
Shandon Church
oil on board 179 x 257
GV 1947.1015

Lewis, Edward Morland 1903–1943
The Band Plays
oil on card 18.9 x 26.9
GV 1935.652

Lewis, Edward Morland 1903–1943
The Beach
oil on board 31.6 x 39.2
GV 1951.1103

Lewis, Wyndham 1882–1957
The Convalescent 1933
oil on canvas 61 x 76.2
GV 1976.17

Facing page: Preece, Patricia, 1894–1966, *Interior with Figures*, 1935, Glynn Vivian Art Gallery (p. 198)

Lewis, Wyndham 1882–1957
Miss Close 1939
oil on canvas 93 x 61.1
GV 1960.1430

Malthouse, Eric James 1914–1997
Orion 1966
acrylic on canvas 71.1 x 91.2
GV 1969.1758

Manson, James Bolivar 1879–1945
Carreg Cennen Castle 1938
oil on canvas 69.5 x 90
GV 1995.111

Martin, Benito Quinquela 1890–1977
Working at High Pressure
oil on canvas 105 x 125
GV 1930.497

Mayer-Marton, George 1897–1960
Llanthony Valley 1949
oil on canvas 50.9 x 68.6
GV 1951.1096

Mayer-Marton, George 1897–1960
Girl and Bird 1950
oil on board 47.3 x 37.1
GV 1975.12

Mayer-Marton, George 1897–1960
Breakwater, Falmouth Harbour 1955
oil on canvas 48.4 x 66
GV 1975.21

Meager, Nigel
Untitled (Seascape) 1992
oil on canvas 63 x 75.6
GV 1992.3

Mengs, Anton Raphael 1728–1779
Madonna della Scodella (after Correggio)
(detail)
oil on canvas 136.4 x 207.4
108

Methuen, Paul Ayshford 1886–1974
Chinon
oil on board 40.7 x 58.3
GV 1955.1315

Monahan, Richard b.1979
Portrait with Pencil 2005
oil on canvas 170 x 120
GV 2006.3

Monet, Claude 1840–1926
Bateaux en Hollande, près de Zaandam 1871
oil on canvas 35.2 x 71
GV 1974.95.a

Morgan, Glyn b.1926
Pontypridd 1954
oil on board 59.5 x 120.2
GV 2002.32

Morris, Carey Boynes 1882–1968
Landscape with Haystack 1910
oil on canvas 25.4 x 30.2
GV 1989.31

Morris, Cedric Lockwood 1889–1982
Llanmadoc Hill, Gower 1928
oil on canvas 66.2 x 81
GV 1930.485

Morris, Cedric Lockwood 1889–1982
The Sparrow Hawks 1929
oil on canvas 78 x 61.6
GV 1931.552

Morris, Cedric Lockwood 1889–1982
Pontypridd 1945
oil on canvas 51 x 76.2
GV 1952.1121

Morris, Cedric Lockwood 1889–1982
River Zezere, Portugal 1950
oil on canvas 74.5 x 99.5
GV 1991.38

Morris, Cedric Lockwood 1889–1982
Margaret's Pots 1965
oil on canvas 90 x 76
GV 2002.33

Morse-Brown, Sam 1903–2001
Grey Day, Newquay 1936
oil on hardboard 41.9 x 31.7
GV 1937.795

Morse-Brown, Sam 1903–2001
Grey Day, Tenby 1937
oil on board 45.8 x 50.8
GV 1937.796

Muhl, Roger b.1929
Le champ de colza 1962
oil on canvas 27.1 x 22.3
GV 1963.1482

Mulloy, Daniel b.1977
Nikki with Hanging Chair
oil on canvas 122 x 91.8
GV 1996.17

Murata, Eitaro
Landscape of Japan 1927
oil on plyboard 37.2 x 44.6
GV 1930.486

Murray, William Grant 1877–1950
Carreg Cennen Castle 1924
oil on plyboard 29 x 38.7
GV 1994.193

Murray, William Grant 1877–1950
Gorsedd y Beirdd Abertawe 1926
oil on board 23.8 x 140.4
GV 1994.179

Murray, William Grant 1877–1950
The Old Mumbles Train 1928
oil on board 61 x 91.5
GV 1994.192

Murray, William Grant 1877–1950
Swansea for Business 1929
oil on canvas 85.5 x 85.3
GV 1994.204

Murray, William Grant 1877–1950
Swansea for Pleasure 1929
oil on canvas 85.4 x 85.2
GV 1994.203

Murray, William Grant 1877–1950
Lilac and Laburnum
oil on plyboard 31.5 x 46.4
GV 1944.937

Murray, William Grant 1877–1950
Oxwich Bay
oil on canvas 61.4 x 91.6
GV 1994.191

Myn, Agatha van de 1700–c.1768
Study of Fruit and Flowers
oil on canvas on board 28.5 x 24.1
49

Nash, Paul 1889–1946
Landscape of the Bagley Woods 1943
oil on canvas 56 x 86.3
GV 1960.1437

Nash, Thomas John b.1931
Promontory 1961
oil on board 79 x 54.3
GV 1961.1450

Neep, Victor 1921–1979
The Tip
oil on board 51 x 73.5
GV 1965.1505

Netscher, Caspar 1639–1684
Lady with Fruit and Attendant
oil on panel 42.4 x 48.3
29

Neuschul, Ernst 1895–1968
Cockle Woman 1940
oil on canvas 100.4 x 81.8
GV 1946.998

Neuschul, Ernst 1895–1968
Untitled (Two Mothers and Babies) 1943
oil on canvas 49.6 x 59.1
GV 1992.21

Neuschul, Ernst 1895–1968
Untitled (Cockle Picker)
oil on board 63.4 x 49.6
GV 1979.59

Neyn, Pieter de 1597–1639
Leyden
oil on panel 27.5 x 37.1
GV 1984.2

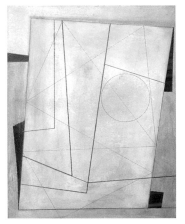

Nicholson, Ben 1894–1982
October 12th 1952 1952
oil & pencil on board 29.5 x 23.3
GV 1998.24

Nicol, Philip b.1953
Tongue in Cheek 1987
oil on plyboard 42 x 48.2
GV 1987.36

Opie, John 1761–1807
Portrait of a Girl
oil on canvas 18 x 14
13

Ostade, Adriaen van (follower of)
1610–1685
Interior of a Tavern
oil on board 35.6 x 46.7
31

Panting, Arlie 1914–1994
Still Life with Mushrooms 1956
oil on canvas 58.5 x 33
GV 2001.11

Panting, Arlie 1914–1994
Guild Houses 1964
oil on canvas 55.8 x 76
GV 2001.12

Panting, Arlie 1914–1994
Welsh Landscape 1969
oil on canvas 71.1 x 91.4
GV 2001.13

Panting, Arlie 1914–1994
Still Life with Leeks
oil on canvas 30.5 x 41
GV 2001.10

Parminter, Agnes Vye c.1836–1915
James Rodgers, JP, Mayor of Swansea (1878)
1878
oil on canvas 112.4 x 86.3
GV 1994.186

Petts, John 1914–1991
Brenda Chamberlain by Candlelight 1939
oil on canvas 51.2 x 45
GV 1975.69

Pfeninger, R. E.
R. Glynn Vivian 1882
oil on canvas 88.2 x 67.7
110

Philipson, Robin 1916–1992
Cockfight Blue
oil on hardboard 51.5 x 67.3
GV 1963.1483

Phillips, Jane 1957–2011
Hurricane Charlie 1986
acrylic on canvas 167 x 167
GV 1986.53

Pickersgill, Henry William 1782–1875
The Hop Pickers
oil on canvas 43.6 x 35.6
12

Piloty, Karl von 1826–1886
Seated Figure, Germany
oil on canvas 13.5 x 10.7
GV R 504

Pissarro, Lucien 1863–1944
Cefn Bryn, Gower 1933
oil on canvas 47.3 x 55
GV 1962.1472. 02

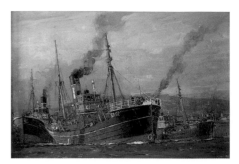

Pitcher, Neville Sotheby 1889–1959
Tide Time, Swansea 1939
oil on canvas 58.3 x 67.5
GV 1939.893

Povey, Edward b.1951
The Herb of the Field (Self Portrait) 1999–2000
oil on canvas 35.5 x 25.2
GV 2000.6

Preece, Patricia 1894–1966
Interior with Figures 1935
oil on canvas 45 x 54.8
GV 1935.673

Prendergast, Peter 1946–2007
Carneddi on a Summer's Day 1978
oil on paper on board 110.5 x 106.4
GV 1983.5

Prendergast, Peter 1946–2007
Bethesda Quarry 1982
acrylic on paper 107.8 x 121.8
GV 1983.39

Prendergast, Peter 1946–2007
Bethesda Quarry 1982
acrylic on paper 38.3 x 47.5
GV 1983.43

Prendergast, Peter 1946–2007
Landscape 1983
acrylic on paper 25 x 35.2
GV 1983.8

Facing page: Hitchens, Ivon, 1893–1979, *Blue vase*, Glynn Vivian Art Gallery (p. 182)

Prendergast, Peter 1946–2007
Landscape Sketch c.1983
acrylic on paper 25 x 35.2
GV 1983.9

Priestly, E. active 19th C
Pecca Falls, Ingleton
oil on canvas 61.1 x 40.6
GV 1994.126

Procter, Dod 1892–1972
Early Morning, Newlyn 1926
oil on canvas 49.7 x 60.2
GV 1929.471 ❀

Protheroe, Handel 1921–2007
Penclawdd
oil on canvas 31 x 40.7
GV 1948.1056

Ranken, William Bruce Ellis 1881–1941
Macaw and Sunflowers
oil on canvas 85.8 x 76.3
GV 1946.1000

Raphael (copy after) 1483–1520
Self Portrait
oil on canvas 21.5 x 16.5
GV 1994.163

Rapp, Ginette 1928–1998
The Beach, Audierne
oil on canvas 45.1 x 63.8
GV 1956.1322

Rathmell, Thomas Roland 1912–1990
Coracle Man
oil on canvas 152.5 x 122
GV 1964.1493

Rees, John Bromfield Gay 1912–1965
Still Life with Fruit and Bonbonnière 1952
mixed media on canvas on hardboard
35.7 x 62.4
GV 1957.1338

Reni, Guido 1575–1642
Susanna and the Elders
oil on canvas 121 x 151.1
37

Reynolds, Alan b.1926
Nocturne 1953
oil on board 41.2 x 52.7
GV 1961.1446

Rhys-James, Shani b.1953
The Mirror 1994
oil on linen 75.4 x 60.2
GV 1994.14

Rhys-James, Shani b.1953
Head I (Self Portrait) 2002
oil on linen 31 x 25
GV 2003.3

Rhys-James, Shani b.1953
Head II (Self Portrait) 2002
oil on linen 31 x 25
GV 2003.4

Rhys-James, Shani b.1953
Head III (Self Portrait) 2002
oil on linen 31 x 25
GV 2003.5

Richards, Anthony b.1962
Llandeilo
oil on paper 21.4 x 36.5
GV 1991.31

Richards, Ceri Giraldus 1903–1971
The Artist's Wife 1932
oil on canvas 76 x 63.5
GV 1981.5

Richards, Ceri Giraldus 1903–1971
Costerwoman 1939
oil on canvas 82.1 x 69.1
GV 1973.7

Richards, Ceri Giraldus 1903–1971
The Force that through the Green Fuse: The Source 1945
oil on canvas 88 x 106
GV 2007.38

Richards, Ceri Giraldus 1903–1971
The Pianist 1948
oil on canvas 63.4 x 76.2
GV 1948.1062

Richards, Ceri Giraldus 1903–1971
The Sculptor's Landscape (homage to Henry Moore) 1948
oil on board 45 x 35.5
GV 1980.17

Richards, Ceri Giraldus 1903–1971
Bouquet 1952
oil on canvas 56 x 71.5
GV 2002.39

Richards, Ceri Giraldus 1903–1971
The Artist's Father 1955
oil on canvas 96.3 x 81.3
GV 1961.1452

Richards, Ceri Giraldus 1903–1971
The Ravine 1955
oil on canvas 49.2 x 49.2
GV 1961.1453

Richards, Ceri Giraldus 1903–1971
La cathédrale engloutie III 1960
oil on canvas 152.2 x 152.9
GV 1960.1432

Richards, Ceri Giraldus 1903–1971
Enclosed in Deep Blue 1962
oil on canvas 41 x 44.5
GV 1963.1481

Richards, Ceri Giraldus 1903–1971
The Lion Hunt 1963
oil on canvas 25.8 x 30.8
GV 1965.1710

Richards, Ceri Giraldus 1903–1971
The Lion Hunt IV 1963
oil on canvas 76.2 x 76.4
GV 1976.13

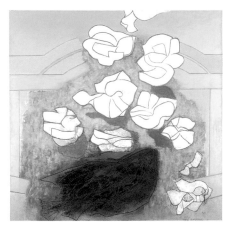

Richards, Ceri Giraldus 1903–1971
Music of Colours, White Blossom 1968
oil on canvas 152.3 x 151
GV 1977.1

Richards, Ceri Giraldus 1903–1971
Hammerclavier Theme
oil on canvas 101 x 71
GV 1960.1420

Richards, Frances 1903–1985
Metamorphosis 1967
oil on board 31 x 20.3
GV 1967.1722.2

Ridinger, Johan Elias 1695–1767
Three Portraits of Countess Ansbach
oil on canvas 43.2 x 100.5
62

Rigaud, John Francis 1742–1810
Mrs Hartle
oil on canvas 126 x 101
GV 1955.1280

Roberts, Will 1907–2000
Winter 1963
oil on hardboard 91.3 x 121.7
GV 1964.1485

Roberts, Will 1907–2000
Public Reading Room 1986
oil on canvas 58.5 x 73.8
GV 1987.20

Roberts, William Patrick 1895–1980
Miss Jane Tupper-Carey 1924
oil on canvas 41 x 31
GV 1928.399

Roos, Philipp Peter 1657–1706
Landscape with Bull, Goats and Attendant
oil on canvas 72.4 x 110.7
44

Rowntree, Kenneth 1915–1997
Vase of Flowers in a Landscape
oil on canvas 40.5 x 50.7
GV 1967.1722

Rubens, Peter Paul 1577–1640
Abraham and Melchisedek
oil on panel 33.5 x 48.2
51

Saunders, Gerald
Cockle Pickers
oil on board 35.4 x 44.5
GV 1993.9

Sauvage, Piat Joseph 1744–1818
Diana and Nymphs
oil on canvas 64.4 x 141.5
89

Sauvage, Piat Joseph 1744–1818
The Boar Hunt
oil on canvas 64.7 x 143.5
86

Schalcken, Godfried 1643–1706
Good Night
oil on canvas 57.5 x 80.7
83

Schwabeda, Johann Michael 1734–1794
Cupids and Fruit
oil on canvas 48.3 x 62.7
55

Schwabeda, Johann Michael 1734–1794
Cupids and Goat
oil on canvas 48.6 x 62.8
58

Scott, Peter Markham 1909–1989
Widgeon Asleep in the Noonday Sun 1936
oil on canvas 38.2 x 45.7
GV 1948.1058

Setch, Terry b.1936
Once upon a Time there Was… 1981
oil & encaustic on canvas 31 x 41
GV 2007.36

Setch, Terry b.1936
Explosion III 1983
oil & wax on canvas 182.7 x 203
GV 1984.14

Shanks, Duncan b.1937
Waterfall 1987
oil on canvas 177.5 x 177.7
GV 1988.17

Sheppard, Maurice Raymond b.1947
Gypsy Men Logging in the Wood
oil on board 112.7 x 150
GV 1996.3 🐝

Sheringham, George 1884–1937
Mabinogion Series (design for a silk panel)
oil on paper (possibly lined on to board)
33 x 22
GV 1938.816

Sickert, Walter Richard 1860–1942
La Nera 1903
oil on canvas 46.3 x 39.2
GV 1952.1122

Smith, Alan b.1956
Six Months in a Closet of Rushing Water with Cold Tea and All the Time in the World 1985
acrylic on paper 72 x 51.7
GV 1986.29

Smith, Alan b.1956
Water Tower No.3 1985
acrylic on paper 107 x 52.2
GV 1986.32

Smith, Alan b.1956
Watertower No.2 1985
acrylic on paper 107.5 x 52.3
GV 1986.31

Smith, Alan b.1956
T piece No.1
acrylic on paper 95.2 x 94.6
GV 1986.30

Smith, Matthew Arnold Bracy 1879–1959
Winter Landscape, Cornwall 1920
oil on canvas 54.2 x 64.8
GV 1957.1331

Smith, Matthew Arnold Bracy 1879–1959
Marguerites and Pears
oil on canvas 60.9 x 50.9
GV 1960.1436

Soo Pieng, Cheong 1917–1983
Abstraction II 1963
oil on canvas 70.9 x 106.4
GV 1963.1480

Spear, Ruskin 1911–1990
River in Winter 1951
oil on canvas 196.5 x 96
GV 1957.1335

Spear, Ruskin 1911–1990
Winter Evening
oil on board 76.5 x 61
GV 1955.1314

Spencer, Stanley 1891–1959
Garden at Whitehouse, Northern Ireland 1952
oil on canvas 52.2 x 76.7
GV 1974.81

Spencer, Stanley 1891–1959
Marriage at Cana, Bride and Bridegroom
1953
oil on canvas 66 x 51
GV 1958.1384

Stapleton, Niemann
*Landscape with River and Boy Fishing** 1943
oil on canvas 38.5 x 76.5
GV 1977.19

Stapleton, Niemann
Chiselhurst Church and Landscape
oil on canvas
GV 1977.21

Stapleton, Niemann
Whitby
oil on canvas
GV 1977.20

Steele-Morgan, Tony 1930–2009
Tiger Mirror Box 1995
oil on hardboard 59.6 x 59.6
GV 1997.2

Stothard, Thomas 1755–1834
The Fall
oil on canvas 25.7 x 50.8
17

Stuart, Gordon b.1924
Daniel Jones
oil on canvas 47.6 x 37
GV 1996.26

Stuart, Gordon b.1924
Will Roberts, Painter
oil on canvas 38.8 x 28.8
GV 1992.31

Swan, Douglas 1930–2000
Michael Sweeping into Air 1982
oil & ink on plexiglass & canvas 119.4 x 89.1
GV 1984.13a

Swan, Douglas 1930–2000
Michael Sweeping into Air 1982
oil on canvas 119.7 x 119.3
GV 1984.13b

Swan, Douglas 1930–2000
Michael Sweeping into Air 1982
oil & ink on plexiglass & canvas 119.6 x 89.1
GV 1984.13c

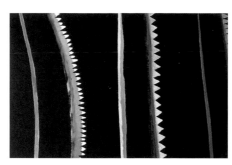

Tatarczyk, Tomasz
Seven Deadly Sins 1984
oil & wax 119.7 x 170
GV 1985.10

Taylor, Edward Ingram 1855–1923
Oxwich Bay, Gower 1907
oil on canvas 69.5 x 90
GV 1976.2

Thomas, J. B.
Farm, Rudry
oil on board 20.5 x 24.5
GV 1998.7

Thomson, Henry 1773–1843
Icarus after His Fall, Found on the Sea Shore
oil on canvas 197.8 x 218.5
GV 1973.8

Tischbein, Johan Wilhelm
Reuszin und Heinrich XXXVII Juneere Reusz
1748
oil on canvas 142 x 109
80

Tischbein, Johan Wilhelm
Heinrich der XXXVII Heinrich der XXXIX
Junge Reusz 1750
oil on canvas 142 x 109
81

Toulcher, Sylvia
Picking Out the Coal Seam 1993
oil on board 29.3 x 39.8
GV 1994.11

Tuke, Henry Scott 1858–1929
On the Beach, Bournemouth, March 1882
oil on canvas 23.8 x 38.5
GV 1998.42

Facing page: Bratby, John Randall, 1928–1992, *Janet and Lilies*, 1961, Glynn Vivian Art Gallery (p. 165)

Tyzack, Michael 1933–2007
Scarlet Fissure
acrylic on hardboard 122 x 122
GV 1965.1711

Uhlman, Fred 1901–1985
Welsh Farm
oil on canvas 59.6 x 90
GV 1954.1258

unknown artist
Mrs Mary Morgan c.1700
oil on canvas 87.6 x 61
GV 1977.49

unknown artist
Jane Ann Edmond c.1800
oil on canvas 25.3 x 22
GV 1994.139

unknown artist
John Edmond c.1800
oil on canvas 25.2 x 21.5
GV 1994.138

unknown artist
View of Swansea 1860
oil on canvas 34.5 x 122.5
GV 1943.922

unknown artist
Jacob's Dream
oil on glass 33 x 26.7
GV R 139

unknown artist
Landscape with Animals
oil on canvas 37 x 54.2
GV 1994.164

unknown artist
Portrait of a Man
oil on panel
GV R 132

unknown artist
Portrait of a Woman
oil on panel 24 x 20.3
GV R 134

unknown artist
The Virgin Mary
oil on glass 24 x 18.5
GV R 144

unknown artist
Untitled (mythological subject)
oil on canvas
GV 1994.168

unknown artist
Untitled (mythological subject)
oil on glass 22.6 x 30.1
GV R 141

unknown artist
Untitled (mythological subject)
oil on glass 20.5 x 17
GV R 147

unknown artist
Untitled (A Lady at Her Mirror)
oil on glass 24 x 18.5
GV R 142

unknown artist
Untitled (Cavalry Charge)
oil on canvas 78 x 106
GV 1994.111

unknown artist
Untitled (Landscape)
oil on paper 17.5 x 27
GV 1994.115

unknown artist
Untitled (Landscape)
oil on canvas 23 x 35.5
GV 1994.117

unknown artist
Untitled (Landscape)
oil on canvas 30.5 x 45.5
GV 1994.119

unknown artist
Untitled (Landscape)
oil on glass 24 x 18.5
GV R 145

unknown artist
Untitled (View of a City)
oil on canvas
GV 1994.112

unknown artist
Untitled (Woman Carrying a Basket of Flowers on Her Head)
oil on glass 24 x 17.5
GV R 146

Varley I, John 1778–1842
Harlech Castle
oil on canvas 64.2 x 76.8
GV 1948.1050

Vaughan, John Keith 1912–1977
Warrior 1959
oil on canvas 124 x 93.5
GV 1960.1433

Vicari, Andrew b.1938
Three Welsh Colliers 1958
oil on board 50.3 x 69
GV 1994.177

Vignet, Henri 1857–1920
West Front of Rouen Cathedral at Sunset 1903
oil on canvas 50 x 61
GV 1911.4

Walters, Evan 1893–1951
Still Life Study of Fish c.1911
oil on canvas 28.5 x 43
GV 2008.1

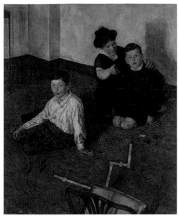

Walters, Evan 1893–1951
Mrs Coombe-Tennant, JP, and Sons,
Alexander and Henry 1920
oil on canvas 152.4 x 127.8
GV 1957.1350

Walters, Evan 1893–1951
Mrs Grant Murray 1920
oil on canvas 61.4 x 50.9
GV 1961.1463

Walters, Evan 1893–1951
Rear Admiral Walker-Heneage-Vivian 1920
oil on canvas 137.8 x 97.2
GV 1988.22

Walters, Evan 1893–1951
Doctor Edith Anne Evans, née Jones 1922
oil on canvas 58.4 x 48.3
GV 2011.1

Walters, Evan 1893–1951
Blind Pianist 1925
oil on canvas 102 x 85
GV 1953.1233

Walters, Evan 1893–1951
Boy with Feather 1925
oil on canvas 61.3 x 50.8
GV 1927.395

Walters, Evan 1893–1951
Eva 1926
oil on canvas 45.6 x 35.8
GV 1964.1499

Walters, Evan 1893–1951
Mr William Hopkins, a Welsh Collier 1926
oil on canvas 61.3 x 50.9
GV 1926.373

Walters, Evan 1893–1951
Pennard Castle 1926
oil on canvas 30.7 x 45.6
GV 1926.372

Walters, Evan 1893–1951
Mr and Mrs Rowlands 1927
oil on canvas 63.5 x 76.4
GV 1973.10

Walters, Evan 1893–1951
Brothers c.1927
oil on canvas 51.1 x 61.1
GV 1930.496

Walters, Evan 1893–1951
Miner c.1927
oil on canvas 59.6 x 47.6
GV 1953.1228

Walters, Evan 1893–1951
Street Scene 1929
oil on canvas 60.2 x 50.4
GV 1994.123

Walters, Evan 1893–1951
Portrait of a Young Woman c.1929
oil on canvas 76.5 x 63.6
GV 1953.1223

Walters, Evan 1893–1951
Village Lane, Mumbles c.1929
oil on canvas 24.9 x 20.1
GV 1994.121

Walters, Evan 1893–1951
A Welsh Miner c.1930
oil on canvas 74.5 x 62
GV 1931.549

Walters, Evan 1893–1951
An Empty Frame 1936
oil on panel 56.3 x 37.7
GV 1979.20

Walters, Evan 1893–1951
Stout Man with Jug c.1936
oil on canvas 63.7 x 76.9
GV 1953.1222

Walters, Evan 1893–1951
Portrait of a Woman c.1936–1939
oil on canvas 74.5 x 62.7
GV 1994.154

Walters, Evan 1893–1951
Hampstead through a Window 1937
oil on canvas 76.1 x 63.6
GV 1953.1225

Walters, Evan 1893–1951
The Artist's Mother Asleep c.1937
oil on canvas 46 x 35.5
GV 1953.1219

Walters, Evan 1893–1951
Lady in a Black Hat (Mrs Erna Meinel) 1938
oil on canvas 59.7 x 50.4
GV 1992.1

Walters, Evan 1893–1951
Landscape with Farm 1938
oil on canvas 61.5 x 74.2
GV 1953.1221

Walters, Evan 1893–1951
Girl in Kitchen c.1938
oil on canvas 61.3 x 51.3
GV 1953.1231.1

Walters, Evan 1893–1951
South Wales Landscape under Cloud c.1938
oil on canvas 50.7 x 61.6
GV 1953.1229

Walters, Evan 1893–1951
The Artist's Mother Reading the Bible c.1938
oil on canvas 76.4 x 63.7
GV 1953.1226

Walters, Evan 1893–1951
Woman Reading c.1938
oil on canvas 63.7 x 76.5
GV 1953.1224

Walters, Evan 1893–1951
Cockle Woman 1939
oil on canvas 61 x 51
GV 1939.898

Walters, Evan 1893–1951
Self Portrait with Candle c.1939
oil on canvas 61 x 56
GV 1953.1230

Walters, Evan 1893–1951
Still Life with Cricket Ball 1940
oil on hardboard 50.4 x 60.9
GV 1979.13

Walters, Evan 1893–1951
A Study from Life 1942–1943
oil on canvas 30.8 x 45.4
GV 1979.36

Walters, Evan 1893–1951
Colliery Disaster 1943
oil on canvas 76.6 x 50.8
GV 1979.14

Walters, Evan 1893–1951
Miss Thomas 1943
oil on canvas 66.4 x 48.8
GV 1987.19

Walters, Evan 1893–1951
Owain and Luned 1943
oil on canvas 50.8 x 40.8
GV 1979.46

Walters, Evan 1893–1951
Boys at Golf 1945
oil on canvas 50 x 61
GV 1979.23

Walters, Evan 1893–1951
Richard J. Strick 1945
oil on canvas 76.1 x 63.4
GV 1974.82

Facing page: Lewis, Wyndham, 1882–1957, *The Convalescent*, 1933, Glynn Vivian Art Gallery (p. 191)

Walters, Evan 1893–1951
Blackened Face with Reclining Figure c.1945
oil on canvas 39.6 x 50.5
GV 1979.26

Walters, Evan 1893–1951
Self Portrait, Green c.1945
oil on canvas 61 x 51.3
GV 1979.67

Walters, Evan 1893–1951
A Venetian Lady 1948
oil on canvas 39 x 64.5
GV 1979.21

Walters, Evan 1893–1951
Abstract with Woman's Head c.1948
oil on board 48.8 x 69.2
GV 1979.61

Walters, Evan 1893–1951
Abstract Landscape 1950
oil on canvas 51 x 40.5
GV 1979.47

Walters, Evan 1893–1951
View through French Windows c.1950
oil on canvas 51 x 40.3
GV 1979.48

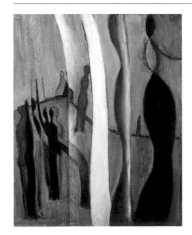

Walters, Evan 1893–1951
Abstract Figures in Landscape
oil on canvas 51 x 40.6
GV 1979.42

Walters, Evan 1893–1951
Abstract Figures in Landscape
oil on canvas 40.4 x 50.7
GV 1979.45

Walters, Evan 1893–1951
Abstract Figures Smoking
oil on board 49.2 x 59.7
GV 1979.39

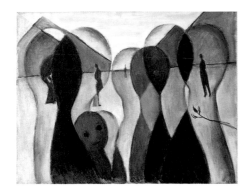

Walters, Evan 1893–1951
Abstract Heads in Grey
oil on canvas 40.6 x 51.1
GV 1979.50

Walters, Evan 1893–1951
Abstract Landscape with Figures
oil on canvas 41 x 50.7
GV 1979.55

Walters, Evan 1893–1951
Abstract View through Window
oil on canvas 41 x 50.5
GV 1979.54

Walters, Evan 1893–1951
Adam and Eve
oil on canvas 61 x 50.5
GV 1979.10

Walters, Evan 1893–1951
Breakfast
oil on canvas 41 x 50.6
GV 1979.18

Walters, Evan 1893–1951
Child in a High Chair
oil on canvas 60.2 x 50.3
GV 1994.124

Walters, Evan 1893–1951
Dead Flowers
oil on canvas on board 47.2 x 28.9
GV 1979.29

Walters, Evan 1893–1951
Double Images No.1
oil on canvas 61 x 50.7
GV 1979.52

Walters, Evan 1893–1951
Execution
oil on canvas 77 x 106.9
GV 1979.66

Walters, Evan 1893–1951
Figures against a Landscape 1
oil on canvas 50 x 60.1
GV 1979.60

Walters, Evan 1893–1951
Figures against a Landscape 2
oil on canvas 50.5 x 39.8
GV 1979.33

Walters, Evan 1893–1951
Flowers in a Vase
oil on canvas 55.2 x 65.4
GV 1986.21

Walters, Evan 1893–1951
Foxgloves
oil on canvas 76.6 x 50.8
GV 1953.1227

Walters, Evan 1893–1951
Garden Scene with Two Doves
oil on board 59 x 38.2
GV 1979.37

Walters, Evan 1893–1951
Gardens No.1
oil on canvas 40.5 x 51
GV 1979.44

Walters, Evan 1893–1951
Geometric Forms
oil on canvas 40.7 x 51
GV 1979.15

Walters, Evan 1893–1951
H. P. Widdup
oil on canvas 126.1 x 100.5
GV 1996.24

Walters, Evan 1893–1951
Jam Pot
oil on panel 35 x 22
GV 1979.32

Walters, Evan 1893–1951
John Jenkins
oil on canvas 74.7 x 61.9
GV 1970.1764

Walters, Evan 1893–1951
Les yeux qui rient
oil on canvas 55.7 x 45.9
GV 1964.1498

Walters, Evan 1893–1951
Medea
oil on canvas 50.5 x 40.5
GV 1979.25

Walters, Evan 1893–1951
Mrs Bessie Jones
oil on canvas 61 x 50.5
GV 1975.70

Walters, Evan 1893–1951
Mrs N. Ledingham as a Young Girl
oil on canvas 101.5 x 68.6
GV 1983.4

Walters, Evan 1893–1951
Mumbles Woman in Window
oil on canvas 50.7 x 40.5
GV 1979.41

Walters, Evan 1893–1951
Nude
oil on canvas 51.2 x 61.5
GV 1953.1232

Walters, Evan 1893–1951
Nude
oil on canvas 63.1 x 76.1
GV 1964.1497

Walters, Evan 1893–1951
Pipe
oil on board 28.5 x 38.3
GV 1979.28

Walters, Evan 1893–1951
Portrait of a Lady
oil on panel 25.3 x 35.4
GV 1979.31

Walters, Evan 1893–1951
Portrait of a Laughing Man
oil on canvas 59.5 x 45.2
GV 1994.122

Walters, Evan 1893–1951
Portrait of a Woman
oil on canvas 62.2 x 47.6
GV 1994.165

Walters, Evan 1893–1951
*Portrait of an Unknown Man**
oil on canvas 60.3 x 45.7
GV 1979.19

Walters, Evan 1893–1951
Pottery Horses
oil on canvas 50.5 x 40.7
GV 1979.53

Walters, Evan 1893–1951
Resolution
oil on canvas 63.5 x 76
GV 1979.64

Walters, Evan 1893–1951
Self Portrait
oil on canvas 61.2 x 51.5
GV 1953.1220

Walters, Evan 1893–1951
Self Portrait
oil on canvas 44.6 x 59.8
GV 1979.11

Walters, Evan 1893–1951
Self Portrait
oil on panel 30.5 x 45.5
GV 1979.30

Walters, Evan 1893–1951
Self Portrait
oil on canvas 61.1 x 50.6
GV 1986.20

Walters, Evan 1893–1951
Self Portrait
oil on canvas 35.4 x 57
GV 2004.4

Walters, Evan 1893–1951
Semi-Abstract
oil on canvas 50.8 x 60.8
GV 1979.34

Walters, Evan 1893–1951
Sir William A. Jenkins, JP
oil on canvas 91.8 x 71.1
GV 1986.4

Walters, Evan 1893–1951
Soho
oil on canvas 91.2 x 60.5
GV 1979.63

Walters, Evan 1893–1951
Still Life with Candle
oil on canvas 50.6 x 61
GV 1979.62

Walters, Evan 1893–1951
Still Life with Crocuses
oil on canvas 40.5 x 50.8
GV 1979.17

Walters, Evan 1893–1951
The Ascension
oil on canvas 76 x 63.4
GV 1979.65

Walters, Evan 1893–1951
Toby Jug and Flowers
oil on canvas 40.8 x 50.7
GV 1979.12

Walters, Evan 1893–1951
Tree Trunks
oil on canvas 50.7 x 40.3
GV 1979.24

Walters, Evan 1893–1951
Two Heads
oil on canvas 40.4 x 50.7
GV 1979.51

Walters, Evan 1893–1951
Untitled
oil on canvas 50.7 x 61
GV 1979.40

Walters, Evan 1893–1951
Waiting for Charon
oil on canvas 60.5 x 51.2
GV 1979.22

Walters, Evan 1893–1951
War Abstract
oil on canvas 71 x 43.2
GV 1979.58

Walters, Evan 1893–1951
White Flowers and Apples
oil on canvas 45.7 x 30.2
GV 1979.27

Walters, Evan 1893–1951
William Daniel Rees
oil on canvas 76.2 x 63.5
GV 1939.894

Walters, Evan 1893–1951
Woman in an Arch of Trees
oil on canvas 76 x 63.2
GV 1994.153

Walters, Evan 1893–1951
Woman Peeling Potatoes
oil on board 57.5 x 42.1
GV 1979.38

Walters, Evan 1893–1951
Woman Playing with a Cat
oil on canvas 49.7 x 49.7
GV 1994.125

Watson, Harry 1871–1936
Summer Day on the Flats
oil on panel 28.6 x 36.2
GV 1938.822

Webster, Catrin b.1966
Hafod 2 2005
acrylic on canvas 162.5 x 213
GV 2009.3

Weight, Carel Victor Morlais 1908–1997
From Robert Buhler's Cottage
oil on canvas 50.4 x 60.2
GV 1957.1340

West, W.
Wreck off Rocky Coast
oil on canvas 74 x 132.8
GV 1972.2

Wilkins, William Powell b.1938
A Dance 1983
oil on canvas 79.9 x 111.3
GV 1993.7

Williams, Archie 1922–1993
Salubrious Passage, Swansea
acrylic on board 36.9 x 27.8
GV 1996.16

Williams, B. H.
Untitled
oil on board 29.2 x 39.5
GV 1988.20

Williams, Christopher 1873–1934
A Fresh Morning, Llangranog
oil on canvas 29.3 x 38.3
GV 1936.702

Williams, Christopher 1873–1934
Atalanta
oil on canvas 59 x 59
GV 1935.662

Williams, Christopher 1873–1934
Branwen
oil on canvas 150.1 x 135.5
GV 1934.646

Williams, Christopher 1873–1934
Ceridwen
oil on canvas 158.9 x 137
GV 1934.645

Williams, Christopher 1873–1934
Coast near Holyhead
oil on canvas 29.5 x 38.7
GV 1936.706

Williams, Christopher 1873–1934
Criccieth Castle
oil on canvas on board 29.2 x 38.7
GV 1935.669

Williams, Christopher 1873–1934
Family on Barmouth Island
oil on board 28.2 x 37.2
GV 1973.21

Williams, Christopher 1873–1934
In North Wales
oil on canvas 30.4 x 39.2
GV 1936.704

Williams, Christopher 1873–1934
Near Merthyr Mawr
oil on canvas 30 x 39.3
GV 1936.705

Williams, Christopher 1873–1934
Remorse of Saul
oil on canvas 159.7 x 139.1
GV 1935.671

Facing page: Neuschul, Ernst, 1895–1968, *Cockle Woman*, 1940, Glynn Vivian Art Gallery (p. 196)

Williams, Christopher 1873–1934
Santa Maria della Salute, Venice
oil on canvas
GV 1936.703

Williams, Christopher 1873–1934
View from Arthog
oil on canvas 30.2 x 39
GV 1936.701

Williams, Emrys b.1958
Woman on the Promenade 1986
oil on board 30.5 x 35.5
GV 1990.28

Williams, Emrys b.1958
On the Pier II 1989
acrylic on card 13.6 x 17.1
GV 1996.25

Williams, Kyffin 1918–2006
Highgate Schoolboy c.1953
oil on canvas 92 x 50.6
GV 1956.1323

Williams, Kyffin 1918–2006
Jack Jones c.1959
oil on canvas 58.2 x 45.7
GV 1997.3

Williams, Kyffin 1918–2006
Deposition
oil on board 22 x 32.5
GV 1948.1053

Williams, Kyffin 1918–2006
Eryri (Snowdon)
oil on canvas 38.8 x 76.4
GV 1951.1087

Williams, Kyffin 1918–2006
Mountainous Landscape
oil on board 21 x 37
GV 1998.30

Williams, Kyffin 1918–2006
Snowdon from near Harlech
oil on board 21 x 35.7
GV 1998.27

Williams, Kyffin 1918–2006
Tre'r Ceiri
oil on canvas 35.5 x 45.5
GV 1948.1052

Williams, Kyffin 1918–2006
View of Snowdon in Winter
oil on canvas 27.1 x 76.5
GV 1953.1217

Williams, Margaret Lindsay 1888–1960
Martha, the Artist's Mother
oil on canvas 195 x 80
GV 1986.5

Williams, Penry 1798–1885
The Assumption of the Virgin (after Jacopa
Cavedone) c.1827
oil on canvas 31.3 x 17.7
72

Williams, Penry 1798–1885
The Vision of Saint Bruno (after Guercino)
c.1827
oil on canvas 38.1 x 22.5
76

Williams, Penry 1798–1885
The Visitation (after Albertinelli) c.1827
oil on canvas 29.4 x 17.9
77

Williams, Penry 1798–1885
Two Saints (after Albertinelli) c.1827
oil on canvas 28.3 x 18.8
78

Williams, Penry 1798–1885
Massacre of the Innocents
oil on canvas 38.1 x 23.3
73

Williams, Penry 1798–1885
Repose
oil on canvas 56.7 x 70.2
20

Williams, Penry 1798–1885
Saint John (after Guercino)
oil on canvas 25.9 x 19.7
75

Williams, Sue b.1956
Beach View 1993
oil on canvas 91.5 x 91.5
GV 1993.3

Williams, Sue b.1956
Scorched 1993
oil on canvas 91.5 x 91.5
GV 1993.2

Williams, William 1808–1895
Fabian's Bay, Swansea, 1844
oil on canvas 61 x 91.4
GV 1988.5

Wilson, Frank Avray 1914–2009
Configuration
oil on hardboard 121.5 x 29.7
GV 1960.1426

Wilson, Richard 1713/1714–1782
Lake Averno
oil on canvas 50 x 75.5
GV 1943.928

Wilson, Richard 1713/1714–1782
Landscape with Old Castle
oil on canvas 37.3 x 54.7
14

Wilson, Richard 1713/1714–1782
River Scene in Italy
oil on canvas 32.9 x 47
16

Wilson, Richard 1713/1714–1782
Solitude
oil on canvas 101 x 125
GV 1971.2

Wilson, Richard 1713/1714–1782
The White Monk
oil on canvas 35 x 44.5
GV R 131

Wit, Jacob de 1695–1754
Blind Man's Buff
oil on canvas 75 x 118
94

Wit, Jacob de 1695–1754
Decorative Panel (with putti)
oil on canvas 118.5 x 60.5
85

Wit, Jacob de 1695–1754
Decorative Panel
oil on canvas 48.2 x 143.5
88

Wit, Jacob de 1695–1754
Decorative Panel with Three Portraits
oil on canvas 32.5 x 127.4
87

Wit, Jacob de 1695–1754
Decorative Panel with Two Central Figures
oil on canvas 48.2 x 143
92

Wit, Jacob de 1695–1754
Triumphal Procession
oil on board 58.4 x 92.3
82

Wit, Jacob de 1695–1754
Triumphal Procession
oil & gilt on panel 57.7 x 72.7
84

Wolkowsky
The Vintage in Umbria
oil on canvas 155.2 x 174.7
GV 1957.1351

Wright, John b.1931
Out of the Hills 1962
oil & sand on board 182.9 x 121.8
GV 1965.1503

Zajac, Ryszard b.1929
Umbrian Landscape 1964
oil on canvas 60.4 x 81.1
GV 1964.1496

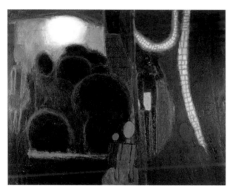

Zobole, Ernest 1927–1999
Ystrad and People No.1 1960
oil on hardboard 121.9 x 153.2
GV 1965.1504

Zobole, Ernest 1927–1999
Landscape around December 1977–1978
oil on canvas 152.2 x 121.7
GV 2002.38

Zobole, Ernest 1927–1999
Painter and Subject Matter No.7
oil on canvas 122 x 182
GV 2006.24

Gower Heritage
Centre

Jones, D. B. R.
Three Cliffs Bay, Gower
oil on board 41 x 71
PCF2

Marchant, David
Three Cliffs Bay, Gower
oil on canvas 39 x 79.5
PCF1

Maggie's Swansea

Prendergast, Peter 1946–2007
Over the Hill 1997
oil on canvas 198.1 x 137.2
PCF1

Weil, Barbara b.1933
Forest of Love 1991
acrylic on cotton 200 x 250
PCF2

Swansea Metropolitan University

Cox, Richard C. b.1946
Red Beard Diptych, I 2000
acrylic on cotton duck 144.8 x 330.2
PCF1

Cox, Richard C. b.1946
Red Beard Diptych, III 2001
acrylic on cotton duck 144.8 x 355.6
PCF2

Cox, Richard C. b.1946
Red Beard Series Black 2005
acrylic on cotton duck 144.8 x 200.7
PCF4

Cox, Richard C. b.1946
Red Beard Series Blue 2003
acrylic on cotton duck 175.3 x 167.6
PCF3

Donovan, James b.1974
Tower Colliery Miner c.1999
acrylic on board 149.8 x 233.7
PCF5

Donovan, James b.1974
Tower Colliery Miner c.1999
acrylic on board
PCF7

Donovan, James b.1974
Tower Colliery Miners c.1999
acrylic on board 120 x 150
PCF6

unknown artist
Abstract (in Mustard and Blue)*
oil on canvas (?)
PCF14

unknown artist
Abstract (in Red and Black)*
oil on canvas (?)
PCF13

unknown artist
Apocalyptic Scene 1
oil on canvas (?) 150 x 120
PCF9

unknown artist
Apocalyptic Scene 2
oil on canvas (?) 181 x 154
PCF10

unknown artist
Apocalyptic Scene 3
oil on canvas (?) 153 x 120
PCF11

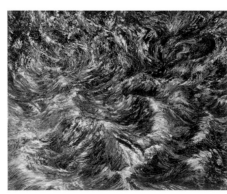

unknown artist
Choppy Sea*
acrylic on board 124 x 166.5
PCF8

unknown artist
Man with Closed Eyes*
oil on canvas (?) 150 x 90
PCF12

Facing page: Landseer, Edwin Henry, 1802–1873, *Lord Ellesmere, and His Pony, 'Jack'*, Glynn Vivian Art Gallery (p. 189)

Swansea Museum

Swansea (Abertawe) is the second largest city in Wales situated on the mouth of the river Tawe, in the middle of the bay which stretches from Mumbles head to Port Talbot. In the eighteenth and nineteenth centuries the settlement became the largest town in Wales with the development of the coal and copper industries. Swansea was known as Copperopolis to reflect its importance as the centre of the worldwide copper trade.

Swansea Museum, the oldest museum in Wales, was built in 1841 by the Royal Institution of South Wales to house the collections accumulated by members. The art collection began in 1835 with the aim to accumulate pictures of local relevance. This idea remains at the heart of the collections policy today and has led to an eclectic range of paintings spanning assorted styles, periods and subject matter. We have a significant collection of landscapes, seascapes and portraits of local dignitaries. Artists include members of the Harris (James Senior and Junior) and Duncan (Allan and Edward) families. Recently there has been an emphasis on collecting local topographical views and images covering the social history of the area. These provide visual representations of local areas at specific moments in time.

There are over 100 oil paintings in the collection stretching from the seventeenth century to the present day. The earliest oil painting accessioned to the collections reflects the growing importance of the Port of Swansea – the painting is of Captain Joseph Huddart (1741–1816) by John Hoppner RA (1758–1810). Huddart was appointed as the Engineer of the first Swansea Harbour Trust and is shown wearing the uniform of the Elder Brethren of the Corporation of Trinity House. Another important work which reflects another 'lost' industry is Landing Oysters at Mumbles, a fine painting by George Wolfe.

Works from the collection are displayed throughout the galleries and are rotated through a series of themed temporary exhibitions.

Many of the works in the collection have been donated by local people or purchased with support from the City and County of Swansea, the Royal Institution of South Wales (The Friends of Swansea Museum), or with the assistance of grant aid bodies such as the Art Fund and Victoria and Albert Purchase Grant Fund. This generosity continues today and the ongoing additions of new acquisitions enable the collection to develop and expand.

Garethe E. El Tawab, Curator

Adams, Edward active 1880–1884
'Inchmaru' 1880
oil on canvas 60 x 90.7
SM 2006.1.1

Adams, Edward active 1880–1884
'Inchgarvie' 1884
oil on canvas 63.3 x 99.7
SM 2006.1.2

Birchall, H. B. active 19th C
Pilot Cutter 'Tom Rosser'
oil on canvas 25 x 35
SM MI 6469

Brandon, A. K.
Brigantine 'Agnes Ellen'
oil on canvas 59.3 x 92
SM MI 5203

Butler, William 1824–1870
Loughor Glass Works c.1850
oil on canvas 15.4 x 33.5
SM 1927.109

Butler, William 1824–1870
Kidwelly Castle
oil on canvas 35.3 x 58
SM 1975.23

Butler, William 1824–1870
Loughor Castle and Town
oil on canvas 15.4 x 33.5
SM 1927.110

Buttersworth, Thomas 1768–1842
HMS 'Daedalus'
oil on canvas 81.6 x 102
SM A 53

Carter, William 1863–1939
Caroline Julia Talbot Dillwyn Llewelyn 1889
oil on canvas 75 x 62.3
SM A 16

Carter, William 1863–1939
John Talbot Dillwyn Llewelyn
oil on canvas 75 x 62.5
SM A 17

Chamney, J. S.
The Sheet Steel Rolling Mill, Pontardawe 1957
oil on canvas 60 x 101
SM MI 4421

Chapman, George R. active 1863–1874
Emma Crichton (1837–1923) and Lily Marion Anne 1866
oil on canvas 167 x 106.5
SM 2001.33.1

Clayton, Tommy F.
Steam Ship 'LO333'
oil on canvas 40.7 x 61
SM MI T 1637

Cleaves, Percy
Henry J. Macdonnell 1921
oil on canvas 125 x 100
SM 2007.197.3

Davidson
'The Amethyst'
oil on wood 22 x 38 (E)
SM 1989.492

Davies, Chas
Mr John Evans 1987
oil on canvas 38.7 x 28.8
SM 2007.3.1

Davies, K.
Penny Ferry, Foxhole to St Thomas 1975
oil on board 57 x 85.5
SM MI 4473

Davis of Shrewsbury
Anne, Wife of William Lloyd
oil on canvas 123 x 95
SM A 63

Dicksee, Frank 1853–1928
Elizabeth Clarke Richardson
oil on canvas 89 x 69
SM 2005.6.2

Dicksee, Frank 1853–1928
John Richardson II
oil on canvas 89 x 69
SM 2005.6.1

Dixon, Alfred 1842–1919
Artists at 'The Mermaid' in Mumbles 1886
oil on canvas 62 x 75
SM 1924.7

Dixon, George
Oystermouth, West End
distemper on canvas 126 x 319 (E)
LIB PCF1

Dixon, George
Oystermouth, West End
distemper on canvas 130 x 340 (E)
LIB PCF1

Emslie, Alfred Edward 1848–1918
Worshipful Brother John Rogers 1905
oil on canvas 90 x 68
SM 2007.197.1

Evans, Will 1888–1957
St Mary's Square after the Blitz, Swansea 1941
oil on canvas 43 x 58
SM 2012.24.3

Evans, Will 1888–1957
Swansea Blitz 1941
oil on canvas on plyboard 47 x 71
SM 2012.24.1

Evans, Will 1888–1957
St Mary's Square after the Blitz, Swansea 1942
oil on canvas on plyboard 61 x 65.7
SM 2012.24.2

Francis, John Deffett 1815–1901
Doctor Wiliam Hewson 1843
oil on canvas 91.5 x 61
SM A 41

Francis, John Deffett 1815–1901
Doctor William Nichol 1843
oil on board 76 x 63
SM A 42

Goddard, Walter W. 1858–after 1910
Neath Abbey 1895
oil on canvas 39 x 60
SM 2006.18

Goddard, Walter W. 1858–after 1910
A View of Mumbles Lighthouse c.1895
oil on canvas 20.3 x 30.6
SM A 14

Goddard, Walter W. 1858–after 1910
Mumbles Islands from Bracelet Bay
oil on canvas 60.5 x 89
SM 1989.574

Harris Junior, James
Off Gower Coast
oil on canvas 22.2 x 43
SM 1927.104

Harris Senior, James 1810–1887
Swansea Bay in Stormy Weather 1834
oil on canvas 60.3 x 88.9
SM 1927.98

Harris Senior, James 1810–1887
Oystermouth from the Sea c.1860
oil on canvas 60.3 x 103.7
SM 1927.102

Harris Senior, James 1810–1887
Pilot Cutter in Stormy Sea
oil on canvas 27 x 42.8
SM 1927.96

Harris Senior, James 1810–1887
Pilot Cutters
oil on canvas 31 x 48.5
SM 1927.99

Harris Senior, James 1810–1887
Ships in Calm Water
oil on canvas 27 x 42.8
SM 1927.95

Harris Senior, James 1810–1887
Ships in Rough Sea
oil on canvas 35.3 x 47.8
SM 1927.100

Harris Senior, James 1810–1887
Ships in Swansea Bay
oil on canvas 19 x 35
SM 1927.97

Harris Senior, James 1810–1887
Ships off Mumbles
oil on canvas 22.2 x 42.5
SM 1927.103

Harris Senior, James 1810–1887
Ships Off Mumbles
oil on canvas 33 x 57.5
SM 1968.11

Hayman, Mary b.1955
Fishing Boats, Summer, Swansea
acrylic on wood 39 x 60
SM 2011.57

Heard, Hugh Percy 1866–1940
Oxwich Bay 1938
oil on canvas 28.7 x 48.6
SM 1938.56

Hepburn, David
Harbour and Salt House, Port Eynon 1907
oil on canvas 30.5 x 46
SM 1965.6.4

Hepburn, David
Port Eynon 1907
oil on canvas 25.5 x 46
SM 1965.6.3

Hepburn, David
Overton Meer, Gower 1908
oil on canvas 25.5 x 46
SM 1965.6.1

Hepburn, David
Port Eynon Bay
oil on canvas 25.5 x 46
SM 1965.6.2

Hepburn, David
Sunrise at Port Eynon
oil on canvas 25.5 x 46
SM 1965.6.5

Herkomer, Hubert von 1849–1914
Portrait of a Lady (said to be Frida Mond)
oil on canvas 127.3 x 101
SM A 28

Herkomer, Hubert von 1849–1914
Portrait of a Man (said to be Ludwig Mond)
oil on canvas 127 x 101
SM A 32

Hoppner, John 1758–1810
Captain Joseph Huddart
oil on canvas 75 x 62.2
SM 1896.110

Hughes, John Joseph (attributed to)
1820–1909
The Oystermouth Railway
oil on canvas 48.9 x 69
SM 2008.3

Ince, Joseph Murray (attributed to)
1806–1859
Swansea Castle 1840
oil on canvas 59.2 x 49.6
SM 1996.64

Janes, Alfred (possibly) 1911–1999
Brother C. J. Tazewell 1931
oil on canvas 120 x 90
SM 2007.197.6

Jones, Calvert Richard 1804–1877
View of the Harbour at Valetta, Malta 1836
oil on canvas 51 x 77
SM A 55

Jones, John J.
Edgar Evans 1940
oil on canvas 57.2 x 96.5
SM A 56

Jones, John J.
Edgar Evans 1940
oil on canvas 85 x 77.5
SM A 57

Jones, M. Russell
Sentimental Journey
oil on board 43.7 x 69
SM A 44

Lance, George 1802–1864
Thomas Duncan 1840
oil on canvas 30.8 x 25.5
SM A 15

Lance, George 1802–1864
Edward Duncan (1803–1882)
oil on canvas 91.5 x 71 (E)
SM 1965.8

Lawrence, Thomas 1769–1830
Lady Anna Powell (1773–1809) 1794
oil on canvas 74 x 61
SM 1920.9

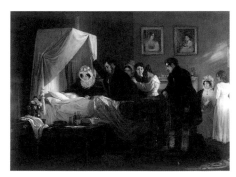

Leslie, Charles Robert 1794–1859
Sarah Dillwyn's Deathbed 1829
oil on canvas 58 x 78.7
SM 1985.179

Lewis, Richard Jeffreys (possibly)
1822/1823–1883
Turning the First Sod, the South Docks 1852
oil on wood 43.7 x 73
SM 2012.3

Marchi, Giuseppe Filippo Liberati
c.1735–1808
Portrait of a Man 1770
oil on canvas 76 x 63
SM A 43

Mendus, V.
Landscape of a Lake 1914
oil on canvas 29 x 59.5
SM A 38

Mercier, J. D. active 1877
Worshipful Brother T. Powell
oil on canvas 75 x 61.7
SM 2007.197.5

Owen, William (possibly) 1769–1825
John Richardson
oil on canvas 73.5 x 61
SM A 54

Pather, Walter
William Simon 1934
oil on canvas 91.5 x 71
SM 2007.197.4

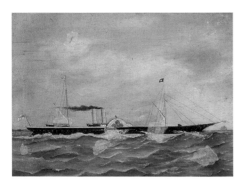

Pearson, W.
The Steam Yacht 'Lynx' 1898
oil on canvas 45.2 x 60.7
SM MI 7482.1

Pearson, W.
The Paddle Ship 'Alexandra'
oil on canvas 45.3 x 60.7
SM MI 7482.2

Rathmell, Thomas Roland 1912–1990
Man Carrying His Coracle
oil on canvas 61 x 46 (E)
SM 2008.60.1

Facing page: Procter, Dod, 1892–1972, *Early Morning, Newlyn,* 1926, Glynn Vivian
Art Gallery (p. 200)

Rees, Rhiannon
Thinking
oil on gesso ground 70 x 55
SM A 47

Rees, Rhiannon
Waiting
oil on gesso ground 80 x 60
SM A 59

Renault, Luigi active 1845–1877
Brigantine 'Constance Ellen'
oil on canvas 46 x 68
SM MI 4715

Rothwell, Thomas
The Old Rectory, Oxwich 1790
oil on canvas 53 x 65.2
SM 1978.12

Rothwell, Thomas
Oxwich Landscape
oil on canvas 67.5 x 88
SM 1980.34

Schweickhardt, Heinrich Wilhelm
1747–1797
Landscape with River
oil on wood 19.8 x 25
SM A 20

Scott, Derek
Christmas Visit 1987
oil on canvas 49.5 x 75
SM 2007.193

Scott, Derek
Pulling and Sailing a Lifeboat
oil on canvas 49.5 x 75
SM 2007.194

Shee, Martin Archer 1769–1850
Pascoe Grenfell (1761–1838), MP
oil on canvas 125 x 100.5
SM MI 7777

Syer, John 1815–1885
Shipping off Mumbles
oil on canvas 44.3 x 75
SM A 31

unknown artist
Pilot Cutter Off Mumbles Head 1865
oil on wood 35.7 x 51
SM 2011.39

unknown artist
John Aeron Thomas (1850–1935) 1923
oil on canvas 75 x 62
SM 1994.91

unknown artist
Worshipful Brother J. Broad Excell 1992
oil on canvas 90 x 61.5
SM 2007.197.2

unknown artist
A Man Holding a Pomander
oil on panel 43 x 33.3
SM A 50

unknown artist
A Man with Money Bags
oil on canvas 53 x 42.3
SM 1989.490

unknown artist
Abigail Pacifying David
oil on tin tray 58 x 78
SM 2007.192

unknown artist
Broad Gauge Train on a Dual-Gauge Track
oil on board 31 x 47
SM MI 3015

unknown artist
Harris Lane
oil on board 30.3 x 45.7
SM 1989.267

unknown artist
Limebeer's Farm
oil on board 30.2 x 45.7
SM 1989.240

unknown artist
Major John Hanbury (1664–1734), Father of the Tinplate Trade
oil on tin 60.5 x 42
SM 2007.195

unknown artist
Meleager Presenting the Boar's Head to Atalanta
oil on cedar panel 89 x 114.3
SM A 30

unknown artist
Portrait of a Bearded Man
oil on canvas 111.5 x 86
SM UNK 581

unknown artist
Portrait of a Man (possibly Lord Glantawe)
oil on canvas 61 x 50.5
SM A 61

unknown artist
Portrait of a Woman
oil on canvas 67 x 53
SM A 22

unknown artist
Siloam Congregational Church
oil on canvas 48 x 61
SM 2003.22.4

unknown artist
Steam Ship 'Menantic'
oil on canvas 40 x 90
SM MI T 1641

unknown artist
Swansea from Kilvey Hill
oil on board 16.7 x 28
SM 1989.486

unknown artist
Two Masted Ship
oil on board 57 x 74
SM MI T 1640

unknown artist
Wooden Motor Trawler 'Holkar' and Tug 'Pilot Jack'
oil on board 28 x 38
SM MI 4485

Warren, Frances Bramley active 1889–1901
J. H. M. Middleton Powell (1837–1912)
oil on canvas 125 x 100
SM 1937.29

Watkeys, William John 1800–1873
Mrs Hewson 1832
oil on canvas 45.2 x 38.2
SM 1910.4.2

Watkeys, William John 1800–1873
Ann of Swansea (1764–1838) 1835
oil on copper 16.7 x 13 (E)
SM 1985.159

Watkeys, William John 1800–1873
Doctor Hewson (1782–1845), Vicar of Swansea
oil on canvas 47 x 39.5
SM 1910.4.1

Wolfe, George 1834–1890
Landing Oysters at Mumbles
oil on canvas 59.6 x 90.3
SM MI 7769

Paintings Without Reproductions

This section lists all the paintings that have not been included in the main pages of the catalogue. They were excluded as it was not possible to photograph them for this project. Additional information relating to acquisition credit lines or loan details is also included. For this reason the information below is not repeated in the Further Information section.

Carmarthenshire Museums Service Collection

Edwards, Lionel Dalhousie Robertson 1878–1966, *Lieutenant Colonel W. H. Buckley,* 1964, oil on canvas, 60 x 90.5, 2000.0562, gift, image unavailable due to copyright restrictions

Lodwick, Edith Mary 1905–1993, *View from the Green, Llanstephan,* c.1956, oil on board, 41 x 57, 1988.0094, purchased, not available at the time of photography

Owen, Wyn *Foel Cwm Cerwyn II '81,* 1981, oil on canvas, 61.5 x 120.5, 1982.0001, purchased, not available at the time of photography

Pratt, Derrick Edward Henry 1895–1979, *Talley Abbey,* 1932, oil on canvas, 35.6 x 45.7, 1988.0079, purchased, not available at the time of photography

Rowlands, Glenys active 1960–1967, *Llandybie Church (and 'Red Lion'),* 1963, oil on board, 50.5 x 76, 1988.0103, purchased, not available at the time of photography

Smith, Dudley active 1958–1983, *Llanelli House and Vaughan Street,* 1963, oil on canvas, 50.5 x 76, 1981.0062, purchased, not available at the time of photography

Thomas, Gareth b.1955, *Llanstephan,* 1981, oil on canvas, 30.5 x 45.5, 1981.0243, purchased, not available at the time of photography

University of Wales Trinity Saint David

Barclay, Ceri b.1937, *Tower Colliery, Hirwaun,* 1991, acrylic on canvas, 58.4 x 99.1, 449, not available at the time of photography

Crabtree, Jack b.1938, *Collier at Merthyr Vale,* 1977, oil on canvas, 30.5 x 38.1, 452, not available at the time of photography

Cundell, Charles *St David's Cathedral,* oil on canvas, 446, not available at the time of photography

Davies, Adrian *Mynydd Y Gwain,* 1978, oil on paper, 20.3 x 23, 193, not available at the time of photography

Davies, Adrian *Rainfall,* 1978, acrylic, 15.2 x 22.9, 541, not available at the time of photography

Davies, Adrian *Rift,* 1989, acrylic & oil, 43.2 x 53.3, 540, not available at the time of photography

Davies, Adrian *Ascension,* 1992, oil & acrylic on board, 38.1 x 45.7, 333, not available at the time of photography

Davies, Adrian *Echo,* 1992–1993, acrylic on board, 329, not available at the time of photography

Davies, Adrian *Dance,* 1994, acrylic on board, 330, not available at the time of photography

Evans, L. B. L. *St Ediths, Llanedi,* oil on canvas, 38.1 x 58.4, 264, not available at the time of photography

Gillick, James *Ray White (b.1940), President of the University of Wales Lampeter (2002–2006),* 2006, oil on linen, 104 x 70, TSD_PCF23, commissioned, image unavailable due to copyright restrictions

Gillick, James *Robert Alasdair Pearce (b.1951), Vice-Chancellor of the University of Wales Lampeter (2008–2009),* 2010, oil on linen, 90 x 136, TSD_PCF24, commissioned, image unavailable due to copyright restrictions

Lloyd, Stephen *Hand Sculpted,* pastel, oil & acrylic, 30.5 x 40.6, 370, not available at the time of photography

Lloyd, Stephen *Odd Head in Water?,* pastel, oil & acrylic, 30.5 x 40.6, 373, not available at the time of photography

Lowe, Ronald 1932–1985, *Above the Usk,* 1974, acrylic on paper, 27.9 x 38.1, 454, not available at the time of photography

Morgan, Abi *Still Life with Orange and Yellow Fruits,* acrylic, 58.4 x 68.6, 310, not available at the time of photography

Nash, Thomas John b.1931, *Incise Green Blue,* 1970, acrylic, 35.6 x 48.3, 456, not available at the time of photography

Nash, Thomas John b.1931, *Interior Venice,* acrylic, 33 x 48.3, 496, not available at the time of photography

Neep, Victor 1921–1979, *Objects on a Beach,* oil on board, 507, not available at the time of photography

Owens, Nichola *Still Life with Green Bottle and Green Apples,* acrylic, 58.4 x 78.7, 311, not available at the time of photography

Owens, Nichola *Still Life with Venetian Blind and Red Fruit,* acrylic, 50.8 x 68.6, 312, not available at the time of photography

Pelts, Kusha *Poppies in a Morning Light,* 1985, acrylic, 17.8 x 27.9, 504, not available at the time of photography

Rathmell, Thomas Roland 1912–1990, *The Floating Nude,* oil on canvas, 73.7 x 101.6, 498, not available at the time of photography

Record, Rob *MD 1556,* acrylic & oil, 38.1 x 48.3, 212, not available at the time of photography

Skinner, Sheila *Monet 1884 Self Portrait 1914,* 2001, oil on canvas (?), 20.3 x 68.6, 295b, not available at the time of photography

Skinner, Sheila *Paul Klee Self Portrait 1933,* 2001, oil on canvas (?), 20.3 x 68.6, 295c, not available at the time of photography

Skinner, Sheila *Piet Mondrian Self Portrait 19/2/B,* 2001, oil on canvas (?), 20.3 x 68.6, 295a, not available at the time of photography

Stall, James *Abstract*,* 2004, acrylic on canvas, 78.7 x 99.1, 548, not available at the time of photography

Stock, James *Fishfingers No.1,* 2005, acrylic on canvas, 111.8 x 114.3, 558, not available at the time of photography

Sutton, Philip b.1928, *Heather Cook,* acrylic on paper, 53.3 x 55.9, 260, not available at the time of photography

Thomas, Gareth b.1955, *Snow above Llyn Brianne,* oil on card, 17.9 x 25.4, 508, not available at the time of photography

unknown artist *Dr Hillary Lewis,* 1987, acrylic on canvas, 33.2 x 43.2, 450, not available at the time of photography

unknown artist *Moonlit Tango,* 1989, acrylic on board, 15.2 x 25.4, 447, not available at the time of photography

unknown artist *Four Faces,* 1990, acrylic on board, 91.4 x 121.9, 342, not available at the time of photography

unknown artist *Abstract*,* acrylic on wood, 45.7 x 76.2, 547, not available at the time of photography

unknown artist *Gauguin Type Scene,* acrylic on board, 30.5 x 58.4, 316, not available at the time of photography

unknown artist *Klee Type Soft Cubist Piece,* acrylic on board, 63.5 x 76.2, 293, not available at the time of photography

unknown artist *Rocks, Water and Hills,* oil on canvas (?), 343, not available at the time of photography

unknown artist *Rural Landscape with Horse or Mule and Trees Behind,* acrylic on canvas, 48.3 x 88.9, 262, not available at the time of photography

unknown artist *Surrealist Scene with Patterned Floor,* acrylic on board, 61 x 61, 292, not available at the time of photography

unknown artist *Tree with Green Grass and Blue Sky,* acrylic on canvas, 81.3 x 121.9, 376, not available at the time of photography

Walters, Evan *Interior with Artist's Mother by the Fire,* oil on canvas, 48.3 x 58.4, 458, not available at the time of photography

Neath Port Talbot County Borough Council

Craig, Andrew *Kelly's Yard,* oil (?), NEA2_PCF18, gift from the Arts Council of Wales, 2003, not available at the time of photography

Craig, Andrew *Meeting,* oil (?), NEA2_PCF17, gift from the Arts Council of Wales, 2003, not available at the time of photography

Davies, Roger *Icarus,* oil (?), NEA2_PCF19, gift from the Arts Council of Wales, 2003, not available at the time of photography

Freeman, Michael John b.1936, *Shipwreck,* oil (?), NEA2_PCF21, gift from the Arts Council of Wales, 2003, not available at the time of photography

Freeman, Michael John b.1936, *Tristan and Isolde,* oil (?), NEA2_PCF20, gift from the Arts Council of Wales, 2003, not available at the time of photography

Mynton, R. W. *View of Neath Abbey,* oil on canvas, 61 x 91.5, NEA2_PCF13, on permanent loan from Neath Town Council, not available at the time of photography

unknown artist *Mr Edward Vaughan,* before 1900, oil on canvas (?), 1996.P.22, unknown acquisition method, not available at the time of photography

West, Benjamin 1738–1820, *Abraham and Isaac,* oil on canvas, 137.2 x 259, NEA2_PCF8, unknown acquisition method, not available at the time of photography

Williams, Harry *Gower Theme,* oil (?), NEA2_PCF22, gift from the Arts Council of Wales, 2003, not available at the time of photography

Pembrokeshire County Council's Museums Service

Calver, Fanny *Hook Farm, Marloes,* 1915, oil on board, 17.5 x 26.5, SCO_FA_Op_239, not

Facing page: Herkomer, Hubert von, 1849–1914, *Portrait of a Lady*, Swansea Museum, (p. 242)

available at the time of photography

Cramp, Jonathan D. b.1930, *Expressionist Landscape,* oil on hardboard, 49 x 71.5, SCO_FA_Op_233, gift from the Contemporary Art Society for Wales, 1967, not available at the time of photography

Könekamp, Frederick 1897–1977, *Lanzarote,* 1956, oil (?) & mixed media on paper, 48.3 x 81.2, SCO.FA.Mm.006, gift from the Contemporary Art Society for Wales, not available at the time of photography

Llewellyn Davies, Lyn b.1947, *The Old Cottage,* 1989, oil (?) & mixed media on paper, 24.9 x 37.6, SCO.FA.Mm.007, purchased from 'Sea & Sky' Exhibition, 1990, not available at the time of photography

Morris, Carey Boynes 1882–1968, *Harbour Scene,* oil on canvas, 23 x 28, SCO.FA.Op.240, purchased at Sykes Auctioneers, 1975, not available at the time of photography

Morris, Carey Boynes 1882–1968, *Woman,* c.1900, oil on canvas, 28 x 23, SCO.FA.Op.245, not available at the time of photography

Reynolds, Ernie active 1969–1982, *Bird and Butterflies,* 1979, oil on glass, 38 x 29, SCO.FA.Op.243, gift from the artist, 1979, not available at the time of photography

Reynolds, Ernie active 1969–1982, *Two Birds on a Thistle,* 1979, oil on glass, 38 x 29, SCO.FA.Op.244, gift from the artist, 1980, not available at the time of photography

Shellard *Cattle and Landscape,* oil on cardboard, 19.3 x 31, SCO.FA.Op.241, not available at the time of photography

unknown artist *Man,* oil on canvas, 91 x 70.5, SCO.FA.Op.234, not available at the time of photography

unknown artist *Maritime Figurehead,* oil on canvas, 144 x 76, SCO.FA.Op.235, not available at the time of photography

unknown artist *Trees, River and Cottage,* oil on cardboard, 22.8 x 42.8, SCO.FA.Op.236, not available at the time of photography

unknown artist *Trees, River and Mountains,* oil on cardboard, 22.8 x 42.8, SCO.FA.Op.237, not available at the time of photography

unknown artist *Wren and Chicks on Branch,* oil on cardboard, 18.5 x 14, SCO.FA.Op.242, not available at the time of photography

Milford Haven Heritage and Maritime Museum

Rickard, Robert *'Gerberdina Johanna',* oil on board, 65 x 91, 1996.0515, not available at the time of photography

unknown artist *HMS 'Warrior',* oil on board, 1998.0275, not available at the time of photography

unknown artist *Steam Trawler 'Caliph' M197,* oil on board, 2001.0008, not available at the time of photography

Puncheston School

Tress, David b.1955, *Caerfai,* oil on canvas, 35.7 x 50.7, PCF10, gift from the artist, image unavailable due to copyright restrictions

Abertawe Bro Morgannwg University Health Board

unknown artist *Steamboat,* poster paint on paper, 63.5 x 90 (E), PCF128, not available at the time of photography

Glynn Vivian Art Gallery

Appleyard, Frederick 1874–1963, *St David's Cathedral,* 1938, oil on canvas, 90.2 x 69.7, GV 1995.109, unknown acquisition method, not available at the time of photography

Boucher, François (attributed to) 1703–1770, *Cupids,* oil on paper, 17.8 x 18.5, 52, bequeathed by Richard Glynn Vivian, 1911, not available at the time of photography

Brangwyn, Frank 1867–1956, *British Empire Panel, Preparatory Work* (triptych) c.1930 tempera on canvas, 420 x 368, GV 1934.646.1.18, gift from The Iveagh Trust, 1934, not available at the time of photography

Collins, W. J. *The Waterwheel,* oil on canvas, 59.8 x 49.1, GV 1913.44, gift from Roger Beck, 1913, not available at the time of photography

Cooper-Mason, G. *Untitled (Fantasy scene),* oil on board, 175 x 443, GV 1982.204, unknown acquisition method, not available at the time of photography

Cox the elder, David 1783–1859, *Castell Carreg Cennen,* 1844, oil on canvas, 37 x 31, GV 1943.927, gift from Richard J. Strick and The Art Collection Fund, 1943, not available at the time of photography

Denner, Balthasar (style of) 1685–1749, *Untitled (Portrait of a Man),* oil on canvas, 49.5 x 38.4, GV 1994.170, bequeathed by Richard Glynn Vivian, 1911, not available at the time of photography

Evans, Will 1888–1957, *Castle Street, Swansea, 22nd February 1941,* oil on canvas, 61.4 x 66.5, GV 1994.105, gift, not available at the time of photography

Evans, Will 1888–1957, *Temple Street, Swansea,* oil on canvas, 70.9 x 92, GV 1994.104, gift, not available at the time of photography

French School *Madame de Florensac,* oil on canvas, 40.2 x 31.5, 65, bequeathed by Richard Glynn Vivian, 1911, not available at the time of photography

Gainsborough, Thomas (attributed to) 1727–1788, *Miss Elwes,* oil on canvas, 127 x 101, GV 1960.1438, bequeathed by Gwenny Griffiths, 1960, not available at the time of photography

Gerard, Charles *Siesta,* oil on plywood, 63 x 72.9, GV 1938.813, gift from the Contemporary Art Society, 1938, not available at the time of photography

Goodall, Frederick 1822–1904, *The Artist's Wife,* oil on canvas, 150 x 92.2, GV 1911.2, gift from Thomas Griffith, 1911, not available at the time of photography

Goyen, Jan van 1596–1656, *Leyden or The Hague,* oil on panel, 21 x 27, GV 1984.3, bequeathed by Edgar Hodges, 1984, not available at the time of photography

Griffier I, Jan c.1645–1718, *View of the Danube,* oil on oak panel, 36 x 48.7, GV 1920.326, gift from John Dyer, 1920, not available at the time of photography

Griffiths, Archie Rhys 1902–1971, *Testing a Collier's Lamp,* oil on canvas, 61.1 x 51.1, GV 1932.567, purchased from the artist, 1932, not available at the time of photography

Gurschner, Herbert 1901–1975, *The Silent Lake,* oil on canvas, 39.6 x 36.7, GV 1932.563, purchased

from the Art Exchange Bureau, not available at the time of photography

Harris Senior, James 1810–1887, *Off the Gower Coast,* oil on canvas, 101.4 x 157, GV 1935.647, gift from William Lewis, 1935, not available at the time of photography

Harris Senior, James 1810–1887, *Worm's Head,* oil on canvas, 20.8 x 37.6, GV 1943.917, gift from Ernest H. Leeder, 1943, not available at the time of photography

Herman, Josef 1911–2000, *Two Miners Against a Lamp Post,* oil on canvas, 44.1 x 59.9, GV 1963.1477, purchased from Rowland, Browse and Delbarco, 1963, not available at the time of photography

Hickin, George Arthur 1821–1885, *Untitled (Landscape),* oil on canvas, 30.5 x 45.5, GV 1994.114, gift, not available at the time of photography

Italian (Venetian) School *Belshazzar's Feast,* oil on canvas, 105.6 x 215.5, GV 1920.330, purchased from John Dyer, 1920, not available at the time of photography

Johns, John White *Untitled (Boy and Girl on a Beach)* (unfinished), oil on canvas, 38 x 30.4, GV 1994.120, gift, not available at the time of photography

Jones, Calvert Richard 1804–1877, *Picking Up the Pilot, Swansea Bay,* oil on canvas, 50.8 x 68.9, GV 1974.64, purchased from the Colin Lacey Gallery, 1974, not available at the time of photography

Leslie, Charles Robert 1794–1859, *Countess of Blessington, as Juliet,* oil on canvas, 84.2 x 68.1, 61, bequeathed by Richard Glynn Vivian, 1911, not available at the time of photography

Lucas, John Seymour 1849–1923, *Sir Griffiths Thomas, JP, Mayor of Swansea (1901–1902),* oil on canvas, 134 x 103.5, GV 1994.184, unknown acquisition method, not available at the time of photography

Mitchell, William c.1806–1900, *Entrance to Solway Firth,* oil on canvas, 25.5 x 38, GV 1975.54, gift from L. Rees, 1975, not available at the time of photography

Morgan, T. *Untitled,* oil on canvas, 46.1 x 33.4, GV 1994.129, gift from Roger Beck, not available at the time of photography

Neuschul, Ernst 1895–1968, *D. R. Grenfell,* 1939, oil on canvas, GV

2011.12, gift from Bryan Grenfell, 2011, not available at the time of photography

Neyn, Pieter de 1597–1639, *Encampment,* oil on panel, 33 x 44.5, GV 1974.60, purchased from Regency Antiques, not available at the time of photography

Piazzetta, Giovanni Battista (attributed to) 1683–1754, *Untitled (Portrait of a Man),* oil on canvas, 39.7 x 28.4, GV R 133, bequeathed by Richard Glynn Vivian, 1911, not available at the time of photography

Short, Richard 1841–1919, *Untitled (Painting of a Steam Ship),* oil on canvas, 50 x 75, GV 1979.80, purchased from Regency Antiques, 1979, not available at the time of photography

Solomon, Leopold active 1940s, *Mollie Mullins,* oil on sacking, 41.5 x 35.9, GV 1994.12, gift from Bert McKee, 1994, not available at the time of photography

unknown artist *Lord and Lady Mansel,* oil on canvas, 74.2 x 61.1, GV 1951.1099, gift from Earl Jersey, 1951, not available at the time of photography

unknown artist *Ludwig VIII,* oil on canvas, 53.5 x 40, GV 1994.167, bequeathed by Richard Glynn Vivian, 1911, not available at the time of photography

unknown artist *Oystermouth Castle,* oil on canvas, 30.6 x 45.9, GV 1913.46, gift from Roger Beck, 1913, not available at the time of photography

unknown artist *Portrait of a Lady in a Blue Dress,* oil on canvas, 84.5 x 68, 64, bequeathed by Richard Glynn Vivian, 1911, not available at the time of photography

unknown artist *Spring,* oil on glass, GV R 140, bequeathed by Richard Glynn Vivian, 1911, not available at the time of photography

unknown artist *Untitled (Man and Woman in a Landscape),* oil on canvas, 22.5 x 30.5, GV 1994.116, gift, not available at the time of photography

unknown artist *W. M. J. of Neath,* oil on paper on canvas, 44 x 67.5, GV 1979.84, gift from Mrs Lloyd, not available at the time of photography

Walters, Evan 1893–1951, *Abstract Faces,* oil on canvas, 50.6 x 40.6,

GV 1979.16, gift from William Meinel, 1979, not available at the time of photography

Walters, Evan 1893–1951, *Abstract Landscape with Figures No.2,* oil on canvas, 51 x 40.7, GV 1979.56, gift from William Meinel, 1979, not available at the time of photography

Walters, Evan 1893–1951, *Boy's Head,* oil on canvas, GV 1926.368, purchased from the artist, 1925, not available at the time of photography

Walters, Evan 1893–1951, *David Davies, JP,* oil on canvas, 76.3 x 63.2, GV 1933.632, gift from David Davies, 1933, not available at the time of photography

Walters, Evan 1893–1951, *Feeding Time,* oil on canvas, 35.7 x 50.9, GV 1979.43, gift from William Meinel, 1979, not available at the time of photography

Walters, Evan 1893–1951, *Lieutenant S. G. Johns,* oil on board, 60.1 x 45, GV 1996.4, gift from The British Legion, 1996, not available at the time of photography

Walters, Evan 1893–1951, *Miss Rowlands,* oil on canvas, 46 x 35.7, GV 1973.9, gift from Miss Rowlands, 1973, not available at the time of photography

Walters, Evan 1893–1951, *Mr Bardo,* oil on canvas, 60.9 x 50.7, GV 1995.3, gift from Paul Vining, 1995, not available at the time of photography

Walters, Evan 1893–1951, *Rest and Unrest,* oil on canvas, 133.1 x 109.6, GV 1942.912, bequeathed by T. Walters, 1942, not available at the time of photography

Williams, Penry 1798–1885, *Adoration of the Magi* (after Jacopo Cavedone) c.1827, oil on board, 20 x 32.2, 74, bequeathed by Richard Glynn Vivian, 1911, not available at the time of photography

Further Information

The paintings listed in this section have additional information relating to one or more of the five categories outlined below. This extra information is only provided where it is applicable and where it exists. Paintings listed in this section follow the same order as in the illustrated pages of the catalogue.

I   The full name of the artist if this was too long to display in the illustrated pages of the catalogue. Such cases are marked in the catalogue with a (…).

II   The full title of the painting if this was too long to display in the illustrated pages of the catalogue. Such cases are marked in the catalogue with a (…).

III   Acquisition information or acquisition credit lines as well as information about loans, copied from the records of the owner collection.

IV   Artist copyright credit lines where the copyright owner has been traced. Exhaustive efforts have been made to locate the copyright owners of all the images included within this catalogue and to meet their requirements. Any omissions or mistakes brought to our attention will be duly attended to and corrected in future publications.

V   The credit line of the lender of the transparency if the transparency has been borrowed. Bridgeman images are available subject to any relevant copyright approvals from the Bridgeman Art Library at www.bridgemanart.com

Carmarthenshire Museums Service Collection

Alison, J. active 1900s, *Sir James Williams-Drummond (1857–1913), of Edwinsford, Llandeilo, 4th Bt Hawthornden, CB, Lord-Lieutenant of Carmarthenshire*, gift

Anthony, Sonia active 1960s, *Llygad Llwchwr*, purchased, © the copyright holder

Aplin, Herbert Lawrence 1907–1993, *Gelli Aur, Autumn*, purchased, © the copyright holder

Ardron, Annette Matilda 1875–1952, *Portrait of an Unknown Boy*, gift, © the copyright holder

Barham, George active c.1850–1858, *Laugharne Castle*, gift

Barham, George active c.1850–1858, *Laugharne Church*, gift

Barnard, J. Langton 1853–1902, *The Makers of England*, gift

Bevan, J. G. active 1950s–1960s, *Deserted Farm, Coedcae*, purchased, © the copyright holder

Beynon, E. B. active 1970s, *St Paul's Depot*, purchased, © the copyright holder

Blanchard, Jacques 1912–1992, *Still Life with Cherries*, gift from the Contemporary Art Society for Wales, © the copyright holder

Bonnor, Rose Dempster 1875–1967, *Ernest Trubshaw*, gift, © the copyright holder

Bonville, William *Bridge over River Taff, Pontypridd*, gift

Bowen, John 1914–2006, *Self Portrait*, gift, © the copyright holder

Bowen, John 1914–2006, *Mediterranean Fishing Boat*, purchased, © the copyright holder

Bowen, John 1914–2006, *Aegean Variations II, Temple Ruins*, purchased, © the copyright holder

Bowen, John 1914–2006, *Sunset*, purchased, © the copyright holder

Bowen, John 1914–2006, *Melting Snow Evening*, purchased, © the copyright holder

Bowen, John 1914–2006, *Farmer in a Field*, purchased, © the copyright holder

Bowen, John 1914–2006, *Nevills Channel*, purchased, © the copyright holder

Bowen, John 1914–2006, *April Morning Wet Pavements*, gift, © the copyright holder

Bowen, John 1914–2006, *Terrace near Bridge with Pole*, purchased, © the copyright holder

Bowen, John 1914–2006, *Winter Landscape*, purchased, © the copyright holder

Bowen, John 1914–2006, *Autumn Evening*, purchased, © the copyright holder

Bowen, John 1914–2006, *Landscape with Tiger Moth*, purchased, © the copyright holder

Bowen, John 1914–2006, *Woman in Lamplight (1)*, purchased, © the copyright holder

Bowen, John 1914–2006, *Woman in Lamplight (2)*, purchased, © the copyright holder

Bowen, John 1914–2006, *Autumn Mist, Llanelli Beach*, purchased, © the copyright holder

Bowen, John 1914–2006, *Chapel No.3*, purchased, © the copyright holder

Bowen, John 1914–2006, *Elegy Autumn*, purchased, © the copyright holder

Bowen, John 1914–2006, *Park in Autumn*, purchased, © the copyright holder

Bowen, John 1914–2006, *The Blue Shirt (Graffiti)*, purchased, © the copyright holder

Bowen, John 1914–2006, *Spanish Hill Village, Twilight* (recto), purchased, © the copyright holder

Bowen, John 1914–2006, *Colour Abstract* (verso), purchased, © the copyright holder

Bowen, John 1914–2006, *Breezes from the Sea*, purchased, © the copyright holder

Bowen, John 1914–2006, *A Window: Tossa de Mar*, purchased, © the copyright holder

Bowen, John 1914–2006, *Evening Thunder, Tossa*, purchased, © the copyright holder

Bowen, John 1914–2006, *Woman Packing Flowers, Nice*, purchased, © the copyright holder

Bowen, John 1914–2006, *Still Life with Fruit and Peppers*, gift, © the copyright holder

Bowen, John 1914–2006, *Noonday Heat, Provence*, purchased with the assistance of the Friends of Llanelli Museum, © the copyright holder

Bowen, Leslie *Devon Lane*, purchased

Brenton, Ruth 1922–2007, *Local Derby*, purchased, © the artist's estate

Brenton, Ruth 1922–2007, *Autumn Scene*, gift, © the artist's estate

Brenton, Ruth 1922–2007, *View from Libanus, Pwll*, purchased, © the artist's estate

Brenton, Ruth 1922–2007, *Daniel's Cottage, Pwll*, purchased, © the artist's estate

Brenton, Ruth 1922–2007, *Penwlch Farm, Pwll*, purchased, © the artist's estate

Brenton, Ruth 1922–2007, *Burry Port Harbour*, © the artist's estate

Brigstocke, Thomas 1809–1881, *John Jones, Esq. (1777–1842), MP, of Ystrad*, transferred

Brigstocke, Thomas 1809–1881, *General Sir William Nott (1782–1845)*, transferred

Brigstocke, Thomas 1809–1881, *David Morris (1800–1869), MP and Whig Politician*, transferred

Brigstocke, Thomas (attributed to) 1809–1881, *John Jones, Esq. (1777–1842), MP, of Ystrad*, gift

Brown, Geoff b.1948, *Jersey Beach Hotel*, purchased, © the copyright holder

Brown, Julian b.1934, *Free Fibres*, gift, © the artist

Bush, Reginald Edgar James 1869–1956, *J. E. Jones*, gift, © the copyright holder

Chalmers, George (attributed to) c.1720–c.1791, *Lady Maude of Westmead (1697–1779)*, purchased with the assistance of the Victoria and Albert Museum Purchase Grant Fund

Charles, Anthony Stephen *Garnant 1*, gift from the Arts Council of Wales, © the copyright holder

Charles, Anthony Stephen *Garnant 2*, gift from the Arts Council of Wales, © the copyright holder

Charles, Julian Peter *The Stranger*, purchased, © the copyright holder

Cole, Philip Tennyson 1862–1939, *Owen Cosley Philipps, 1st Baron Kylsant, MP*, gift

Cole, Walter Stevens 1883–1967, *Aneurin Bevan (1897–1960)*, gift, © the copyright holder

Cole, Walter Stevens 1883–1967, *Winston Churchill (1874–1965)*, gift, © the copyright holder

Cole, Walter Stevens 1883–1967, *Our Factory in Winter*, gift, © the copyright holder

Cole, Walter Stevens 1883–1967, *Henry Giles*, gift, © the copyright holder

Cole, Walter Stevens 1883–1967, *Old Welsh Woman*, purchased, © the copyright holder

Cole, Walter Stevens 1883–1967, *Still Life, Musical Corner*, purchased, © the copyright holder

Collier, Ernest Vale 1859–1932, *The Gate at the Vicarage, St Ishmael's*

Collier, Ernest Vale 1859–1932, *The Parsonage Garden*

Collier, Ernest Vale 1859–1932, *The Palace, St David's*, gift

Collier, John 1850–1934, *William Rosser*, gift

Crabtree, Jack b.1938, *Pithead Scene*, gift from the Contemporary Art Society for Wales, © the artist

Davies, Arthur *La Perdix, Dordogne*, purchased, © the copyright holder

Davies, D. J. *James Buckley*, gift

Davies, Gareth *Ned Kelly's Ball*, © the copyright holder

Davies, Gareth *Y Clwb Rygbi*, purchased, © the copyright holder

Lewis, Edward Morland 1903–1943, *Harbour Scene* (recto), gift, © the artist's estate

Lewis, Edward Morland 1903–1943, *Seascape with a Ship and a Jetty* (verso), gift, © the artist's estate

Lewis, Edward Morland 1903–1943, *Harbour Scene*, gift, © the artist's estate

Lewis, Edward Morland 1903–1943, *Harbour Scene*, gift, © the artist's estate

Lewis, Edward Morland 1903–1943, *Harbour Scene*, gift, © the artist's estate

Lewis, Edward Morland 1903–1943, *Harbour Scene*, gift, © the artist's estate

Lewis, Edward Morland 1903–1943, *Landscape*, gift, © the artist's estate

Lewis, Edward Morland 1903–1943, *Landscape*, gift, © the artist's estate

Lewis, Edward Morland 1903–1943, *Landscape*, gift, © the artist's estate

Lewis, Edward Morland 1903–1943, *Landscape*, gift, © the artist's estate

Lewis, Edward Morland 1903–1943, *Landscape* (recto), gift, © the artist's estate

Lewis, Edward Morland 1903–1943, *Portrait of a Woman* (verso), gift, © the artist's estate

Lewis, Edward Morland 1903–1943, *Landscape, Ferryside (?)*, gift, © the artist's estate

Lewis, Edward Morland 1903–1943, *Landscape, Ferryside (?)*, gift, © the artist's estate

Lewis, Edward Morland 1903–1943, *Lifeboat Station at Ferryside (?)*, gift, © the artist's estate

Lewis, Edward Morland 1903–1943, *Man in an Armchair*, gift, © the artist's estate

Lewis, Edward Morland 1903–1943, *Old Man Seated at a Table*, gift, © the artist's estate

Lewis, Edward Morland 1903–1943, *People Seated*, gift, © the artist's estate

Lewis, Edward Morland 1903–1943, *River Quayside*, gift from the Arts Council of Wales, © the artist's estate

Lewis, Edward Morland 1903–1943, *River Scene*, gift, © the artist's estate

Lewis, Edward Morland 1903–1943, *Scotch Quay, Waterford*, purchased with the assistance of the Victoria and Albert Museum Purchase Grant Fund, © the artist's estate

Lewis, Edward Morland 1903–1943, *Seated Figures*, gift, © the artist's estate

Lewis, Edward Morland 1903–1943, *Still Life*, gift, © the artist's estate

Lewis, Edward Morland 1903–1943, *Street Scene*, gift, © the artist's estate

Lewis, Edward Morland 1903–1943, *Street Scene*, gift, © the artist's estate

Lewis, Edward Morland 1903–1943, *Street Scene, Carmarthen*, gift, © the artist's estate

Lewis, Edward Morland 1903–1943, *The Beach and Estuary with Boats*, gift, © the artist's estate

Lewis, Edward Morland 1903–1943, *Three Figures in a Room*, gift, © the artist's estate

Lewis, Edward Morland 1903–1943, *Townscape, Carmarthen Quay (?)*, gift, © the artist's estate

Lewis, Edward Morland 1903–1943, *Two Members of a Brass Band in a Bandstand*, gift, © the artist's estate

Lewis, Edward Morland 1903–1943, *Two Members of a Brass Band in a Bandstand*, gift, © the artist's estate

Lewis, Edward Morland 1903–1943, *Village Scene with Gate, Ferryside (?)*, gift, © the artist's estate

Lewis, Edward Morland 1903–1943, *Village Scene, Houses and Grassy Bank*, gift, © the artist's estate

Lewis, Edward Morland 1903–1943, *Welsh Kitchen*, gift, © the artist's estate

Lewis, Edward Morland 1903–1943, *The Bandstand*, gift from the Arts Council of Wales, © the artist's estate

Lewis, Edward Morland 1903–1943, *Three Profiles*, gift from the Arts Council of Wales, © the artist's estate

Lewis, Edward Morland 1903–1943, *The Spanish Tutor*, gift from the Arts Council of Wales, © the artist's estate

Lewis, Edward Morland 1903–1943, *General Sir William Nott (1782–1845)*, purchased, © the artist's estate

Lewis, Edward Morland 1903–1943, *Quayside with Reflections*, gift from the Arts Council of Wales, © the artist's estate

Lewis, Edward Morland 1903–1943, *Solva*, gift, © the artist's estate

Lewis, Edward Morland 1903–1943, *Backs of Houses, Wales*, gift, © the artist's estate

Lewis, Edward Morland 1903–1943, *Carmarthen Market and Clock Tower*, gift, © the artist's estate

Lewis, Edward Morland 1903–1943, *Snow at Undercliff*, gift, © the artist's estate

Lewis, Edward Morland 1903–1943, *St Ishmael's Sand Dunes*, gift, © the artist's estate

Lewis, Edward Morland 1903–1943, *Townscape, South of France (?)*, gift, © the artist's estate

Lewis, Edward Morland 1903–1943, *Townscape, South of France (?)*, gift, © the artist's estate

Lewis, Edward Morland 1903–1943, *Townscape, South of France (?)*, gift, © the artist's estate

Lewis, Edward Morland 1903–1943, *Welsh Houses*, gift, © the artist's estate

Lewis, Edward Morland 1903–1943, *Welsh Landscape*, purchased, © the artist's estate

Lewis, Edward Morland 1903–1943, *Carmarthen Quay*, gift, © the artist's estate

Lewis, Edward Morland 1903–1943, *A Farm in the Tywi Valley*, gift, © the artist's estate

Lewis, John active 1736–1776, *Elizabeth Eleanor Lloyd, Lady Stepney*, purchased with the assistance of the Heritage Lottery Fund, the Victoria and Albert Museum Purchase Grant Fund and the Friends of Carmarthen Museum.

Lewis, John active 1736–1776, *Bridget Vaughan, Madam Bevan (1698–1779)*, purchased with the assistance of the Heritage Lottery Fund, the Victoria and Albert Museum Purchase Grant Fund and the Friends of Carmarthen Museum.

Lewis, John active 1736–1776, *Landscape*, gift

Lewis, John active 1736–1776, *Buwchllaethwen*, gift

Lewis, John (attributed to) active 1736–1776, *Mrs Lloyd of Laques, near Llanstephan*, gift

Lewis, John (attributed to) active 1736–1776, *Arthur Bevan (1689–1743) (after John Vanderbank)*, purchased with the assistance of the Heritage Lottery Fund, the Victoria and Albert Museum Purchase Grant Fund and the Friends of Carmarthen Museum.

Lewis, Stanley Cornwall 1905–2009, *Carmarthen Hill Farm, Cwmllyfri Farm*, purchased, © the artist's estate

Lewis, Stanley Cornwall 1905–2009, *Dylan Thomas' Cottage*, purchased, © the artist's estate

Lewis, Stanley Cornwall 1905–2009, *Winter, Wauniago*, gift, © the artist's estate

Lewis, Stanley Cornwall 1905–2009, *Old Cockle Factory, Laugharne*, purchased, © the artist's estate

Lewis, Stanley Cornwall 1905–2009, *The Old Chapel*, purchased, © the artist's estate

Lewis, V. P. *Springtime at Carreg Cennen*, purchased, © the copyright holder

Lloyd, A. *Portrait of an Unknown Gentleman*, gift

Lodwick, Edith Mary 1905–1993, *Pontynys Wen, near Brechfa*, purchased, © the copyright holder

Lynn, Jenny active 1970s, *Town Hall, Llanelli*, purchased, © the copyright holder

Lynn, Jenny active 1970s, *Station Road*, purchased, © the copyright holder

MacCallum, Andrew 1821–1902, *Evening Glow*, gift

Malcolm, Victoria b.1957, *Teifi III*, purchased, © the artist

Malcolm, Victoria b.1957, *Tulips on Black Card*, purchased, © the artist

Markey, Peter b.1930, *Cypress Trees*, purchased, © the artist

McCann, Susan *Old Quay and River Towy*, gift from the Arts Council of Wales, © the copyright holder

Meyler, Stephen b.1956, *The Riots of 1911, a Reconstruction of the Event*, purchased, © the artist

Meyler, Stephen b.1956, *Dining Out*, purchased, © the artist

Meyler, Stephen b.1956, *Industrial Landscape*, purchased, © the artist

Midgley, J. C. active 1925–1930, *Carmarthen Quay*, gift

Miers, Christopher b.1941, *Lieutenant Colonel W. Kemmis Buckley*, gift, © the artist

Milner, Joseph 1880–1940, *George Eyre Evans (1857–1939)*, gift

More, Guinevere *Carmarthen Bay Power Station*, purchased, © the copyright holder

Morgan, Maldwyn active 1970s, *Two Red Lorries*, gift from the Arts Council of Wales, © the copyright holder

Morgan (Miss) *Bull Lane, Carmarthen*, gift, © the copyright holder

Morris, Carey Boynes 1882–1968, *Sir Lewis Morris (1833–1907)*, purchased, © the artist's estate

Morris, Carey Boynes 1882–1968, *Sir Lewis Morris (1833–1907)*, gift, © the artist's estate

Morris, Carey Boynes 1882–1968, *Colonel Delmé William Campbell Davies-Evans (1873–1953)*, gift, © the artist's estate

Morris, Carey Boynes 1882–1968, *Three Cliffs Bay Gower, Morning*, purchased, © the artist's estate

Morse-Brown, Sam 1903–2001, *Fog, Frost and Sunlight*, gift, © the copyright holder

Morse-Brown, Sam 1903–2001, *Sir Rhys Hopkins Morris (1888–1956), MBE, QC, MP, LID, MP for Cardiganshire*, purchased by public subscription, sponsored by the Rotary Club and presented to Carmarthen County Council, 1959, © the copyright holder

Moss, Sally b.1949, *Relief: Green Shirt*, purchased, © the copyright holder

Narbett, W. N. active c.1963–c.1967, *Derwen Fawr Farm*, purchased, © the copyright holder

Narbett, W. N. active c.1963–c.1967, *Woodlands in May*, purchased, © the copyright holder

Nash, Thomas John b.1931, *Llandybie Quarry*, purchased, © the copyright holder

Nash, Thomas John b.1931, *Coastal Wave*, gift from the Arts Council of Wales, © the copyright holder

Nash, Thomas John b.1931, *Primordial Image*, gift from the Arts Council of Wales, © the copyright holder

Oliver, William 1823–1901, *Haymaking Scene*, gift

Patrick, David 1822–1899, *John Williams*, gift

Patrick, David 1822–1899, *Mrs Mary and Miss Sarah Williams*, gift

Petts, David b.1947, *No Good Boyo*, purchased, © the copyright holder

Petts, David b.1947, *A Window on the Hill*, purchased, © the copyright holder

Petts, David b.1947, *Ark No.6*, purchased, © the copyright holder

Petts, John 1914–1991, *Red Structure*, purchased, © the copyright holder

Petts, Kusha 1921–2003, *Lieutenant Colonel W. Kemmis Buckley*, gift, © the copyright holder

Phillips, Ethne active after 1990, *Raby's Furnace*, gift, © the copyright holder

Phillips, P. *Stac Fawr*, gift

Pratt, Derrick Edward Henry 1895–1979, *Anne*, purchased, © the copyright holder

Pratt, Derrick Edward Henry 1895–1979, *Llwyn Farm, Llanelli*, purchased, © the copyright holder

Pratt, Derrick Edward Henry 1895–1979, *Hydrangeas*, gift, © the copyright holder

Pratt, Derrick Edward Henry 1895–1979, *Island Place*, purchased, © the copyright holder

Pratt, Derrick Edward Henry 1895–1979, *Llanelli Railway Station*, purchased, © the copyright holder

Pryor, S. J. active 20th C, *Llanelli Hospital*, purchased, © the copyright holder

Prytherch, Thomas 1864–1926, *Portrait of an Unknown Lady with a Lace Cap*, gift

Prytherch, Thomas 1864–1926, *Portrait of an Unknown Man with Full Beard*, gift

Ramsay, Frances Louisa Margaret 1858–1928, *Charlotte Cookman née Johnes (1825–1911)*, gift

Ramsay, Frances Louisa Margaret 1858–1928, *Lady Elizabeth Hills Johnes of Dolaucothi (1834–1927)*, gift

Ramsay, Isabelle *St Paul's Church*, purchased, © the copyright holder

Ratcliffe, William Whitehead 1870–1955, *Hertford Landscape*, gift, © the artist's estate

Rayner, A. E. *Carreg Cennen Castle*, gift

Rees, Becky 1921–2010, *Roses*, purchased, © the artist's estate

Rees, John Bromfield Gay 1912–1965, *Still Life with a Chianti Bottle*, gift from the Arts Council of Wales, © the copyright holder

Reynolds, J. *A Scene in Kidwelly*, gift

Richards, Frances 1903–1985, *Nun*, presented by the Contemporary Arts Society for Wales, © the copyright holder

Roberts, Diana b.1941, *The Scrap Metal Man*, gift from the Arts

Council of Wales, © the copyright holder

Roberts, Diana b.1941, *Maliphant*, gift from the Arts Council of Wales, © the copyright holder

Roberts, Dylan T. active 1960s, *Industrial Lights*, purchased, © the copyright holder

Roberts, Dylan T. active 1960s, *High Tide, Amlwch*, © the copyright holder

Roberts, Gwyn b.1953, *Croth*, gift from the Arts Council of Wales, © the artist

Roberts, Jeremy active 1970s, *Blodeuwedd*, gift from the Arts Council of Wales, © the copyright holder

Roberts, Will 1907–2000, *The Doubler*, gift from the Contemporary Art Society for Wales, © Will Roberts' estate

Roe, John (attributed to) active 1771–1811, *Portrait of an Unknown Lady with a Velvet Choker*, gift

Roos, William (attributed to) 1808–1878, *Reverend David Lloyd (1805–1863), MA*, gift

Rowan, Eric b.1931, *Parable*, gift from the Arts Council of Wales, © the artist

Rowlands, Glenys active 1960–1967, *The Melting Shop*, purchased, © the copyright holder

Rowlands, Glenys active 1960–1967, *Bonllwyn Bridge, Ammanford*, purchased, © the copyright holder

Rowlands, Glenys active 1960–1967, *Kidwelly Castle*, purchased, © the copyright holder

Rowlands, Glenys active 1960–1967, *Talley Abbey and Lake*, purchased, © the copyright holder

Saunders, B. A. active 20th C, *'The Farriers'*, purchased, © the copyright holder

Scrutton, B. E. M. active 20th C, *Still Life*, purchased, © the copyright holder

Scrutton, Ella *December Morning with Snow*, purchased, © the copyright holder

Secco, L. *Townscape, Evening in Llanelli from Bigyn Hill*, purchased, © the copyright holder

Selway, John b.1938, *The Factory Inspector*, gift from the Arts Council of Wales, © John Selway (Arlunydd)

Shee, Martin Archer 1769–1850, *Lieutenant General Sir Thomas Picton (1758–1815)*, transferred

Sirrell, Wilfred John 1901–1979, *Capel Bethlehem, Coed Poeth*, gift from the Contemporary Art Society for Wales, © the copyright holder

Sirrell, Wilfred John 1901–1979, *Llanerch Cottage, Llandindrod Wells*, gift from the Contemporary Art Society for Wales, © the copyright holder

Smith, Dudley active 1958–1983, *Cothi near Abercothi House*, purchased, © the copyright holder

Smith, Dudley active 1958–1983, *Polperro Harbour*, purchased, © the copyright holder

Smith, Dudley active 1958–1983, *Mynydd Mawr Bridge, North Dock, Llanelli*, gift, © the copyright holder

Smyth, Henry active c.1800–1873, *A View of Kidwelly*, purchased

Spencer, Richard Barnett d.c.1890, *The 'Carmarthenshire'*, purchased

Steele-Morgan, Tony 1930–2009, *Lord Elwyn Jones (1909–1989)*, purchased, © the artist's estate

Stephens, Brian active 1958–1970, *Low Tide, New Dock (Llanelli)*, purchased, © the copyright holder

Stephens, Brian active 1958–1970, *Towards the Copperworks*, purchased, © the copyright holder

Stuart, Gordon b.1924, *The Beach*, purchased, © the artist

Stuart, Gordon b.1924, *The Flag, Gower*, purchased, © the artist

Stuart, Gordon b.1924, *Towy Farm*, purchased, © the artist

Thatcher, C. F. active 1816–1846, *Llangennech Park House*, purchased with the assistance of the Victoria and Albert Museum Purchase Grant Fund, the Friends of Carmarthen Museum and the Art Fund, 1992

Thatcher, C. F. active 1816–1846, *Llangennech Park House*, purchased with the assistance of the Victoria and Albert Museum Purchase Grant Fund, the Friends of Carmarthen Museum and the Art Fund, 1992

Thomas, Bryn active 1980s, *Jackson's Lane, Carmarthen*, gift, © the copyright holder

Thomas, Bryn active 1980s, *Capitol Bingo Hall, Carmarthen*, gift, © the copyright holder

Thomas, Bryn active 1980s, *Carmarthen from the Railway Station*, gift, © the copyright holder

Thomas, Bryn active 1980s, *The Old Art School, Carmarthen*, gift, © the copyright holder

Thomas, E. active 1970s, *View of Tycroes*, purchased, © the copyright holder

Thomas, Gareth b.1955, *Abergwili Church in Mist*, purchased, © the copyright holder

Thomas, Jefferson active c.1930–1983, *Llandeilo Church*, purchased, © the copyright holder

Thomas, Sid active 20th C, *Llanelli Old Church*, purchased, © the copyright holder

unknown artist *John Vaughan (?)*, purchased with the assistance of the Victoria and Albert Museum Purchase Grant Fund

unknown artist *Francis, Lord Vaughan (1638–1667), MP*, purchased with the assistance of the Victoria and Albert Museum Purchase Grant Fund

unknown artist *Richard Vaughan (1600–1686), 2nd Earl of Carbery (possibly after Adriaen Hanneman)*, purchased with the assistance of the Victoria and Albert Museum Purchase Grant Fund

unknown artist *Sir John Altham Vaughan (1640–1713), 3rd Earl of Carbery*, purchased with the assistance of the Victoria and Albert Museum Purchase Grant Fund

unknown artist *Lady Frances Vaughan*, purchased with the assistance of the Victoria and Albert Museum Purchase Grant Fund

unknown artist *Portrait of an Unknown Gentleman*, purchased with the assistance of the Victoria and Albert Museum Purchase Grant Fund

unknown artist *Reverend George Bull (1634–1710), DD*, gift

unknown artist *Richard Vaughan, Auditor of Wales*, purchased with the assistance of the Victoria and Albert Museum Purchase Grant Fund

unknown artist *Portrait of an Unknown Lady in Green*, purchased with the assistance of the Victoria and Albert Museum Purchase Grant Fund

unknown artist *Richard Vaughan, Esq. (1726–c.1780)*, purchased with the assistance of the Victoria and Albert Museum Purchase Grant Fund

unknown artist *Captain Ro(w)e*, gift

unknown artist *Golden Grove*, on loan from the Cawdor Estate

unknown artist *Portrait of an Unknown Woman*, gift

unknown artist *The Surrender of the French at Fishguard*, gift, on loan to Scolton Manor

unknown artist *Vale of Towy*, gift

unknown artist *Judge John Wilson (1785–1851)*, gift

unknown artist *Portrait of an Unknown Gentleman*, gift

unknown artist *Ann Wilson, née Shutt (1796–1874)*, gift

unknown artist *General Andrew Cowell (d.1821)*, gift

unknown artist *Elizabeth Buckley, née Wedge*, gift

unknown artist *Captain David Davies (1789–1873)*, gift

unknown artist *James Buckley (1802–1883), JP, DL*, gift

unknown artist *James Buckley (1802–1883), JP, DL*, gift

unknown artist *Portrait of the Wife of Captain David Davies*, gift

unknown artist *Portrait of an Unknown Gentleman with a Checked Waistcoat*, gift

unknown artist *James Francis Hughes Buckley (b.1869), JP, MA, FSA*, gift

unknown artist *Reverend Llewellyn Bevan*, gift

unknown artist *Still Life – Red and Pink Roses*, gift

unknown artist *Portrait of an Unknown Girl*, gift

unknown artist *Portrait of an Unknown First World War Officer*, gift

unknown artist *William Joseph Buckley*, gift

unknown artist *View of Llanelli Town Hall and Town Centre*, purchased

unknown artist *A View of Swiss Valley*, gift

unknown artist *Haloed Figure*, gift

unknown artist *Lady Anne, Countess of Carbery (1663–1669)*, purchased with the assistance of the Victoria and Albert Museum Purchase Grant Fund

unknown artist *Pembroke Castle*, gift

unknown artist *Portrait of an Unknown Gentleman*, gift

unknown artist *Portrait of an Unknown Gentleman (said to be called John Lewis)*, gift

unknown artist *Portrait of an Unknown Gentleman with Glasses*, gift

unknown artist *Portrait of an Unknown Gentleman with Purple Flowers*, gift

unknown artist *Portrait of an Unknown Man with Whiskers*, gift

unknown artist *Portrait of Luke*, gift

unknown artist *Reverend David Griffiths*, gift

unknown artist *Richard, Lord Vaughan (1600–1686), 2nd Earl of Carbery*, purchased with the assistance of the Victoria and Albert Museum Purchase Grant Fund

unknown artist *Seascape*, gift

unknown artist *Still Life*

unknown artist *Trinity College, Carmarthen*

unknown artist *View of Laugharne Castle*

Walker, Christopher *Mount Gabriel*, purchased, © the copyright holder

Walters, Evan 1893–1951, *Eve*, bequeathed, © the artist's estate

Walters, Evan 1893–1951, *Still Life with Chrysanthemums*, bequeathed, © the artist's estate

Walters, Evan 1893–1951, *Winter Cherries*, bequeathed, © the artist's estate

Walters, Evan 1893–1951, *Rural District*, bequeathed, © the artist's estate

Walters, Evan 1893–1951, *Daffodils*, bequeathed, © the artist's estate

Walters, Evan 1893–1951, *Self Portrait*, bequeathed, © the artist's estate

Walters, Evan 1893–1951, *The Artist's Mother Asleep*, bequeathed, © the artist's estate

Walters, Evan 1893–1951, *Artist's Father*, bequeathed, © the artist's estate

Walters, Evan 1893–1951, *The Artist's Mother*, bequeathed, © the artist's estate

Walters, Evan 1893–1951, *The Cockle Woman*, bequeathed, © the artist's estate

Walters, Evan 1893–1951, *Bishop Havard*, on loan from the Diocese of St Davids, © the artist's estate

Walters, James Lewis active c.1900–1922, *Llanboidy Mole Catcher*, gift

Walters, James Lewis active c.1900–1922, *The Artist's Mother*, gift

Walters, James Lewis active c.1900–1922, *John Hinds, Esq. (1862–1928), MP*, gift

Walters, W. R. *The Cottage*, gift from the Arts Council of Wales, © the copyright holder

Westmacott, Phyllis active 1948–1972, *Lieutenant Colonel William Howell Buckley, DL*, gift, © the copyright holder

Williams, C. M. active c.1960–1967, *Country Scene*, purchased, © the copyright holder

Williams, C. M. active c.1960–1967, *Cenarth Falls*, © the copyright holder

Williams, Christopher 1873–1934, *Dryslwyn Castle*, transferred

Williams, Christopher 1873–1934, *Barmouth Estuary*, gift

Williams, Christopher 1873–1934, *In the Alhambra*, gift

Williams, Christopher 1873–1934, *John Hinds, Esq. (1862–1928)*

Williams, D. H. active 1973–1974, *Steel Works by Night*, purchased, © the copyright holder

Williams, D. H. active 1973–1974, *Dockland Scene*, purchased, © the copyright holder

Williams, E. R. M. active 20th C, *Court Farm 1908 – A Reconstruction*, purchased, © the copyright holder

Williams, Jacqueline b.1962, *Still Life with Lamplight*, gift from the Contemporary Art Society for Wales, © the artist

Williams, Joel R. *Winter*, purchased, © the copyright holder

Williams, Kyffin 1918–2006, *Tom Owen*, gift from Arts Council of Wales, © Llyfrgell Genedlaethol Cymru / The National Library of Wales

Williams, Lauretta 1910–1993, *A. W. Williams*, gift, © the copyright holder

Williams, Lauretta 1910–1993, *Ann*, gift, © the copyright holder

Williams, Lauretta 1910–1993, *Blodau Mawrth Cyntaf*, gift, © the copyright holder

Williams, Lauretta 1910–1993, *Cactus*, gift, © the copyright holder

Williams, Lauretta 1910–1993, *Castiau'r Haul I*, gift, © the copyright holder

Williams, Lauretta 1910–1993, *Castiau'r Haul II*, gift, © the copyright holder

Williams, Lauretta 1910–1993, *Castiau'r Haul III*, gift, © the copyright holder

Williams, Lauretta 1910–1993, *Cat*, © the copyright holder

Williams, Lauretta 1910–1993, *Catherine*, gift, © the copyright holder

Williams, Lauretta 1910–1993, *Celyn y mor o Towyn Bach*, gift, © the copyright holder

Williams, Lauretta 1910–1993, *Cennin Pedr a Lorwg (recto)*, gift, © the copyright holder

Williams, Lauretta 1910–1993, *Still Life (verso)*, gift, © the copyright holder

Williams, Lauretta 1910–1993, *Cwm Lliedi*, gift, © the copyright holder

Williams, Lauretta 1910–1993, *Cyfoesal*, gift, © the copyright holder

Williams, Lauretta 1910–1993, *Er Cof am Smiw*, gift, © the copyright holder

Williams, Lauretta 1910–1993, *Ffenestr Siop*, gift, © the copyright holder

Williams, Lauretta 1910–1993, *Florie*, gift, © the copyright holder

Williams, Lauretta 1910–1993, *G and Ruggeri*, gift, © the copyright holder

Williams, Lauretta 1910–1993, *G. W. Williams*, gift, © the copyright holder

Williams, Lauretta 1910–1993, *Garthychau*, gift, © the copyright holder

Williams, Lauretta 1910–1993, *Glan y Fferi 1880 Hen Lun, Old Photograph*, gift, © the copyright holder

Williams, Lauretta 1910–1993, *Kidwelly Castle*, gift, © the copyright holder

Williams, Lauretta 1910–1993, *Lafant y mor o Towyn Bach*, gift, © the copyright holder

Williams, Lauretta 1910–1993, *M. Williams*, gift, © the copyright holder

Williams, Lauretta 1910–1993, *Machlud Haul*, gift, © the copyright holder

Williams, Lauretta 1910–1993, *Machlud Haul I*, gift, © the copyright holder

Williams, Lauretta 1910–1993, *O Bydded I'r Hen iaith Barhau*, gift, © the copyright holder

Williams, Lauretta 1910–1993, *Poinsetta*, gift, © the copyright holder

Williams, Lauretta 1910–1993, *Rhedeg*, gift, © the copyright holder

Williams, Lauretta 1910–1993, *Roses*, gift, © the copyright holder

Williams, Lauretta 1910–1993, *Self Portrait*, gift, © the copyright holder

Williams, Lauretta 1910–1993, *W. H. Williams*, gift, © the copyright holder

Williams, Lauretta 1910–1993, *W. W. Williams*, gift, © the copyright holder

Williams, Lauretta 1910–1993, *Y Diddiwedd*, gift, © the copyright holder

Williams, Lauretta 1910–1993, *Y Llanc Glas*, gift, © the copyright holder

Williams, Lauretta 1910–1993, *Yr Hen Neuadd y Plwyf a'r Llys Ynadon Newyd yn Llanelli*, gift, © the copyright holder

Williams, Lauretta 1910–1993, *Hickling Broad Gaeaf*, gift, © the copyright holder

Williams, Lauretta 1910–1993, *Still Life with a Coffee Pot and Mug* (recto), gift, © the copyright holder

Williams, Lauretta 1910–1993, *Autumn Scene* (verso), gift, © the copyright holder

Williams, Lauretta 1910–1993, *Village Scene*, gift, © the copyright holder

Williams, Lauretta 1910–1993, *Cyfoesal*, gift, © the copyright holder

Williams, Lauretta 1910–1993, *Cyfresol 1973*, gift, © the copyright holder

Williams, Lauretta 1910–1993, *Glan y Fferi 1944 Atgof, Recollects*, gift, © the copyright holder

Williams, M. R. *Between Tides*, purchased, © the copyright holder

Williams, Vivienne b.1955, *Still Life Fresco*, purchased, © the artist

Williams (Davies) (Mrs), E. R. M. *Sosban Fach*, gift from the Arts Council of Wales, © the copyright holder

Winterhalter, Franz Xaver (possibly) 1805–1875, *Lady Stepney*, gift

Wissing, Willem (attributed to) 1656–1687, *Portrait of an Unknown Man* (either Sir Edward Vaughan or George Savile, 1st Marquis of Halifax), purchased with the assistance of the Victoria and Albert Museum Purchase Grant Fund

Woodland, S. *Our Freedom – Their Price*, gift, © the copyright holder

Wright, John b.1931, *Rama*, purchased, © the copyright holder

Wright, John b.1931, *Green Legend*, gift from the Arts Council of Wales, © the copyright holder

Zobole, Ernest 1927–1999, *Figure in a Chair*, gift from the Arts Council of Wales, © the artist's estate

University of Wales Trinity Saint David

Alpin, H. L. *Christmas Tree*, © the copyright holder

Andrews, Janette *Still Life with Washing Vase and Basin*, © the copyright holder

Beal, Nick 1885–1971, *The Canterbury Building*, gift from the Lampeter Society Alumni, © the copyright holder

Brason, Paul b.1952, *Brian Robert Morris (1930–2001), Baron Morris of Castle Morris, Principal of St David's University College (1980–1991)*, commissioned, © the artist

Brason, Paul b.1952, *Keith Gilbert Robbins (b.1940), Principal and Vice-Chancellor of University of Wales Lampeter, St David's University College (1992–2003)*, commissioned, © the artist

Brason, Paul b.1952, *Brian Robert Morris (1930–2001)* (triptych), © the artist

Chapman, George 1908–1993, *Industrial Buildings at Blackburn*, purchased, © the artist's estate

Davies, Adrian *Welsh Cauldron*, © the copyright holder

Davies, Adrian *Looking Through*, © the copyright holder

Davies, Adrian *Abstract**, © the copyright holder

Davies, Adrian *Abstract**, © the copyright holder

Edwards, Peter Douglas b.1955, *John Elfed Jones (b.1933), President of University of Wales Lampeter, St David's University College (1992–1998)*, commissioned, © the artist

Foster, Ruth active 1919–1921, *Hugh Walker (1855–1939), Professor of English at St David's College (1890–1939)*, © the copyright holder

Giaconia, Emmanuel *Thomas Price 'Carnhuanawc' (1748–1848)*

Graves, J. *Edward Harold Browne (1811–1891), Vice-Principal of St David's College (1843–1850)*, acquired, 1822–1850

Griffiths, David b.1939, *Eric Sunderland (1930–2010), President of the University of Wales Lampeter (1998–2002)*, commissioned, © the artist

Griffiths, David b.1939, *Alfred Cosier Morris (b.1941), Vice-Chancellor of the University of Wales Lampeter (2003–2008)*, commissioned, © the artist

Hayter, George 1792–1871, *Sir Charles Cockerell (1755–1837), Bt*, gift

Hunter, Hoi May *Still Life* (recto), © the copyright holder

Hunter, Hoi May *Portrait Studies* (verso), © the copyright holder

Lawrence, Thomas after 1769–1830, *John Scandrett Harford II (1785–1866), Donor of the Site for St David's College, Benefactor and Sub Visitor*, gift

Mason, Arnold 1885–1963, *Henry Kingsley Archdall (1866–1976), Principal of St David's College (1938–1953)*, commissioned, © the artist's estate

Mason, Arnold 1885–1963, *Alfred Edwin Morris (1894–1971), Bishop of Monmouth (1945–1967), Archbishop of Wales (1957–1967)*, commissioned, © the artist's estate

Mason, Arnold 1885–1963, *John Roland Lloyd Thomas (1908–1984), Principal of St David's College/St David's University College (1953–1975)*, commissioned, © the artist's estate

Owen, William 1769–1825, *Bishop Thomas Burgess (1756–1837), Bishop of St David's (1803–1825), Bishop of Salisbury (1825–1837), Founder of St David's College*

Pickersgill, Henry William 1782–1875, *Llewelyn Llewellin (1827–1878), First Principal of St David's College*

Rathmell, Thomas Roland 1912–1990, *John Richards (1901–1990), Bishop of St David's University College (1971–1977)*, commissioned, © the artist's estate

Robertson, James *Rowland Williams (1817–1870), Vice-*

Principal of St David's College (1843–1850), presented by King's College, Cambridge, 1935

Todd, Daphne b.1947, *Evan Roderic Bowen (1913–2001), President of St David's University College (1977–1992)*, commissioned, © the artist

unknown artist *Abstract Composition**, © the copyright holder

unknown artist *Abstract Flower Forms on Black**, © the copyright holder

unknown artist *Abstract Forms on Lemon Yellow**, © the copyright holder

unknown artist *Abstract Pastel Forms on Black**, © the copyright holder

unknown artist *Analytical Cubist Style Abstract Landscape**, © the copyright holder

unknown artist *Assembled Composition**, © the copyright holder

unknown artist *Canon Evan Thomas Davies (1847–1927) (?)*, unknown acquisition method

unknown artist *Composition with Figure, Building and Other Scenes**, © the copyright holder

unknown artist *Figure Looking through Archway**, © the copyright holder

unknown artist *Green, Yellow and Blue Geometric Forms**, © the copyright holder

unknown artist *Mary**, © the copyright holder

unknown artist *Mary**, © the copyright holder

unknown artist *Mixed Composition with Figures in Various Locations**, © the copyright holder

unknown artist *Mixed Composition, Stripes, Figures and Cartoon Character**, © the copyright holder

unknown artist *Mother and Son and Other Scenes**, © the copyright holder

unknown artist *Personal Icon*, © the copyright holder

unknown artist *Still Life, Green Vessels**, © the copyright holder

unknown artist *Triptych: Figure with Hat and Other Themes**

unknown artist *Triptych: Figure with Hat and Other Themes**

unknown artist *Triptych: Figure with Hat and Other Themes**

unknown artist *Woman in Mirror**

Walters, Evan 1893–1951, *Maurice Jones (1863–1957), Principal of St David's College (1923–1938)*, commissioned, © the artist's estate

Ware, Margaret *Anthony Bedford Steel (1900–1973), Principal of University College Cardiff (1949–1966), Vice-Chancellor of the University of Wales (1956–1961)*, commissioned, © the copyright holder

Ware, Margaret *Sir David John James (1887–1967), Benefactor*, commissioned, © the copyright holder

Principal of St David's College (1975–1980), commissioned, © the artist's estate

Wright, John b.1931, *Magic Land*, © the copyright holder

Zebole, E. *Red Sunset over Sea*, © the copyright holder

Llandovery Town Council

Chapman, Ronald A. 1928–1982, *Vicar Prichard and the Goat*, donated, © the copyright holder

Hall, Graham 1937–2001, *A Scene of the Upper Towy Valley, near Rhandirmwyn*, donated by Mr John Brand, © the copyright holder

Harvey-Thomas *Pantycelyn Farmhouse, Home of William Williams and His Descendants*, donated by the artist, © the copyright holder

Williams, Peter *Self Portrait*, donated by Mr Gwynne Williams, © the copyright holder

Neath Antiquarian Society

Hill, C. *The River Neath with the Ship 'Viola'*, unknown acquisition method

Neath Port Talbot College

Harris, Jade b.1990, *Aberafon Beach in a Storm*, donated by the artist

Howells, Neale b.1965, *Industrial Scene at Night*, donated by the artist, © the artist

Rees, Paul b.1971, *Pontrhydyfen*, donated by the artist, © the artist

Rinaldi, Jason G. b.1970, *Swansea Docklands*, donated by the artist, © the copyright holder

Woodford, Paul *Pebbles*, donated by the artist, © the copyright holder

Neath Port Talbot County Borough Council

Bevan, Graham 1935–2006, *Bouquet*, gift from the Arts Council of Wales, 2003, © the artist's estate

Bevan, Graham 1935–2006, *Landscape*, gift from the Arts Council of Wales, 2003, © the artist's estate

Burrow, G. *Drymma Hall*, unknown acquisition method, © the copyright holder

Carlson, Ron 1936–2002, *Daffodil Bulbs*, gift from the Arts Council of Wales, 2003, © the copyright holder

Chapman, George 1908–1993, *Blaengwynfi*, unknown acquisition method, © the artist's estate

Cort, Hendrik Frans de 1742–1810, *The Gnoll and Castle, Neath*, unknown acquisition method

Curry, T. H. *Miner Feeding a Pit Pony*, transferred from residential flats in Seven Sisters, © the copyright holder

Davies, Gwyn active c.1950–c.1960, *Cadoxton Church*, unknown acquisition method, © the copyright holder

Davies, Gwyn active c.1950–c.1960, *Crynant Street Scene*, unknown acquisition method, © the copyright holder

Deane, Charles 1794–1874, *Vale of Neath*, unknown acquisition method

Eynon, William Arthur *The Crossroads*, gift from the Arts Council of Wales, 2003, © the copyright holder

Flanagan, John 1895–1964, *Harry Parr Davies (1914–1955)*, unknown acquisition method, © the copyright holder

Gleaves, Percy 1882–1944, *Lloyd George Receiving the Freedom of the Borough of Neath, c.1920*, on permanent loan from Neath Town Council, © the copyright holder

Hump (possibly) *River Scene*, unknown acquisition method

James, Douglas *Companions*, gift from the Arts Council of Wales, 2003, © the copyright holder

Jones, Harry *Alderman M. G. Roberts, Mayor of Neath (1922–1923)*, unknown acquisition method

Jones, V. A. *Neath Abbey*, unknown acquisition method

Kennington, Thomas Benjamin 1856–1916, *Alderman Pendrill Charles, Mayor of Neath (1864–1865)*, unknown acquisition method

Kennington, Thomas Benjamin 1856–1916, *Henry Pendrill Charles III, Mayor of Neath (1864, 1878, 1899, 1901 & 1916)*, on permanent loan from Neath Town Council

Kennington, Thomas Benjamin 1856–1916, *Howel Cuthbertson, Mayor of Neath (1867)*, on permanent loan from Neath Town Council

Kennington, Thomas Benjamin 1856–1916, *J. H. Rowland, Mayor of Neath (1865, 1871, 1879, 1880 & 1886)*, on permanent loan from Neath Town Council

Parminter, Agnes Vye c.1836–1915, *Howel Gwyn, Mayor of Neath (1842 & 1844)*, on permanent loan from Neath Town Council

Phillips, C. *Neath Abbey*, unknown acquisition method

Pyne, James Baker 1800–1870, *Vale of Neath*, unknown acquisition method

Riley, J. *Harry Parr and Guests*, unknown acquisition method, © the copyright holder

Roberts, Will 1907–2000, *Cae Rhys Ddu Cimla*, gift from Mansel J. Griffiths, © Will Roberts' estate

Roberts, Will 1907–2000, *The Gallery*, gift from the Arts Council of Wales, 2003, © Will Roberts' estate

Smith, James Burrell 1822–1897, *The Falls of Dulais, c.1870*, unknown acquisition method

Stuart, Gordon b.1924, *Port Talbot Steelworks*, unknown acquisition method, © the artist

Tennant, Dorothy 1855–1926, *Tom Harri(e)s as a Boy*, unknown acquisition method

Thomas, Dilys *Victoria Gardens, Neath, 1901*, unknown acquisition method, © the copyright holder

unknown artist *Alderman David Davies, Mayor of Neath (1931–1932)*, unknown acquisition method

unknown artist *Portrait of an Unknown Mayor of Neath*, unknown acquisition method

unknown artist *Richard Burton*, unknown acquisition method

Williams, Margaret Lindsay 1888–1960, *Hopkin Morgan, Mayor of Neath (1894, 1911, 1917 & 1921)*, on permanent loan from Neath Town Council, © the copyright holder

South Wales Miners' Museum

Duncan, C. active 1970–1978, *Miner Drilling at the Coalface*, © the copyright holder

Duncan, C. active 1970–1978, *Miner Drilling at the Coalface*, © the copyright holder

Haverfordwest Town Museum

Lindley, David b.1930, *Town Houses*, © the copyright holder

Lindley, David b.1930, *View of Haverfordwest*, © the copyright holder

Lindley, David b.1930, *Haverfordwest Square*, © the copyright holder

Lindley, David b.1930, *St Martin's Church, Haverfordwest*, © the copyright holder

Pitt, William c.1818–c.1900, *Haverfordwest Castle*, purchased at auction

unknown artist *William Walters*, on loan from Pembrokeshire County Council's Museums Service

unknown artist *Sir John Perrot (1528–1592)*, gift from the Sir John Perrot Trust, 1998

Pembrokeshire County Council's Museums Service

Adcock, Doris *Church, Castle and Bay, Manorbier*, purchased from the West Wales Guardian, 1961, © the copyright holder

Allen, H. C. G. *J. H. V. Higgon, Esq.*, on loan from the Higgon family, © the copyright holder

Allen *Sandy Haven*, purchased from Lees & Thomas, 1957, © the copyright holder

Arnold, Victor b.1944, *Scolton Manor: Rhododendron Time*, gift, 1990, © the copyright holder

B., S. J. *Modern Harvesting Scene*, © the copyright holder

Bendtsen, Axel 1893–c.1952, *Portrait of a Gentleman in Regimental Uniform*, gift from Bob and Jackie Butcher, 2010, © the copyright holder

Bright, Beatrice 1861–1940, *Major John Arthur Higgon*, on loan from the Higgon family

Bright, Beatrice 1861–1940, *Mrs Lurline May Higgon*, on loan from the Higgon family

Brown, Gordon active 1957–1958, *Beggar's Reach*, purchased from the artist, 1958, © the copyright holder

Brown, Gordon active 1957–1958, *Cleddau, Benton Woods, Winter Sunrise*, purchased from the artist, 1958, © the copyright holder

Brown, Gordon active 1957–1958, *Winter – Pembrokeshire Lane*, © the copyright holder

Burne-Jones, Philip Edward 1861–1926, *Edward Lucas Jenks Ridsdale (1833–1901)*, on loan from Mrs Susan Hewitt, since 1984

Burne-Jones, Philip Edward 1861–1926, *Sir Edward Aurelian Ridsdale (1864–1923)*, on loan from Mrs Susan Hewitt, since 1984

Burne-Jones, Philip Edward 1861–1926, *Mrs Esther Lucy J. Ridsdale (1840–1909)*, on loan from Mrs Susan Hewitt, since 1984

Burne-Jones, Philip Edward 1861–1926, *Lady Susan Stirling Ridsdale*, on loan from Mrs Susan Hewitt, since 1984

Burton-Richardson, David b.1961, *Preseli Fields and Wild Flowers*, gift from the artist, 2005, © the artist

Burton-Richardson, David b.1961, *Landscape: Rainy Day*, gift from the artist, 2005, © the artist

Burton-Richardson, David b.1961, *Twisted Trees, Efailwen*, gift from the artist, 2005, © the artist

Burton-Richardson, David b.1961, *Dark Autumn*, gift from the artist, 2006, © the artist

Burton-Richardson, David b.1961, *Landscape: Setting Sun*, gift from the artist, 2007, © the artist

Burton-Richardson, David b.1961, *The Clown*, gift from the artist, 2005, © the artist

Burton-Richardson, David b.1961, *Under the Cherry Moon*, gift from the artist, 2005, © the artist

Burton-Richardson, David b.1961, *Valley*, gift from the artist, 2009, © the artist

Burton-Richardson, David b.1961, *The Window*, gift from the artist, 2005, © the artist

Burton-Richardson, David b.1961, *The Window Study (in Blue and Yellow)*, gift from the artist, 2005, © the artist

Burton-Richardson, David b.1961, *Julie*, gift from the artist, 2005, © the artist

Burton-Richardson, David b.1961, *Landscape with Castle*, gift from the artist, 2005, © the artist

Burton-Richardson, David b.1961, *Skrinkle*, gift from the artist, 2005, © the artist

Burton-Richardson, David b.1961, *The Room*, gift from the artist, 2008, © the artist

Christopherson, John 1921–1996, *Hill Farm*, purchased through Yr Oriel Fach, St David's, © the copyright holder

Cole, Ethel 1892–1934, *Landscape with Trees*

Cole, Ethel 1892–1934, *Trees and Lakeside*

Colley, Cyril *Flower Piece*, gift from the Contemporary Art Society for Wales, 1961, © the copyright holder

Cramp, Jonathan D. b.1930, *Standing Stones* (recto), purchased from the artist, 1961, © the artist

Cramp, Jonathan D. b.1930, *Gnarly Tree* (verso), purchased from the artist, 1961, © the artist

Cramp, Jonathan D. b.1930, *Pembrokeshire Landscape*, purchased, © the artist

Cramp, Jonathan D. b.1930, *Still Life with Geraniums*, gift from the Arts Council of Wales, © the artist

Crawford, David *Oil Refinery*, © the copyright holder

Crome, Vivian 1842–c.1926, *View of Castle Pill and Castle Hall*, purchased from Milford Haven Antiques, 1975

Cross, Tom 1931–2009–2009, *Light Catch*, gift from the Contemporary Art Society for Wales, 1975, © the artist's estate

Davies, M. J. active 1896–1913, *Picton Castle*

Dorrington, Barbara *Blue and Green Abstract Shapes*, © the copyright holder

Dorrington, Barbara (attributed to) *Still Life with Vegetables* (unfinished), © the copyright holder

Edmunds, Michael *The Fishtrap*, gift from the Contemporary Art Society for Wales, 1957, © the copyright holder

Ellis, Lawrence Martin 1905–1981, *Bosherston Lily Pond*, accessioned, 1986, © the copyright holder

Ellis, Lawrence Martin 1905–1981, *Main Road, near Redberth*, © the copyright holder

Ellis, Lawrence Martin 1905–1981, *Stackpole Woods*, left after retrospective exhibition, © the copyright holder

Ellis, Lawrence Martin 1905–1981, *Treffgarne Quarry Workings*, © the copyright holder

Elwyn, John 1916–1997, *Landscape*, purchased from the artist, 1967, © the artist's estate

Evans, J. *Fishing Boats*, © the copyright holder

Evans-Thomas, Martin *The Front at Dale*, gift from the Arts Council of Wales, © the copyright holder

Fisher, Mark 1841–1923, *Still Life*, presented to the County of Pembroke by Dorothy Evelyn Garratt, 1936

Fisher, Samuel Melton 1859–1939, *Mabel Carlisle, Wife of Hugh Edwardes, 6th Baron Kensington*

Fisher, Samuel Melton 1859–1939, *Hugh Edwardes (1873–1938), 6th Baron Kensington*

Ford, Harry E. active 1892–1956, *Beach Scene*

Frith, William Powell 1819–1909, *Tenby Fisherwoman*, purchased

G., S. *Church near Weir*

Game, Aaron (attributed to) c.1791–1842, *Portrait of a Military Gentleman*

Green, T. W. *'Margaret'*, © the copyright holder

H., M. *Waiting for the Music to Start*

Hoare, William 1707–1792, *William Edwardes (c.1711–1801), 1st Lord Kensington*, transferred from the old County Hall

Hock, G. (attributed to) *F. C. Meyrick, CB*, gift from the Meyrick family, 2008

Holland, Harry b.1941, *The Breadwinner*, presented by the Contemporary Art Society for Wales, 1985, © the artist

Hopson, Royston 1927–2003, *Fishguard Invasion*, gift from Philippa Widdows, 2009, © the copyright holder

Howard-Jones, Ray 1903–1996, *Island of Scalmeye, Welshway*, purchased from the artist, 1992, © Amgueddfa Cymru – National Museum Wales and Nicola Howard-Jones

Icke, Glllian Sybll 1925–1989, *St Martin's, Haverfordwest*, gift from the Arts Council of Wales, © the copyright holder

Jones, Clifford active 1936–1982, *New Bridge, Haverfordwest*, gift from the artist, 1982, © the copyright holder

Jones, Selwyn 1928–1998, *Two Labourers*, gift from the Contemporary Art Society for Wales, 1967, © the copyright holder

Kay, Bernard b.1927, *Brantome*, gift from the Contemporary Art Society for Wales, 1956, © the artist

Knapp-Fisher, John b.1931, *House and Shed, North Pembrokeshire*, © the artist

Könekamp, Frederick 1897–1977, *Canadian Forest*, gift from Dillwyn Miles, © the copyright holder

Könekamp, Frederick 1897–1977, *Abstract*, gift from Dillwyn Miles, © the copyright holder

Könekamp, Frederick 1897–1977, *Nucleus*, purchased from the artist, 1957, © the copyright holder

Könekamp, Frederick 1897–1977, *Low Tide at Newport*, purchased from the artist, 1969, © the copyright holder

Könekamp, Frederick 1897–1977, *Jetsam on the beach*, gift from the Arts Council of Wales, © the copyright holder

Könekamp, Frederick 1897–1977, *Fire on the Mountain*, © the copyright holder

unknown artist *Farmhouse with Cows*

unknown artist *Foreign Beach Scene with Cattle*

unknown artist *Frederick (1847–1911), 3rd Lord Cawdor*, presented by Lord St Davids; transferred from the old County Hall

unknown artist *General Sir Thomas Picton (1758–1815)*, transferred from the old County Hall

unknown artist *Honestas optima politia*

unknown artist *Industrial Scene*

unknown artist *John Meyrick*, gift from the Meyrick family, 2008

unknown artist *Lady Riding a Horse*

unknown artist *Landscape of a Cottage and Lake*

unknown artist *Landscape of a River and Cottage*

unknown artist *Landscape with a Church and a Figure with a Boat*

unknown artist *Landscape with a Mountain*

unknown artist *Laurence Hugh Higgon*

unknown artist *Life Drawing Class*

unknown artist *Mediterranean View*

unknown artist *Neda Kathleen Cecil Higgon, née Rennick*

unknown artist *Pembrokeshire View*, found at Haverfordwest Library and transferred to Pembrokeshire Museums Service

unknown artist *Pier Scene*

unknown artist *Portrait of a Baroque Lady*, gift from the Meyrick family, 2008

unknown artist *Portrait of a Gentleman in Regency Dress*

unknown artist *Portrait of a Georgian Gentleman*, gift from the Meyrick family, 2008

unknown artist *Portrait of a Georgian Gentleman*

unknown artist *Portrait of a Georgian Man in a Decorative Waistcoat*, gift from the Meyrick family, 2008

unknown artist *Portrait of a Lady in a Ballgown and Tiara*, transferred from the old County Hall

unknown artist *Portrait of a Man*

unknown artist *Portrait of a Man in a Clerical Collar*

unknown artist *Portrait of a Man in a White Shirt*, gift from the Royston Brown family

unknown artist *Portrait of a Man Wearing a Tie*, on long-term loan from the County Library

unknown artist *Portrait of a Man with a Beard*

unknown artist *Portrait of a Naval Cadet*

unknown artist *Portrait of a Victorian Gentleman*, transferred from Hill House College

unknown artist *Portrait of a Victorian Lady in a Frilly Bonnet*

unknown artist *Portrait of a Victorian Man*

unknown artist *Portrait of a Victorian Man*

unknown artist *Portrait of a Victorian Woman in a Bonnet*, transferred from Hill House College

unknown artist *Portrait of a Victorian Woman in a Bonnet*

unknown artist *Portrait of a Woman with a Bonnet*

unknown artist *Portrait of a Woman with a Veil*

unknown artist *Portrait of a Young Woman*

unknown artist *Portrait of an Elizabethan Man*, transferred from the old County Hall

unknown artist *Primitive Cattle*

unknown artist *Primitive Horse*

unknown artist *Primitive Horses*

unknown artist *Primitive Landscape of Sea and Buildings*

unknown artist *Richard Fenton (1747–1821), KC, FAS*, presented by Lord St Davids; transferred from the old County Hall

unknown artist *Road near St David's*, found at Haverfordwest Library and transferred to Pembrokeshire Museums Service

unknown artist *Robert Anstice*

unknown artist *Sir John Henry Philipps Scourfield (1808–1876), Bt, MP*, transferred from the old County Hall

unknown artist *Sir John Meyrick*, gift from the Meyrick family, 2008

unknown artist *Sir John Owen (d.1861), Bt*, presented by Lord St Davids; transferred from the old County Hall

unknown artist *Standing Man*

unknown artist *The Dream of George Stephenson*

unknown artist *'The Duke of Sussex'*, purchased, 1995

unknown artist *Thomas James, Mayor of Haverfordwest (1887, 1896 & 1897)*

unknown artist *Three Tree Stumps*

unknown artist *Two Soldiers*

unknown artist *View of Haverfordwest from Uzmaston Road (looking west towards Quay Street and Castle from New Road)*

unknown artist *William Edwardes (1835–1896), 4th Baron Kensington*, transferred from the old County Hall

Vale, Edith *Bormes-les-Mimosas*, © the copyright holder

Wells, Arthur *Female Field, Smile Please*, gift from the Arts Council of Wales, © the copyright holder

Williams, Elizabeth *Little Haven*, purchased from the artist, 1960, © the copyright holder

Williams, Margaret Lindsay 1888–1960, *Lady Gwilym Lloyd George (d.1971), Lady Tenby*, purchased, 1972, © the copyright holder

Williams, Margaret Lindsay 1888–1960, *Lord Gwilym Lloyd George (1894–1967), Lord Tenby*, purchased, 1972, © the copyright holder

Milford Haven Heritage and Maritime Museum

Allen, Elsie *'Sybil'*, © the copyright holder

Bell, John H. *Off Landshipping in Milford Haven*, presented by N. A. Beal, 1956, © the copyright holder

Brett, Oswald Longfield b.1921, *A View of Milford Haven, Wales, 1798*, © the artist

Cadme, Christabel *Vessels in Castle Pill*

Clayton, Tommy F. *The Trawler 'David Ogilvie'*, © the copyright holder

Clayton, Tommy F. *The Trawler 'The Merit' LO56 Passing the Trawler 'Pheneas Beard' LO283*, © the copyright holder

Clayton, Tommy F. *Tug 'Turmoil' and Cargo Ship 'Flying Enterprise'*, © the copyright holder

Harrison *HMS 'Ardent'*, © the copyright holder

McIntosh *Milford Docks*, © the copyright holder

McIntosh *Milford Docks*, © the copyright holder

Murray, G. *Side Trawler 'Notts County' GY 643*, © the copyright holder

Rickard, Robert *'Esso', Pembrokeshire*, © the copyright holder

Rickard, Robert *German Minelaying Aircraft Dropping Parachute Mines near the Entrance to Milford Haven*, © the copyright holder

S., R. M. *Milford Haven, 1979*, © the copyright holder

T., D. T. *Passenger Liner 'Aquitania'*, © the copyright holder

unknown artist *Cardiff Vessel*

unknown artist *'Alert' H264*

unknown artist *Cliffs with Vessel in the Background*

unknown artist *'Kinellen' Leaving Dock*

unknown artist *'Norrard Star' on the Slip*

unknown artist *Padstow, Cornwall*

unknown artist *Schooner 'Gypsy'*

unknown artist *Steam Trawler 'Yezo' LO74*

unknown artist *Stokehold of Trawler 'Tamura' LOG3*

unknown artist *Trawler 'Lephreto' LO458*

Vaughan, Richard *'Kandahar' GY123*, © DACS 2013

Pembroke Dock Sunderland Trust

Banks, Arthur active 1984–1990, *X/210 P. D. 1944 (To John Evans, the inspiration for this theme)*, donated by the artist, © the copyright holder

Banks, Arthur active 1984–1990, *The New Sunderlands, Dar-es-salaam, Catalina and Sunderlands*, on loan from Pembroke Dock Museum Trust, © the copyright holder

Banks, Arthur active 1984–1990, *Study for 'Canadian Homecoming' (422 Squadron RCAF)*, presented to the Royal Airforces Association by the artist, 1987; acquired, © the copyright holder

Banks, Arthur active 1984–1990, *Cruikshank's VC*, donated by the artist, © the copyright holder

Banks, Arthur active 1984–1990, *Sunderland ML814 'Islander' at Lord Howe Island* (acknowledgments to Angela Smith), presented by the artist to 648 Branch RAFA, 1990; acquired, © the copyright holder

Bearman, Robert D. b.1927, *Seaplane 201 A over White Cliffs*, presented to Sunderland Trust by the artist, 2010, © the artist

Curtis, Ian J. *Royal Dockyard, Pembroke Dock (one of two)*, presented by the artist

Curtis, Ian J. *Royal Dockyard, Pembroke Dock (two of two)*, presented by the artist

Griffiths, A. T. active c.1980–1990s, *'AOZ'*, © the copyright holder

Griffiths, A. T. active c.1980–1990s, *Sunderland Flying Boat*, © the copyright holder

Hughes, G. S. *Sea Plane at Traitors Gate, Tower of London*, © the copyright holder

Hughes, S. S. *Aircraft RN303 with Crane*, © the copyright holder

Jarvis, Robin *Another Sortie Over*, donated by the artist, © the copyright holder

Martin, T. J. *Sea Plane over Headland*, donated by the artist, © the copyright holder

Palmer, D. *Seaship 2661*, donated by the artist, © the copyright holder

Rickard, Robert *'AOB' and 'AOC'*, gift from the artist, © the copyright holder

Rickard, Robert *Sea Plane with Purple Sky*, gift from the artist, © the copyright holder

Roberts, K. *Sea Plane and Tender*, presented by Vince Roberts, © the copyright holder

Robin, E. *RAF Hamworthy*, presented to Pembroke Dock Museum by John and Mary Witcomb, 2002, © the copyright holder

Spencer, Kenneth *Return to Pembroke Dock (Sunderland DV967 of No.228 Squadron RAF Coastal Command returns to Pembroke Dock after a successful air-sea Rescue 29th May 1943)*, presented to Pembroke Dock, RAFA, by Ron and Vivian Birchall, 1986; acquired, © the copyright holder

Tee, Jonny active c.1980–1990s, *Short Sunderland, 'On Patrol'*, gift from Trevor Bryant, 2011, © the copyright holder

unknown artist *Champion Gibraltar Bound F7 304, 'Depicting a Catalina of 270 Squadron'*, gift to Pembroke Dock RAFA Branch; acquired

unknown artist *Police Station*, donated to Pembroke Dock Museum Trust; acquired

unknown artist *'VA715'*, donated

unknown artist *'Z' W4004, 10 Squadron RAAF Drake's Island*, presented to Pembroke Dock Museum by John and Mary Witcomb, 2003; acquired

Puncheston School

Cooper, Ken *Puncheston*, gift from the artist, © the copyright holder

Curry, Denis b.1918, *Sheep and Rain*, gift from the artist, © the copyright holder

Gwyn, Elis *Beardsey*, gift from the artist, © the copyright holder

Heal, Katrina *Colour of Coal*, gift from the artist, © the copyright holder

Howard-Jones, Ray 1903–1996, *Rock Pool*, gift from the artist, © Amgueddfa Cymru – National Museum Wales and Nicola Howard-Jones

Lloyd, Ben b.1973, *Eggshell Brewery*, gift from the artist, © the copyright holder

MacKeown, James b.1961, *The Classroom*, gift from the artist, © the copyright holder

Owens, Wyn *Trych Mynachbyddu*, gift from the artist, © the copyright holder

Prichard, Gwilym b.1931, *Big Bala/ Byrnau Mawr*, gift from the artist, © the artist

Robinson, Beth b.1959, *The Sea*, gift from the artist, © the artist

Rosenthal, Stan b.1933, *Black Cows*, gift from the artist, © the copyright holder

Williams, Claudia b.1933, *Mother and Child*, gift from the artist, © the artist

Young, Sarah b.1971, *Pilgrims Road*, gift from the artist, © the artist

Young, Sarah b.1971, *Porthgain*, commissioned for reproduction in 'Clawdd Cam'; gift from the artist, © published in 'Clawdd Cam', Gwasg Carreg Gwalch

Tenby Museum & Art Gallery

Adams, K. D. *Brother Thomas's Garden*, gift, 2009, © the copyright holder

Adlam, Hank b.1922, *Trawler out of Tenby in a South West Wind, c.1895*, gift from the artist, 2001, © the copyright holder

Allen, Herbert Charles Goodeve Allen 1878–1965, *Tenby from Waterwynch*, gift, 1944, © the copyright holder

Allen, Herbert Charles Goodeve Allen 1878–1965, *Louis Kingdom (owner and skipper of 'The Hermes')*, gift, © the copyright holder

Allen, Herbert Charles Goodeve Allen 1878–1965, *Tenby Lifeboat 'J. R. Webb II' and Coxswain Benjamin*

Richards, unknown acquisition method, © the copyright holder

Allen, Herbert Charles Goodeve Allen 1878–1965, *Preselly's*, gift, 2009, © the copyright holder

Allen, Herbert Charles Goodeve Allen 1878–1965, *St Julian's Church*, gift, 2009, © the copyright holder

Artz active 20th C, *Portrait of a Mother and Children*, unknown acquisition method, © the copyright holder

Blake-Reed, John 1882–1966, *Tenby Five Arches*, gift, 2009, © the copyright holder

Bowen, Augusta M. 1869–1944, *Cottage near the Sluice*, gift, © the copyright holder

Bowen, Augusta M. 1869–1944, *Quay Hill*, gift, 1944, © the copyright holder

Bowen, Augusta M. 1869–1944, *Tenby Harbour*, gift, 1944, © the copyright holder

Bowen, Augusta M. 1869–1944, *The Sluice, Tenby*, gift, 1944, © the copyright holder

Bradforth, Eric b.1920, *Pembrokeshire Corner, Hodgeston*, purchased, © the copyright holder

Bradforth, Eric b.1920, *The Mayor's Slip*, purchased, 1995, © the copyright holder

Bradforth, Eric b.1920, *Tenby in 1586*, purchased, 1993, © the copyright holder

Buckley, Elizabeth Anne Kershaw 1854–1920, *St Mary's Church Interior*, gift, 1996

Burton-Richardson, David b.1961, *Landscape: Snowfall*, gift from the artist, 2004, © the artist

Burton-Richardson, David b.1961, *Preseli Hills: Evening Sunset*, gift from the artist, 2004, © the artist

Cook, Eric Trayler 1893–1978, *Hotels on the Front at Tenby*, gift, 1984, © the artist's estate

Cook, Eric Trayler 1893–1978, *St Florence Church near Tenby*, gift, 1984, © the artist's estate

Cook, Eric Trayler 1893–1978, *St Lawrence, Gumfreston near Tenby*, gift, 1984, © the artist's estate

Cook, Eric Trayler 1893–1978, *Tenby Castle and Castle Hill*, gift, 1984, © the artist's estate

Coulson, Jerry *Robin Crockford*, gift, © the copyright holder

Devas, Anthony 1911–1958, *Miss Farrant*, purchased, 1997, © the artist's estate/Bridgeman Art Library

Duncan, James Robert b.1939, *Shed on Caldey Island*, gift from the artist, 2006, © the copyright holder

Edwards, John Uzzell b.1937, *Barges*, gift, 2009, © the copyright holder

Edwards, John Uzzell b.1937, *Bride and Groom, Tenby*, gift from the Arts Council of Wales, 2002, © the copyright holder

Edwards, P. D. *HMS 'Tenby' (1941–1946)*, gift, 2007

Felder, J. H. L. (attributed to) *Interior of St Mary's Church*, gift, 1969

Fisher-Hoch, Nesta Donne 1903–1997, *Landscape*, gift, © the copyright holder

Fishley, Reginald *'Edith of Milford' (Captain Clark)*, gift, 1969

Gere, Charles March 1869–1957, *Caldey from Sunny Mead*, gift, 1948, © the artist's estate

Golding, William c.1771–1845, *Tenby from North Cliff*, gift, 1945

Gregson, Anne b.1936, *Magic Symbols, 2010*, gift from the artist, 2010, © the artist

Grupton *Family Life*, unknown acquisition method, © the copyright holder

Guy, Roy b.1944, *Chiaroscuro*, gift from the artist, 2005, © the artist

Haines, Elizabeth b.1945, *Streetscape, Candes*, gift from the Contemporary Art Society for Wales, 2011, © the artist

Hammersley, Doreen b.1926, *Miss Jessie Allen*, gift, 1971, © the artist

Hammersley, Doreen b.1926, *Nurse Marjorie Knowling*, unknown acquisition method, © the artist

Hammersley, Doreen b.1926, *Harry Billing*, gift from the artist, 2005, © the artist

Head, Edward Joseph 1863–1937, *White Roses*, gift, 1967

Head, Edward Joseph 1863–1937, *A Tenby Fisherman*, gift, 1971

Head, Edward Joseph 1863–1937, *Manorbier Castle*, purchased, 1997

Head, Edward Joseph 1863–1937, *Frank B. Mason and Family on the Beach*, on loan from a private collection

Head, Edward Joseph 1863–1937, *The Domino Players*, gift, 1985

Head, Edward Joseph 1863–1937, *Joseph (Currie) Davies*, on loan from a private collection

Head, Edward Joseph 1863–1937, *Eira Rosetta Thomas (Dolly and I)*, purchased, 1997

Head, Edward Joseph 1863–1937, *Nancy Flynn*, gift, 2002

Head, Edward Joseph 1863–1937, *A Bowl of Roses*, gift, 2009

Head, Edward Joseph 1863–1937, *Waggoners Well*, gift, 1991

Head, Edward Joseph (attributed to) 1863–1937, *Mother Hen and Chicks*, acquired, 2002

Howard-Jones, Ray 1903–1996, *Mary Constance*, gift, 2002, © Amgueddfa Cymru – National Museum Wales and Nicola Howard-Jones

Howard-Jones, Ray 1903–1996, *Moment of Perception*, gift, 2002, © Amgueddfa Cymru – National Museum Wales and Nicola Howard-Jones

Hurd-Wood, Grahame Fergus b.1956, *View of St David's*, gift from the artist, 2009, © the artist

John, Augustus Edwin 1878–1961, *Richard Hughes*, bequeathed by the artist, 1962, © the artist's estate/Bridgeman Art Library

John, Augustus Edwin 1878–1961, *David John*, purchased with the assistance of the Victoria and Albert Museum Purchase Grant Fund, 1997, © the artist's estate/Bridgeman Art Library

John, Augustus Edwin 1878–1961, *Self Portrait*, gift, 2011, © the artist's estate/Bridgeman Art Library

John, Gwen 1876–1939, *Landscape at Tenby with Figures*, purchased with the assistance of the Victoria and Albert Museum Purchase Grant Fund, 1996

John, Gwen 1876–1939, *Winifred John*, purchased with the assistance of the Art Fund, 1971

Jones, Ida (attributed to) 1883–1966, *Fisherman and Wife*, unknown acquisition method, © the copyright holder

Knapp-Fisher, John b.1931, *Cresswell Street, Tenby*, gift, 2001, © the artist

Llywelyn Hall, Dan b.1980, *Tenby Harbour*, gift from the artist, 2006, © the artist

Marquis *Fisherman's Cottage (Tenby Harbour)*, unknown acquisition method

Morgan, Oliver *Jubilee Oak, 1889*, unknown acquisition method, © the copyright holder

Morris, Dorothy b.1953, *Dŵr*, gift from the artist, 2008, © the artist

Morris, Reginald 1883–1941, *Gypsy*, gift, 1974

Morris, Reginald 1883–1941, *The 'Gwendoline'*, gift, 1975

Morse-Brown, Sam 1903–2001, *Viaduct and the Green, Tenby*, gift, 1972, © the copyright holder

Nash, Eustace P. E. 1886–1969, *Manorbier Bay*, gift, 1981, © the artist's estate

Noble, W. F. *Fisherman's Wife*, unknown acquisition method, © the copyright holder

Organ, Michael b.1939, *Landscape Study: Craig y Cilau*, gift from the artist, 2004, © the artist

Pearse, Margaretta b.c.1883, *Altar Steps, St Mary's Church*, gift, 1996, © the copyright holder

Perry, Douglas William b.1926, *Caldey from Castle Hill*, gift from the artist, 2006, © the artist

Plunkett, Brendan S. *Green Bridge (Stack Rocks)*, gift, © the copyright holder

Powis Evans, Nellie 1875–1948, *Old Friends*, gift from the artist, 1944, © the copyright holder

Powis Evans, Nellie 1875–1948, *Tommy Parcell*, gift, 1971, © the copyright holder

Powis Evans, Nellie 1875–1948, *Flowers in a Vase*, gift, 2009, © the copyright holder

Powis Evans, Nellie 1875–1948, *Monkstone*, gift, 2009, © the copyright holder

Price-Gwynne, Fanny 1819–1901, *St Catherine's Isle*, gift, 1941

Prichard, Gwilym b.1931, *Snow – South Beach, 2010*, gift from the artist, 2010, © the artist

Pritchard, Ceri b.1954, *Divide or Multiply*, gift from the artist, 2010, © the copyright holder

Rhys-Jones, D. C. active 1975–1977, *Christmas 1975, High Street at Midnight*, gift from the artist, 1975, © the copyright holder

Rhys-Jones, D. C. active 1975–1977, *Tenby 11am Any Day*, unknown acquisition method, © the copyright holder

Rixon, William Augustus 1858–1948, *Cenarth Falls, River Teifi*, gift from the artist, 1944, © the copyright holder

Rixon, William Augustus 1858–1948, *Manorbier Church*, gift from the artist, 1944, © the copyright holder

Rixon, William Augustus 1858–1948, *Pembroke Castle*, gift from the artist, 1944, © the copyright holder

Rosenthal, Stan b.1933, *St David's*, gift from the artist, 1994, © the copyright holder

Salisbury, Frank O. 1874–1962, *Mrs Margaret Perry*, gift, 1985, © estate of Frank O. Salisbury. All rights reserved, DACS 2013

Salisbury, Frank O. 1874–1962, *W. Harold Perry, Esq.*, unknown acquisition method, © estate of Frank O. Salisbury. All rights reserved, DACS 2013

Sivell, Marcia *Ivor Crockford (1911–1990)*, unknown acquisition method, © the artist

Sutton, Philip b.1928, *Tenby Harbour, 1989*, gift, 1995, © Philip Sutton. All rights reserved, DACS 2013

Thompson, Linda b.1950, *'On no account…'*, gift from the artist, 2011, © the artist

unknown artist *Tenby Harbour*, unknown acquisition method

unknown artist *South Gate, Five Arches*, gift, 1941

unknown artist *Steamship 'Éclair'*, gift, 1946

unknown artist *Quay Hill, Tenby*, purchased, 1985

unknown artist *Portrait of a Boy in a Sailor's Suit*, gift, 1970

unknown artist *North Bay*, unknown acquisition method

unknown artist *Caldey from South Beach with Donkey*, unknown acquisition method

unknown artist *Landscape*, unknown acquisition method

unknown artist *M. Thierry, the Past Owner of 'Imperial Hotel'*, unknown acquisition method

unknown artist *Portrait of a Monk*, unknown acquisition method

unknown artist *St Mary's College, Tenby, Looking South*, gift, 1996

unknown artist *Tenby Harbour*, gift, 2009

unknown artist *Thomas Kynaston of Caldy Island*, gift, 1987

Williams, Claudia b.1933, *Boxing Day Plunge, 2001* (at Tenby), gift from the artist, 2005, © the artist

Tenby Town Council

Allen *View of Tenby*, © the copyright holder

Dunbar, J. active 2003–2004, *John Thomas, Tenby Town Crier*, gift from the artist, © the copyright holder

Dunbar, J. active 2003–2004, *Mayoral Group*, gift from the artist, © the copyright holder

Franck, Ellen *Alderman Clement Williams, JP, Mayor of Tenby (1891–1893 & 1898–1901)*, gift from the family of the sitter

unknown artist *Portrait of a Gentleman with a Flute*

unknown artist *Portrait of an Unknown Lady in a Red Dress*

unknown artist *George White, Mayor of Tenby (1862–1864), Descendant of the White Family*, gift from the family of the sitter

Abertawe Bro Morgannwg University Health Board

Atkins, S. A. *A Plate with Two Pears and an Apple*, © the copyright holder

Atkins, S. A. *Blue and White Bowl with an Apple*, © the copyright holder

Atkins, S. A. *Jug and Plate with Apples*, © the copyright holder

Atkins, S. A. *Jug and Two Bowls with Fruit*, © the copyright holder

Atkins, S. A. *Two Bowls, Two Apples, a Pear and a Place Mat*, © the copyright holder

Atkins, S. A. *Two Fish on a Plate*, © the copyright holder

Bannon, Ian *Breaking Wave*, commissioned and funded by Arts in Health, 2010, © the copyright holder

Cresswell, Rebecca b.1980, *Lady from the Lake* (tale from the Mabinogion), commissioned through the Capital Development Scheme, 2008, © the copyright holder

Cresswell, Rebecca b.1980, *Lady from the Lake; Shepherd* (tale from the Mabinogion), commissioned through the Capital Development Scheme, 2008, © the copyright holder

Davies, Alexandra Jane b.1980, *Bird of Prey and Hot Air Balloon in the Black Mountains*, commissioned and funded by Arts in Health, 2006, © the artist

Davies, Alexandra Jane b.1980, *Sea to Garden Journey*, commissioned and funded by Arts in Health, 2006, © the artist

Davies, Alexandra Jane b.1980, *Sea to Garden Journey*, commissioned and funded by Arts in Health, 2006, © the artist

Davies, Alexandra Jane b.1980, *Sea to Garden Journey*, commissioned and funded by Arts in Health, 2006, © the artist

Davies, Alexandra Jane b.1980, *Sea to Garden Journey*, commissioned and funded by Arts in Health, 2006, © the artist

Davies, Alexandra Jane b.1980, *Sea to Garden Journey*, commissioned and funded by Arts in Health, 2006, © the artist

Davies, Alexandra Jane b.1980, *Sea to Garden Journey*, commissioned and funded by Arts in Health, 2006, © the artist

Davies, Alexandra Jane b.1980, *Sea to Garden Journey*, commissioned and funded by Arts in Health, 2006, © the artist

Davies, Alexandra Jane b.1980, *Sea to Garden Journey*, commissioned and funded by Arts in Health, 2006, © the artist

Davies, Alexandra Jane b.1980, *Sea to Garden Journey*, commissioned and funded by Arts in Health, 2006, © the artist

Davies, Alexandra Jane b.1980, *Sea to Garden Journey*, commissioned and funded by Arts in Health, 2006, © the artist

Davies, Alexandra Jane b.1980, *South West Wales Landscapes*, commissioned and funded by Arts in Health, 2006, © the artist

Davies, Alexandra Jane b.1980, *South West Wales Landscapes*, commissioned and funded by Arts in Health, 2006, © the artist

Davies, Alexandra Jane b.1980, *Window View* (triptych, left wing), commissioned and funded by Arts in Health, 2007, © the artist

Davies, Alexandra Jane b.1980, *Window View* (triptych, centre panel), commissioned and funded by Arts in Health, 2007, © the artist

Davies, Alexandra Jane b.1980, *Window View* (triptych, right wing), commissioned and funded by Arts in Health, 2007, © the artist

Davies, Alexandra Jane b.1980, *Tropical Bird Frieze: Leopard*, commissioned through the Capital Development Scheme, 2008, © the artist

Davies, Alexandra Jane b.1980, *Distraction Panels: Fairy Woodland*, commissioned through the Capital Development Scheme, © the artist

Davies, Alexandra Jane b.1980, *Distraction Panels: Mermaids and Underwater Creatures*, commissioned through the Capital Development Scheme, © the artist

Davies, Alexandra Jane b.1980, *Potting Shed Shelf*, commissioned and funded by Arts in Health, © the artist

Davies, Alexandra Jane b.1980, *Tropical Bird Frieze*, commissioned through the Capital Development Scheme, © the artist

Davies, Alexandra Jane b.1980, *Tropical Bird Frieze*, commissioned through the Capital Development Scheme, © the artist

Davies, Alexandra Jane b.1980, *Tropical Bird Frieze*, commissioned through the Capital Development Scheme, © the artist

Davies, Alexandra Jane b.1980, *Window View of Sea*, commissioned and funded by Arts in Health, © the artist

Donovan, James b.1974, *Boxer*, commissioned through the Capital Development Scheme, 1998, © the copyright holder

Donovan, James b.1974, *Gulliver*, commissioned through the Capital Development Scheme, 1998, © the copyright holder

Donovan, James b.1974, *King*, commissioned through the Capital Development Scheme, 1998, © the copyright holder

Donovan, James b.1974, *Man in Fez*, commissioned through the Capital Development Scheme, 1998, © the copyright holder

Donovan, James b.1974, *Man on Tower with Net*, commissioned through the Capital Development Scheme, 1998, © the copyright holder

Hawkins, David *Swansea Bay*, presented to Ward 8, Singleton Hospital, in memory of Pauline Mary Stone (1942–1998), 1998, © the copyright holder

Iles, James *Beach Huts*, commissioned and funded by Arts in Health, 2005, © the copyright holder

Iles, James *Cranes Triptych* (left wing), commissioned and funded by Arts in Health, 2005, © the copyright holder

Iles, James *Cranes Triptych* (centre panel), commissioned and funded by Arts in Health, 2005, © the copyright holder

Iles, James *Cranes Triptych* (right wing), commissioned and funded by Arts in Health, 2005, © the copyright holder

Iles, James *Steps to the Beach*, commissioned and funded by Arts in Health, 2005, © the copyright holder

Iles, James *Waterfront in Red and Blue*, commissioned and funded by Arts in Health, 2005, © the copyright holder

J., S. *Winter Scene*, © the copyright holder

Jenkins, Glyn *Mountain Scene*, © the copyright holder

Le Grice, Kathryn b.1972, *All Saints Church, Mumbles*, commissioned through the Capital Development Scheme, 2008, © the artist

Le Grice, Kathryn b.1972, *Maritime Quarter, Swansea*, commissioned through the Capital Development Scheme, 2008, © the artist

Le Grice, Kathryn b.1972, '*Morgans Hotel', Swansea*, commissioned through the Capital Development Scheme, 2008, © the artist

Le Grice, Kathryn b.1972, *Mumbles Road Methodist Church*, commissioned through the Capital Development Scheme, 2008, © the artist

Le Grice, Kathryn b.1972, *Newton Road, Mumbles, No.1*,

commissioned through the Capital Development Scheme, 2008, © the artist

Le Grice, Kathryn b.1972, *Newton Road, Mumbles, No.2*, commissioned through the Capital Development Scheme, 2008, © the artist

Le Grice, Kathryn b.1972, *Patti Pavilion, Swansea*, commissioned through the Capital Development Scheme, 2008, © the artist

Le Grice, Kathryn b.1972, *Picton Arcade*, commissioned through the Capital Development Scheme, 2008, © the artist

Le Grice, Kathryn b.1972, *Southend, Mumbles, No.1*, commissioned through the Capital Development Scheme, 2008, © the artist

Le Grice, Kathryn b.1972, *Southend, Mumbles, No.2*, commissioned through the Capital Development Scheme, 2008, © the artist

Le Grice, Kathryn b.1972, *Swansea Market*, commissioned through the Capital Development Scheme, 2008, © the artist

Le Grice, Kathryn b.1972, *Wind Street, Swansea*, commissioned through the Capital Development Scheme, 2008, © the artist

Oliveri *Rainy French Street Scene*, unknown acquisition method, © the copyright holder

Potter, Andrew *Boats*, commissioned through the Capital Development Scheme, 2005, © the copyright holder

Potter, Andrew *Boats*, commissioned through the Capital Development Scheme, 2005, © the copyright holder

Potter, Andrew *Boats*, commissioned through the Capital Development Scheme, 2005, © the copyright holder

Potter, Andrew *Boats*, commissioned through the Capital Development Scheme, 2005, © the copyright holder

Potter, Andrew *Float Painting I*, commissioned through the Capital Development Scheme, 2005, © the copyright holder

Potter, Andrew *Float Painting II*, commissioned through the Capital Development Scheme, 2005, © the copyright holder

Potter, Andrew *Float Painting III*, commissioned through the Capital Development Scheme, 2005, © the copyright holder

Potter, Andrew *Float Painting IV*, commissioned through the Capital Development Scheme, 2005, © the copyright holder

Potter, Andrew *Float Painting V*, commissioned through the Capital Development Scheme, 2005, © the copyright holder

Potter, Andrew *Seascape Triptych* (left wing), commissioned through the Capital Development Scheme, 2005, © the copyright holder

Potter, Andrew *Seascape Triptych* (centre panel), commissioned

through the Capital Development Scheme, 2005, © the copyright holder

Potter, Andrew *Seascape Triptych* (right wing), commissioned through the Capital Development Scheme, 2005, © the copyright holder

Potter, Andrew *Single Boat*, commissioned through the Capital Development Scheme, 2005, © the copyright holder

Potter, Andrew *Stepping Stones*, commissioned through the Capital Development Scheme, 2005, © the copyright holder

Potter, Andrew *Beach Huts*, commissioned through the Capital Development Scheme, © the copyright holder

Richards, Helen active 2003–2004, *Floral V*, commissioned through the Capital Development Scheme, © the copyright holder

Richards, Helen active 2003–2004, *Butterfly*, commissioned through the Capital Development Scheme, 2004, © the copyright holder

Richards, Helen active 2003–2004, *Floral VI*, commissioned through the Capital Development Scheme, © the copyright holder

Richards, Helen active 2003–2004, *Brynmill Park*, commissioned through the Capital Development Scheme, © the copyright holder

Richards, Helen active 2003–2004, *Clyne Gardens*, commissioned through the Capital Development Scheme, © the copyright holder

Richards, Helen active 2003–2004, *Cwmdonkin Park*, commissioned through the Capital Development Scheme, © the copyright holder

Richards, Helen active 2003–2004, *Floral I*, commissioned through the Capital Development Scheme, © the copyright holder

Richards, Helen active 2003–2004, *Floral II*, commissioned through the Capital Development Scheme, © the copyright holder

Richards, Helen active 2003–2004, *Floral III*, commissioned through the Capital Development Scheme, © the copyright holder

Richards, Helen active 2003–2004, *Floral IV*, commissioned through the Capital Development Scheme, © the copyright holder

Richards, Helen active 2003–2004, *Victoria Park*, commissioned through the Capital Development Scheme, © the copyright holder

Taylor, Sean b.1951, *Fishing Trip*, commissioned through the Capital Development Scheme, 2008, © the artist

Taylor, Sean b.1951, *Harbour Boats*, commissioned through the Capital Development Scheme, 2008, © the artist

Taylor, Sean b.1951, *Harbour Window*, commissioned through the Capital Development Scheme, 2008, © the artist

Taylor, Sean b.1951, *Seal*, commissioned through the Capital

Development Scheme, 2008, © the artist

Taylor, Sean b.1951, *St Ives Gull*, commissioned through the Capital Development Scheme, 2008, © the artist

Taylor, Sean b.1951, *St Ives Harbour*, commissioned through the Capital Development Scheme, 2008, © the artist

Taylor, Sean b.1951, *Two Gulls and Three Yachts*, commissioned through the Capital Development Scheme, 2008, © the artist

Thomas, Hilda *A Dog and Slipper*, donated by David Thomas in memory of his wife, Hilda Thomas, © the copyright holder

Trust, Peter 1936–2008, *Dragon Express*, © the artist's estate

Trust, Peter 1936–2008, *Laser Appointment Today*, © the artist's estate

Trust, Peter 1936–2008, *Welcome to Bridgend Laserland*, © the artist's estate

Turley, Jessica *Beside the Seaside* (panel 1 of 5), commissioned using money gained through fund raising, © the copyright holder

Turley, Jessica *Beside the Seaside* (panel 2 of 5), commissioned using money gained through fund raising, © the copyright holder

Turley, Jessica *Beside the Seaside* (panel 3 of 5), commissioned using money gained through fund raising, © the copyright holder

Turley, Jessica *Beside the Seaside* (panel 4 of 5), commissioned using money gained through fund raising, © the copyright holder

Turley, Jessica *Beside the Seaside* (panel 5 of 5), commissioned using money gained through fund raising, © the copyright holder

unknown artist *Alpine Scene*

unknown artist *Apples and Plums on a Plate*

unknown artist *Cherries(?) on a Plate*

unknown artist *Cherries(?) on a Plate* (detail)

unknown artist *Eygptian Scene*

unknown artist *Lighthouse with Boat and Left-Hand Wing Mirror*

unknown artist *Lighthouse with Boat and Right-Hand Wing Mirror*

unknown artist *One Fish on a Plate*

unknown artist *Portrait of a Benefactor of Swansea General Hospital*, unknown acquisition method

unknown artist *Portrait of a Benefactor of Swansea General Hospital*, unknown acquisition method

unknown artist *Portrait of a Benefactor of Swansea General Hospital*, unknown acquisition method

unknown artist *Steamboat with Windshelter in the Foreground*

unknown artist *Tulips in a Vase*

unknown artist *Tulips in a Vase with a Boat and a Lighthouse*

unknown artist *View of a Lighthouse, Boat and Balloon with Tulips in a Vase in the Foreground*

Waite, Trevor *Abstract in Blue, Orange, Peach and Green*, © the copyright holder

Waite, Trevor *Abstract in Blue, Tan, Pink and Red*, © the copyright holder

Waite, Trevor *Abstract in Blue, White, Black and Dark Red*, © the copyright holder

Waite, Trevor *Abstract in Tan, Orange and Blue*, © the copyright holder

Waite, Trevor *Abstract in White, Red and Orange*, © the copyright holder

Waite, Trevor *Abstract with a Dark Blue Container in the Foreground*, © the copyright holder

Waite, Trevor *Openings V*, © the copyright holder

Ward, Amy *Orientation Panel; Flowers*, commissioned using money donated by patients' relatives, 2008, © the copyright holder

Ward, Amy *Orientation Panel; Flowers*, commissioned using money donated by patients' relatives, 2008, © the copyright holder

Ward, Amy *Orientation Panel; Flowers*, commissioned using money donated by patients' relatives, 2008, © the copyright holder

Ward, Amy *Orientation Panel; Birds*, commissioned using money donated by patients' relatives, 2008, © the copyright holder

Ward, Amy *Orientation Panel; Birds*, commissioned using money donated by patients' relatives, 2008, © the copyright holder

Ward, Amy *Orientation Panel; Lighthouse*, commissioned using money donated by patients' relatives, 2008, © the copyright holder

Ward, Amy *Orientation Panel; Lighthouse*, commissioned using money donated by patients' relatives, 2008, © the copyright holder

Ward, Amy *Orientation Panel; Peacock*, commissioned using money donated by patients' relatives, 2008, © the copyright holder

Ward, Amy *Orientation Panel; Ponds*, commissioned using money donated by patients' relatives, 2008, © the copyright holder

Ward, Amy *Orientation Panel; Ponds*, commissioned using money donated by patients' relatives, 2008, © the copyright holder

Ward, Amy *Orientation Panel; Ponds*, commissioned using money donated by patients' relatives, 2008, © the copyright holder

Ward, Amy *Orientation Panel; Schooner*, commissioned using money donated by patients'

relatives, 2008, © the copyright holder

Ward, Amy *Orientation Panel; Trees*, commissioned using money donated by patients' relatives, 2008, © the copyright holder

Ward, Amy *Orientation Panel; Trees*, commissioned using money donated by patients' relatives, 2008, © the copyright holder

Ward, Amy *Orientation Panel; Trees*, commissioned using money donated by patients' relatives, 2008, © the copyright holder

Ward, Amy *Orientation Panel; Welsh Dresser*, commissioned using money donated by patients' relatives, 2008, © the copyright holder

Ward, Amy *Orientation Panel; Welsh Dresser*, commissioned using money donated by patients' relatives, 2008, © the copyright holder

Ward, Amy *Orientation Panel; Welsh Dresser*, commissioned using money donated by patients' relatives, 2008, © the copyright holder

Wood, Charlotte *Wild Savannah*, commissioned using money gained through fund raising, 2010, © the copyright holder

Wood, Charlotte *Wild Savannah*, commissioned using money gained through fund raising, 2010, © the copyright holder

Wood, Charlotte *Wild Savannah*, commissioned using money gained through fund raising, 2010, © the copyright holder

Wood, Charlotte *Wild Savannah*, commissioned using money gained through fund raising, 2010, © the copyright holder

Wood, Charlotte *Wild Savannah*, commissioned using money gained through fund raising, 2010, © the copyright holder

Glynn Vivian Art Gallery

Allen, Colin Gard 1926–1987, *Landscape with Snow*, gift from the Contemporary Art Society for Wales, 1957, © the artist's estate, photo credit: City & County of Swansea: Glynn Vivian Art Gallery Collection

Allen, Harry Epworth 1894–1958, *Summer*, purchased from the Art Exhibitions Bureau, 1942, © Geraldine Lattey/Harry Epworth Allen Foundation, photo credit: City & County of Swansea: Glynn Vivian Art Gallery Collection

Babi?, Ljubo 1890–1974, *The Black Flag*, purchased from Yugoslav Exchange, 1930, © the copyright holder, photo credit: City & County of Swansea: Glynn Vivian Art Gallery Collection

Baker, Joan b.1922, *Miss Cotton*, purchased from The South Wales Group, 1949, © the artist, photo credit: City & County of Swansea: Glynn Vivian Art Gallery Collection

Barker, Thomas 1769–1847, *Landscape with Sheep*, bequeathed by Richard Glynn Vivian, 1911,

photo credit: City & County of Swansea: Glynn Vivian Art Gallery Collection

Bassano the elder, Jacopo (attributed to) c.1510–1592, *Virgin and Infant Saviour*, purchased from John Dyer, 1920, photo credit: City & County of Swansea: Glynn Vivian Art Gallery Collection

Baynes, Keith 1887–1977, *Port Meirion, North Wales*, purchased from Thomas Agnew and Sons, 1932, © the artist's estate, photo credit: City & County of Swansea: Glynn Vivian Art Gallery Collection

Bell, David 1915–1959, *Clyne Common*, purchased from Megan Bell, 1961, © the artist's estate, photo credit: City & County of Swansea: Glynn Vivian Art Gallery Collection

Belleroche, Albert de 1864–1944, *Berthe*, purchased from Count William de Belleroche, 1955, © the artist's estate, photo credit: City & County of Swansea: Glynn Vivian Art Gallery Collection

Birchall, Thomas *Seascape to Cliffs*, purchased from F. W. Turner, 1932, photo credit: City & County of Swansea: Glynn Vivian Art Gallery Collection

Birchall, Thomas *Shipping in the Channel*, purchased from F. W. Turner, 1932, photo credit: City & County of Swansea: Glynn Vivian Art Gallery Collection

Bonnor, Rose Dempster 1875–1967, *Herbert Eccles, High Sheriff*, gift, 1994, © the copyright holder, photo credit: City & County of Swansea: Glynn Vivian Art Gallery Collection

Brangwyn, Frank 1867–1956, *Self Portrait with Miners*, gift from the Friends of the Glynn Vivian Art Gallery, 1985, © the artist's estate/ Bridgeman Art Library, photo credit: City & County of Swansea: Glynn Vivian Art Gallery Collection

Brangwyn, Frank 1867–1956, *British Empire Panel (1) England*, gift from The Iveagh Trust, 1934, © the artist's estate/Bridgeman Art Library, photo credit: City & County of Swansea: Glynn Vivian Art Gallery Collection

Brangwyn, Frank 1867–1956, *British Empire Panel (2) Canada*, gift from The Iveagh Trust, 1934, © the artist's estate/Bridgeman Art Library, photo credit: City & County of Swansea: Glynn Vivian Art Gallery Collection

Brangwyn, Frank 1867–1956, *British Empire Panel (3) Canada*, gift from The Iveagh Trust, 1934, © the artist's estate/Bridgeman Art Library, photo credit: City & County of Swansea: Glynn Vivian Art Gallery Collection

Brangwyn, Frank 1867–1956, *British Empire Panel (4) Canada*, gift from The Iveagh Trust, 1934, © the artist's estate/Bridgeman Art Library, photo credit: City & County of Swansea: Glynn Vivian Art Gallery Collection

Brangwyn, Frank 1867–1956, *British Empire Panel (5) Canada*, gift

from The Iveagh Trust, 1934, © the artist's estate/Bridgeman Art Library, photo credit: City & County of Swansea: Glynn Vivian Art Gallery Collection

Brangwyn, Frank 1867–1956, *British Empire Panel (6) West Africa*, gift from The Iveagh Trust, 1934, © the artist's estate/Bridgeman Art Library, photo credit: City & County of Swansea: Glynn Vivian Art Gallery Collection

Brangwyn, Frank 1867–1956, *British Empire Panel (7) West Indies*, gift from The Iveagh Trust, 1934, © the artist's estate/Bridgeman Art Library, photo credit: City & County of Swansea: Glynn Vivian Art Gallery Collection

Brangwyn, Frank 1867–1956, *British Empire Panel (8) Siam*, gift from The Iveagh Trust, 1934, © the artist's estate/Bridgeman Art Library, photo credit: City & County of Swansea: Glynn Vivian Art Gallery Collection

Brangwyn, Frank 1867–1956, *British Empire Panel (9) Burma*, gift from The Iveagh Trust, 1934, © the artist's estate/Bridgeman Art Library, photo credit: City & County of Swansea: Glynn Vivian Art Gallery Collection

Brangwyn, Frank 1867–1956, *British Empire Panel (10) India*, gift from The Iveagh Trust, 1934, © the artist's estate/Bridgeman Art Library, photo credit: City & County of Swansea: Glynn Vivian Art Gallery Collection

Brangwyn, Frank 1867–1956, *British Empire Panel (11) India*, gift from The Iveagh Trust, 1934, © the artist's estate/Bridgeman Art Library, photo credit: City & County of Swansea: Glynn Vivian Art Gallery Collection

Brangwyn, Frank 1867–1956, *British Empire Panel (12) India*, gift from The Iveagh Trust, 1934, © the artist's estate/Bridgeman Art Library, photo credit: City & County of Swansea: Glynn Vivian Art Gallery Collection

Brangwyn, Frank 1867–1956, *British Empire Panel (13) East Africa*, gift from The Iveagh Trust, 1934, © the artist's estate/Bridgeman Art Library, photo credit: City & County of Swansea: Glynn Vivian Art Gallery Collection

Brangwyn, Frank 1867–1956, *British Empire Panel (14) Australia*, gift from The Iveagh Trust, 1934, © the artist's estate/Bridgeman Art Library, photo credit: City & County of Swansea: Glynn Vivian Art Gallery Collection

Brangwyn, Frank 1867–1956, *British Empire Panel (15) East Indies*, gift from The Iveagh Trust, 1934, © the artist's estate/Bridgeman Art Library, photo credit: City & County of Swansea: Glynn Vivian Art Gallery Collection

Brangwyn, Frank 1867–1956, *British Empire Panel (16) Decorative Panel*, gift from The Iveagh Trust,

1934, © the artist's estate/Bridgeman Art Library, photo credit: City & County of Swansea: Glynn Vivian Art Gallery Collection

Brangwyn, Frank 1867–1956, *British Empire Panel (17) North Africa*, gift from The Iveagh Trust, 1934, © the artist's estate/Bridgeman Art Library, photo credit: City & County of Swansea: Glynn Vivian Art Gallery Collection

Brangwyn, Frank 1867–1956, *Caernarvon Castle*, gift, 1995, © the artist's estate/Bridgeman Art Library, photo credit: City & County of Swansea: Glynn Vivian Art Gallery Collection

Brangwyn, Frank 1867–1956, *Venetian Boats*, purchased from the artist, 1943, © the artist's estate/ Bridgeman Art Library, photo credit: City & County of Swansea: Glynn Vivian Art Gallery Collection

Bratby, John Randall 1928–1992, *Janet and Lilies*, purchased at the Zwemmer Gallery, 1962, © the artist's estate/Bridgeman Art Library, photo credit: City & County of Swansea: Glynn Vivian Art Gallery Collection

Breun, John Ernest 1862–1921, *William Thomas of Lan, JP, Mayor of Swansea, 1877*, gift, 1994, photo credit: City & County of Swansea: Glynn Vivian Art Gallery Collection

Breun, John Ernest 1862–1921, *Portrait of a Mayoress of Swansea*, gift, 1994, photo credit: City & County of Swansea: Glynn Vivian Art Gallery Collection

Breun, John Ernest 1862–1921, *William Williams, JP, MP, Mayor of Swansea (1884)*, gift, 1994, photo credit: City & County of Swansea: Glynn Vivian Art Gallery Collection

Breun, John Ernest 1862–1921, *Mayor of Swansea*, gift, 1994, photo credit: City & County of Swansea: Glynn Vivian Art Gallery Collection

Briscoe, Mike b.1960, *Coast Combinations*, gift from the Contemporary Art Society for Wales, 1985, © the artist, photo credit: City & County of Swansea: Glynn Vivian Art Gallery Collection

British (English) School *Landscape with Figures*, bequeathed by Richard Glynn Vivian, 1911, photo credit: City & County of Swansea: Glynn Vivian Art Gallery Collection

British (English) School *Portrait of a French Gentleman*, bequeathed by Richard Glynn Vivian, 1911, photo credit: City & County of Swansea: Glynn Vivian Art Gallery Collection

Brooker, William 1918–1983, *The Green Divan*, purchased from Arthur Tooth, 1958, © the artist's estate, photo credit: City & County of Swansea: Glynn Vivian Art Gallery Collection

Burns, Brendan Stuart b.1963, *Study for 'Petrol Bomb Attack'*, gift from the Contemporary Art Society, 2007, © the artist, photo credit: City & County of Swansea: Glynn Vivian Art Gallery Collection

Burns, Brendan Stuart b.1963, *Taste of Sight Series, 2005 (July 5th)*, gift from the Friends of the Glynn Vivian Art Gallery, 2007, © the artist

Butler, William 1824–1870, *Swansea Bay*, gift, 1956, photo credit: City & County of Swansea: Glynn Vivian Art Gallery Collection

Cadogan, Herbert *Still Life*, purchased from the Eisteddfod, 1932, © the copyright holder, photo credit: City & County of Swansea: Glynn Vivian Art Gallery Collection

Calvin-Thomas, Ursula *Maritime*, gift from the Friends of the Glynn Vivian Art Gallery, 1993, © the copyright holder, photo credit: City & County of Swansea: Glynn Vivian Art Gallery Collection

Caravaggio, Michelangelo Merisi da (after) 1571–1610, *Life Study*, bequeathed by Richard Glynn Vivian, 1911, photo credit: City & County of Swansea: Glynn Vivian Art Gallery Collection

Caravaggio, Michelangelo Merisi da (after) 1571–1610, *Life Study*, bequeathed by Richard Glynn Vivian, 1911, photo credit: City & County of Swansea: Glynn Vivian Art Gallery Collection

Carpanini, David Lawrence b.1946, *Wayward Wind*, gift from the Contemporary Art Society for Wales, 1985, © the artist, photo credit: City & County of Swansea: Glynn Vivian Art Gallery Collection

Carracci, Annibale school of 1560–1609, *Italian Poet*, bequeathed by Richard Glynn Vivian, 1911, photo credit: City & County of Swansea: Glynn Vivian Art Gallery Collection

Carracci, Ludovico (attributed to) 1555–1619, *Holy Family*, bequeathed by Richard Glynn Vivian, 1911, photo credit: City & County of Swansea: Glynn Vivian Art Gallery Collection

Carracci, Ludovico (attributed to) 1555–1619, *Virgin and Infant Saviour*, bequeathed by Richard Glynn Vivian, 1911, photo credit: City & County of Swansea: Glynn Vivian Art Gallery Collection

Center, Edward Kenneth b.1903, *Frank Brangwyn*, purchased from The Royal Society of Portrait Painters, 1954, © the copyright holder, photo credit: City & County of Swansea: Glynn Vivian Art Gallery Collection

Chamberlain, Brenda 1912–1971, *Dora Maar – Intérieur Provençal*, gift, 1994, © the copyright holder, photo credit: City & County of Swansea: Glynn Vivian Art Gallery Collection

Chamberlain, Brenda 1912–1971, *La Carmejane, Menerbes*, purchased, 1994, © the copyright holder, photo credit: City & County of Swansea: Glynn Vivian Art Gallery Collection

Chamberlain, Brenda 1912–1971, *The Acrobats at Practice*, purchased from H. Mitchell, © the copyright holder, photo credit: City & County

of Swansea: Glynn Vivian Art Gallery Collection

Chambers I, George 1803–1840, *View of Swansea*, gift from the Friends of the Glynn Vivian Art Gallery, 1982

Chapman, George 1908–1993, *Wet Roofs*, purchased from the Zwemmer Gallery, 1962, © the artist's estate, photo credit: City & County of Swansea: Glynn Vivian Art Gallery Collection

Chapman, Henry Alfred 1844–1915, *Lawrence Tulloch, JP, Mayor of Swansea*, gift, 1994, photo credit: City & County of Swansea: Glynn Vivian Art Gallery Collection

Chapman, Henry Alfred 1844–1915, *Lewis Llewelyn Dillwyn, JP, MP, Mayor of Swansea (1847)*, gift, 1994, photo credit: City & County of Swansea: Glynn Vivian Art Gallery Collection

Chappell, Dick b.1954, *At Night*, gift from the Friends of the Glynn Vivian Art Gallery, 2006, © the copyright holder, photo credit: City & County of Swansea: Glynn Vivian Art Gallery Collection

Charlton, Evan 1904–1984, *Promenade Restaurant*, gift from the Contemporary Art Society for Wales, 1985, © the copyright holder, photo credit: City & County of Swansea: Glynn Vivian Art Gallery Collection

Charlton, Felicity 1913–2009, *Cineraria*, gift from the Friends of the Glynn Vivian Art Gallery, 1985, © the copyright holder, photo credit: City & County of Swansea: Glynn Vivian Art Gallery Collection

Cirel, Ferdinand 1884–1968, *Lobster Study*, purchased from the artist, 1953, © the copyright holder, photo credit: City & County of Swansea: Glynn Vivian Art Gallery Collection

Cirel, Ferdinand 1884–1968, *Light and Dark Grapes*, purchased from the artist, 1958, © the copyright holder, photo credit: City & County of Swansea: Glynn Vivian Art Gallery Collection

Coats, John F. *Coal Hoist*, purchased from Swansea Art Society, 1948, © the copyright holder, photo credit: City & County of Swansea: Glynn Vivian Art Gallery Collection

Collier, John 1850–1934, *Souvenir of Chu Chin Chow*, gift from the artist, photo credit: City & County of Swansea: Glynn Vivian Art Gallery Collection

Collins, W. J. *Lake and Cattle*, gift from Roger Beck, 1913, photo credit: City & County of Swansea: Glynn Vivian Art Gallery Collection

Constable, John 1776–1837, *Foxgloves*, bequeathed by Richard Glynn Vivian, 1911, photo credit: City & County of Swansea: Glynn Vivian Art Gallery Collection

Cooper, John F. b.1929, *Tirlun Dwydianol yn y Nos, Port Talbot (Industrial Landscape at Night)*, gift from the artist, 2007, © the copyright holder, photo credit: City

& County of Swansea: Glynn Vivian Art Gallery Collection

Correggio c.1489–1534, *Ecce Homo* (detail), bequeathed by Richard Glynn Vivian, 1911, photo credit: City & County of Swansea: Glynn Vivian Art Gallery Collection

Cortona, Pietro da 1596–1669, *Diana and Endymion*, bequeathed by Richard Glynn Vivian, 1911, photo credit: City & County of Swansea: Glynn Vivian Art Gallery Collection

Cour, Glenys b.1924, *Industrial Scene*, gift from the Contemporary Art Society for Wales, 1967, © the artist, photo credit: City & County of Swansea: Glynn Vivian Art Gallery Collection

Cour, Glenys b.1924, *The Pool, Cefn Bryn*, gift from the Arts Council of Wales, 2002, © the artist, photo credit: City & County of Swansea: Glynn Vivian Art Gallery Collection

Cour, Glenys b.1924, *Cliff Path*, purchased from the artist, 1984, © the artist, photo credit: City & County of Swansea: Glynn Vivian Art Gallery Collection

Cox the elder, David 1783–1859 or Cox the younger, David 1809–1885 *Landscape with Shepherd*, bequeathed by Richard Glynn Vivian, 1911, photo credit: City & County of Swansea: Glynn Vivian Art Gallery Collection

Crabtree, Jack b.1938, *Save This Pit*, gift from the Contemporary Art Society for Wales, 1982, © the artist, photo credit: City & County of Swansea: Glynn Vivian Art Gallery Collection

Daborn, Erica b.1951, *Waiting Room 1*, gift from the Contemporary Art Society for Wales, 1985, © the artist, photo credit: City & County of Swansea: Glynn Vivian Art Gallery Collection

Davies, Hanlyn b.1942, *Mr D. Gwynfor Thomas*, gift from Nansi Golton, 1997, © Hanlyn Davies, photo credit: City & County of Swansea: Glynn Vivian Art Gallery Collection

Davies, Margaret Sidney 1884–1963, *A Cornfield*, gift from the artist, 1953, © the copyright holder, photo credit: City & County of Swansea: Glynn Vivian Art Gallery Collection

Delattre, Joseph 1858–1912, *The Seine above Rouen*, gift from François Depeaux, 1911, photo credit: City & County of Swansea: Glynn Vivian Art Gallery Collection

Delattre, Joseph 1858–1912, *The Seine below Rouen*, gift from François Depeaux, 1911, photo credit: City & County of Swansea: Glynn Vivian Art Gallery Collection

Delattre, Joseph 1858–1912, *Vieilles maisons*, gift from François Depeaux, 1919, photo credit: City & County of Swansea: Glynn Vivian Art Gallery Collection

Donaubauer, Wilhelm 1866–1949, *The Mill*, purchased from Howard Martin, 1937, © the copyright

holder, photo credit: City & County of Swansea: Glynn Vivian Art Gallery Collection

Donovan, James b.1974, *Ironman Grandpa*, gift from Clive Graham, 2007, © the copyright holder, photo credit: City & County of Swansea: Glynn Vivian Art Gallery Collection

Donovan, James b.1974, *The Connoisseur*, gift from the Friends of the Glynn Vivian Art Gallery, 1999, © the copyright holder, photo credit: City & County of Swansea: Glynn Vivian Art Gallery Collection

Donovan, James b.1974, *Sleeper*, gift from Clive Graham, 2007, © the copyright holder, photo credit: City & County of Swansea: Glynn Vivian Art Gallery Collection

Doré, Gustave 1832–1883, *Christ Leaving the Praetorium*, bequeathed by Richard Glynn Vivian, 1911, photo credit: City & County of Swansea: Glynn Vivian Art Gallery Collection

Doré, Gustave 1832–1883, *Coin de cellier*, bequeathed by Richard Glynn Vivian, 1911, photo credit: City & County of Swansea: Glynn Vivian Art Gallery Collection

Doré, Gustave 1832–1883, *Ecce Homo*, bequeathed by Richard Glynn Vivian, 1911, photo credit: City & County of Swansea: Glynn Vivian Art Gallery Collection

Doré, Gustave 1832–1883, *Genius Kindled by Fame*, bequeathed by Richard Glynn Vivian, 1911, photo credit: City & County of Swansea: Glynn Vivian Art Gallery Collection

Doré, Gustave 1832–1883, *Judith with the Head of Holofernes*, bequeathed by Richard Glynn Vivian, 1911, photo credit: City & County of Swansea: Glynn Vivian Art Gallery Collection

Doré, Gustave 1832–1883, *La baigneuse*, bequeathed by Richard Glynn Vivian, 1911, photo credit: City & County of Swansea: Glynn Vivian Art Gallery Collection

Doré, Gustave 1832–1883, *La folie*, bequeathed by Richard Glynn Vivian, 1911, photo credit: City & County of Swansea: Glynn Vivian Art Gallery Collection

Doré, Gustave 1832–1883, *La Sainte Trinité*, bequeathed by Richard Glynn Vivian, 1911, photo credit: City & County of Swansea: Glynn Vivian Art Gallery Collection

Doré, Gustave 1832–1883, *Madame Adelina Patti*, bequeathed by Richard Glynn Vivian, 1911, photo credit: City & County of Swansea: Glynn Vivian Art Gallery Collection

Dutch School *The Shepherd*, gift from John Dyer, 1920, photo credit: City & County of Swansea: Glynn Vivian Art Gallery Collection

Edwards, Paul b.1954, *Yellow Table/ Saxophone*, purchased from the artist, 1987, © the artist, photo credit: City & County of Swansea: Glynn Vivian Art Gallery Collection

Elwyn, John 1916–1997, *In the Valley*, purchased, 1948, © the artist's estate, photo credit: City &

County of Swansea: Glynn Vivian Art Gallery Collection

Elwyn, John 1916–1997, *Miners Returning over Waste Ground*, gift from the Arts Council of Wales, 2002, © the artist's estate, photo credit: City & County of Swansea: Glynn Vivian Art Gallery Collection

Elwyn, John 1916–1997, *Dark Shapes in the Rain*, gift from the Friends of the Glynn Vivian Art Gallery, 1998, © the artist's estate, photo credit: City & County of Swansea: Glynn Vivian Art Gallery Collection

Elwyn, John 1916–1997, *Tree Architecture*, gift from J. T. Morgan, 1954, © the artist's estate, photo credit: City & County of Swansea: Glynn Vivian Art Gallery Collection

Elwyn, John 1916–1997, *Ydlan Yn Sir Aberteifi*, gift from J. T. Morgan, 1954, © the artist's estate, photo credit: City & County of Swansea: Glynn Vivian Art Gallery Collection

Evans, Nicholas 1907–2004, *Untitled (Pithead Scene)*, gift from the Arts Council of Wales, 2002, © the artist's estate, photo credit: City & County of Swansea: Glynn Vivian Art Gallery Collection

Evans, Nicholas 1907–2004, *Aberfan*, purchased from the artist, 1986, © the artist's estate, photo credit: City & County of Swansea: Glynn Vivian Art Gallery Collection

Evans, Nicholas 1907–2004, *Coming to the Surface*, gift from the artist, 1986, © the artist's estate, photo credit: City & County of Swansea: Glynn Vivian Art Gallery Collection

Evans, Olive E. *Mount Pleasant*, gift from the Arts Council of Wales, 2002, © the copyright holder, photo credit: City & County of Swansea: Glynn Vivian Art Gallery Collection

Evans, Vincent 1896–1976, *A Snack*, purchased from the artist, 1936, © the copyright holder, photo credit: City & County of Swansea: Glynn Vivian Art Gallery Collection

Evans, Vincent 1896–1976, *Family Life*, gift from A. Lane, 1983, © the copyright holder, photo credit: City & County of Swansea: Glynn Vivian Art Gallery Collection

Evans, Vincent 1896–1976, *At the Coalface*, gift from A. Lane, 1983, © the copyright holder, photo credit: City & County of Swansea: Glynn Vivian Art Gallery Collection

Evans, Vincent 1896–1976, *Mr Stanley Williams*, gift from Gwladys Evans, 1985, © the copyright holder, photo credit: City & County of Swansea: Glynn Vivian Art Gallery Collection

Evans, Will 1888–1957, *Ploughing*, purchased from P. Harvey, 1980, © the copyright holder, photo credit: City & County of Swansea: Glynn Vivian Art Gallery Collection

Evans, Will 1888–1957, *Street Scene*, purchased from the Swansea and West Wales Cancer Aid Society, 1984, © the copyright holder, photo credit: City & County of Swansea:

Glynn Vivian Art Gallery Collection
Evans, Will 1888–1957, *Snow in Swansea*, gift from Swansea Art Society, 1932, © the copyright holder, photo credit: City & County of Swansea: Glynn Vivian Art Gallery Collection
Evans, Will 1888–1957, *Entrance to Swansea Market, 1941*, gift, 1994, © the copyright holder, photo credit: City & County of Swansea: Glynn Vivian Art Gallery Collection
Evans, Will 1888–1957, *Llanberis Pass, North Wales*, purchased from the artist, 1937, © the copyright holder, photo credit: City & County of Swansea: Glynn Vivian Art Gallery Collection
Evans, Will 1888–1957, *Nant Ffrancon Pass, North Wales*, purchased, 1977, © the copyright holder, photo credit: City & County of Swansea: Glynn Vivian Art Gallery Collection
Evans, Will 1888–1957, *Snow, 1945, St Mary's Church, Swansea*, gift, 1994, © the copyright holder, photo credit: City & County of Swansea: Glynn Vivian Art Gallery Collection
Evans, Will 1888–1957, *Wesley Chapel, Swansea, 1941*, gift, 1994, © the copyright holder, photo credit: City & County of Swansea: Glynn Vivian Art Gallery Collection
Fairley, George 1920–2003, *Little Lyric*, purchased from the Howard Roberts Gallery, 1961, © the copyright holder, photo credit: City & County of Swansea: Glynn Vivian Art Gallery Collection
Flemish School *Sleeping Angel with Emblems of Death*, bequeathed by Richard Glynn Vivian, 1911, photo credit: City & County of Swansea: Glynn Vivian Art Gallery Collection
Forbes, Andrew Douglas *Breakfast Eggs*, purchased from the Swansea Art Society, 1993, © the copyright holder, photo credit: City & County of Swansea: Glynn Vivian Art Gallery Collection
Ford, Mabs d.2011, *Daniel Jones*, purchased from the artist, 1995, © the copyright holder, photo credit: City & County of Swansea: Glynn Vivian Art Gallery Collection
Frechon, Charles 1856–1929, *View of Rouen through an Apple Tree*, gift from François Depeaux, 1911, photo credit: City & County of Swansea: Glynn Vivian Art Gallery Collection
Freeman, Michael John b.1936, *Angel Visiting a Shipwreck*, purchased from the artist, 1991, © the copyright holder
French School *Portrait of a Lady with an Ermine Cloak*, bequeathed by Richard Glynn Vivian, 1911, photo credit: City & County of Swansea: Glynn Vivian Art Gallery Collection
Ganz, Valerie b.1936, *Coaling In G8*, purchased from the artist, 1987, © the copyright holder, photo credit: City & County of Swansea: Glynn Vivian Art Gallery Collection
Garner, David b.1958, *Politics Eclipsed by Economics*, gift from the Friends of the Glynn Vivian Art Gallery, 2004, © the artist, photo credit: City & County of Swansea: Glynn Vivian Art Gallery Collection
German School *Chess Players*, bequeathed by Richard Glynn Vivian, 1911, photo credit: City & County of Swansea: Glynn Vivian Art Gallery Collection
German School *Lady in a Blue Dress*, bequeathed by Richard Glynn Vivian, 1911, photo credit: City & County of Swansea: Glynn Vivian Art Gallery Collection
German School *Untitled* (a mythological subject), bequeathed by Richard Glynn Vivian, 1911, photo credit: City & County of Swansea: Glynn Vivian Art Gallery Collection
German School *Untitled* (a mythological subject), bequeathed by Richard Glynn Vivian, 1911, photo credit: City & County of Swansea: Glynn Vivian Art Gallery Collection
Gertler, Mark 1891–1939, *The Artist's Mother*, gift from the Contemporary Art Society, 1954, photo credit: City & County of Swansea: Glynn Vivian Art Gallery Collection
Ginner, Charles 1878–1952, *Penally Hill*, gift from the Contemporary Art Society for Wales, 1923, © the copyright holder, photo credit: City & County of Swansea: Glynn Vivian Art Gallery Collection
Giulio Romano (school of) c.1499–1546, *Two Wrestlers*, bequeathed by Richard Glynn Vivian, 1911, photo credit: City & County of Swansea: Glynn Vivian Art Gallery Collection
Goble, Anthony 1943–2007, *Water Crossing*, purchased from the artist, 1995, © the artist's estate, photo credit: City & County of Swansea: Glynn Vivian Art Gallery Collection
Goodall, Frederick 1822–1904, *The Artist's Daughter*, gift from Thomas Griffith, 1911, photo credit: City & County of Swansea: Glynn Vivian Art Gallery Collection
Govier, James Henry 1910–1974, *Landscape near Brill*, purchased from the artist, 1935, © Stephen Govier, photo credit: City & County of Swansea: Glynn Vivian Art Gallery Collection
Grant, Duncan 1885–1978, *View in Venice*, purchased from Leger Galleries, 1951, © estate of Duncan Grant. All rights reserved, DACS 2013, photo credit: City & County of Swansea: Glynn Vivian Art Gallery Collection
Griffiths, Gwenny b.1867, *Mrs Octavia Howell, Founder of the Swansea Orphan Home*, acquired, 1972, photo credit: City & County of Swansea: Glynn Vivian Art Gallery Collection
Guilbert, Narcisse 1878–1942, *Banks of the Seine at Croisset*, gift from François Depeaux, 1911, photo credit: City & County of Swansea: Glynn Vivian Art Gallery Collection
Gwynne-Jones, Allan 1892–1982, *Emmy as a Bridesmaid*, purchased, 1983, © the artist's estate/Bridgeman Art Library, photo credit: City & County of Swansea: Glynn Vivian Art Gallery Collection
Gwynne-Jones, Allan 1892–1982, *August morning, Suffolk*, gift from the Contemporary Art Society for Wales, 1947, © the artist's estate/ Bridgeman Art Library, photo credit: City & County of Swansea: Glynn Vivian Art Gallery Collection
Haddon, Arthur Trevor 1864–1941, *Lord Glantawe*, gift from Lord Bledisloe, 1960, photo credit: City & County of Swansea: Glynn Vivian Art Gallery Collection
Hagers, Albert Clarence b.1915, *Two Fishermen of Ostend*, gift from the Belgian Government, 1942, © the copyright holder, photo credit: City & County of Swansea: Glynn Vivian Art Gallery Collection
Hall, Oliver 1869–1957, *Welsh Mountains*, acquired, 1995, © the artist's estate, photo credit: City & County of Swansea: Glynn Vivian Art Gallery Collection
Hancock, Kenneth W. 1911–1978, *Ben Davies*, gift from the artist, 1935, © the copyright holder, photo credit: City & County of Swansea: Glynn Vivian Art Gallery Collection
Hancock, Kenneth W. 1911–1978, *Mr Sydney Heath*, gift from Mr/ Mrs/Miss Jones, 1990, © the copyright holder, photo credit: City & County of Swansea: Glynn Vivian Art Gallery Collection
Hancock, Kenneth W. 1911–1978, *Two Figures in a Landscape*, purchased from The South Wales Group, 1951, © the copyright holder, photo credit: City & County of Swansea: Glynn Vivian Art Gallery Collection
Handley-Read, Edward Henry 1870–1935, *Mametz Wood*, gift from Alfred Mond, 1942, photo credit: City & County of Swansea: Glynn Vivian Art Gallery Collection
Harlow, George Henry 1787–1819, *Portrait of a Gentleman* (said to be Burns), bequeathed by Richard Glynn Vivian, 1911, photo credit: City & County of Swansea: Glynn Vivian Art Gallery Collection
Harris, Annie *Grandfather's Darling*, gift, 1980, photo credit: City & County of Swansea: Glynn Vivian Art Gallery Collection
Harris Senior, James 1810–1887, *Shipping off Messina*, purchased at Phillips Fine Art, Cardiff, 1985, photo credit: City & County of Swansea: Glynn Vivian Art Gallery Collection
Harris Senior, James 1810–1887, *Picking up the Pilot*, purchased, 1955, photo credit: City & County of Swansea: Glynn Vivian Art Gallery Collection
Harris Senior, James 1810–1887, *Seascape with Three Barques*, bequeathed by John Dyer, 1921, photo credit: City & County of Swansea: Glynn Vivian Art Gallery Collection
Harris Senior, James 1810–1887, *From Paviland to the Worm*, purchased from P. V. Davies, 1996, photo credit: City & County of Swansea: Glynn Vivian Art Gallery Collection
Harris Senior, James 1810–1887, *Hafod Copper Works, River Tawy, Swansea*, purchased from E. J. Nuggee, 1956, photo credit: City & County of Swansea: Glynn Vivian Art Gallery Collection
Harris Senior, James 1810–1887, *Ship in Distress, Hove To*, purchased at Phillips Fine Art, Cardiff, 1986, photo credit: City & County of Swansea: Glynn Vivian Art Gallery Collection
Haughton, Benjamin 1865–1924, *Spring Evening*, gift from Janet Haughton, 1937, photo credit: City & County of Swansea: Glynn Vivian Art Gallery Collection
Haughton, Benjamin 1865–1924, *Spring Wheat*, gift from J. Mason, 1937, photo credit: City & County of Swansea: Glynn Vivian Art Gallery Collection
Hayter, George 1792–1871, *Lady Belgrave*, bequeathed by Richard Glynn Vivian, 1911, photo credit: City & County of Swansea: Glynn Vivian Art Gallery Collection
Helst, Bartholomeus van der 1613–1670, *Portrait of a Young Lady*, purchased from Thomas Agnew and Sons, 1974, photo credit: City & County of Swansea: Glynn Vivian Art Gallery Collection
Hepworth, Barbara 1903–1975, *Project* (group of figures for sculpture), gift from the Friends of the Glynn Vivian Art Gallery, 1998, © Bowness, Hepworth estate, photo credit: City & County of Swansea: Glynn Vivian Art Gallery Collection
Herman, Josef 1911–2000, *Miners*, purchased from the artist, 1951, © estate of Josef Herman. All rights reserved, DACS 2013, photo credit: City & County of Swansea: Glynn Vivian Art Gallery Collection
Herman, Josef 1911–2000, *Mother and Child*, gift from the Contemporary Art Society for Wales, 1952, © estate of Josef Herman. All rights reserved, DACS 2013, photo credit: City & County of Swansea: Glynn Vivian Art Gallery Collection
Hickin, George Arthur 1821–1885, *Untitled (Landscape)*, gift, 1994, photo credit: City & County of Swansea: Glynn Vivian Art Gallery Collection
Hillier, Tristram Paul 1905–1983, *Flooded Meadow*, bequeathed by Richard J. Strick, 1974, © the artist's estate/Bridgeman Art Library, photo credit: City & County of Swansea: Glynn Vivian Art Gallery Collection
Hitchens, Ivon 1893–1979, *Essex River and Greenhill*, purchased from Howard Bliss, 1955, © Ivon Hitchens' estate/Jonathan Clark & Co., photo credit: City & County of Swansea: Glynn Vivian Art Gallery Collection
Hitchens, Ivon 1893–1979, *Blue vase*, purchased from the Redfern Gallery, 1960, © Ivon Hitchens' estate/Jonathan Clark & Co., photo credit: City & County of Swansea: Glynn Vivian Art Gallery Collection
Holl, Frank 1845–1888, *John Jones Watkins, Lord Glantawe, Mayor of Swansea (1869 & 1879–1880)*, gift, 1994, photo credit: City & County of Swansea: Glynn Vivian Art Gallery Collection
Holland, Harry b.1941, *Preparatory Study for 'Corridor'*, gift from the Friends of the Glynn Vivian Art Gallery, 1982, © the artist, photo credit: City & County of Swansea: Glynn Vivian Art Gallery Collection
Holland, Harry b.1941, *The Corridor*, gift from the Friends of the Glynn Vivian Art Gallery, 1982, © the artist, photo credit: City & County of Swansea: Glynn Vivian Art Gallery Collection
Holland, Harry b.1941, *Phil, Ess and Sue (Ess)*, purchased from the artist, 1986, © the artist, photo credit: City & County of Swansea: Glynn Vivian Art Gallery Collection
Holland, Harry b.1941, *Phil, Ess and Sue (Phil)*, purchased from the artist, 1986, © the artist, photo credit: City & County of Swansea: Glynn Vivian Art Gallery Collection
Holland, Harry b.1941, *Phil, Ess and Sue (Sue)*, purchased from the artist, 1986, © the artist, photo credit: City & County of Swansea: Glynn Vivian Art Gallery Collection
Howard, Henry 1769–1847, *Charles Kemble*, bequeathed by Richard Glynn Vivian, 1911, photo credit: City & County of Swansea: Glynn Vivian Art Gallery Collection
Howard-Jones, Ray 1903–1996, *Seascape from Mumbles*, gift from W. A. Timothy Perkins, 2009, © Amgueddfa Cymru – National Museum Wales and Nicola Howard-Jones, photo credit: City & County of Swansea: Glynn Vivian Art Gallery Collection
Hubbard, Eric Hesketh 1892–1957, *Harlech Castle*, gift, 1995, © the copyright holder, photo credit: City & County of Swansea: Glynn Vivian Art Gallery Collection
Ibbetson, Julius Caesar 1759–1817, *Scene in the Taff Valley*, purchased from the John Mitchell Gallery, 1961, photo credit: City & County of Swansea: Glynn Vivian Art Gallery Collection
Ifold, Cyril 1922–1986, *Welsh Village*, purchased from C. Ifold, 1986, © the copyright holder, photo credit: City & County of Swansea: Glynn Vivian Art Gallery Collection
Innes, James Dickson 1887–1914, *Arenig Mountain*, purchased from the Stepney Estate, 1953, photo credit: City & County of Swansea: Glynn Vivian Art Gallery Collection
Innes, James Dickson 1887–1914, *Garn Lake*, purchased, 1982, photo

credit: City & County of Swansea: Glynn Vivian Art Gallery Collection

Innes, James Dickson 1887–1914, *View in Wales*, purchased from Rowland, Browse & Delbarco, 1951, photo credit: City & County of Swansea: Glynn Vivian Art Gallery Collection

Italian (Venetian) School *The Holy Family*, gift from John Dyer, 1920, photo credit: City & County of Swansea: Glynn Vivian Art Gallery Collection

Italian School *Bacchanals*, bequeathed by Richard Glynn Vivian, 1911, photo credit: City & County of Swansea: Glynn Vivian Art Gallery Collection

Italian School *Bacchanals*, bequeathed by Richard Glynn Vivian, 1911, photo credit: City & County of Swansea: Glynn Vivian Art Gallery Collection

Italian School *Boy and Viper*, bequeathed by Richard Glynn Vivian, 1911, photo credit: City & County of Swansea: Glynn Vivian Art Gallery Collection

Italian School *Daedalus Fastening Wings on Icarus*, bequeathed by Richard Glynn Vivian, 1911, photo credit: City & County of Swansea: Glynn Vivian Art Gallery Collection

Jackson, John 1778–1831, *Mr John Deffett*, purchased from B. B. Brook, 1928, photo credit: City & County of Swansea: Glynn Vivian Art Gallery Collection

James, Merlin b.1960, *Way Up*, gift from the Contemporary Art Society for Wales, 2011, © the artist, photo credit: City & County of Swansea: Glynn Vivian Art Gallery Collection

Jamieson, Alexander 1873–1937, *Wedding at St Cloude*, purchased from the Art Exchange Bureau, 1939, photo credit: City & County of Swansea: Glynn Vivian Art Gallery Collection

Janes, Alfred 1911–1999, *D. Pugsley Gwynne*, gift from J. M. Ashe-Haley, 1989, © the copyright holder, photo credit: City & County of Swansea: Glynn Vivian Art Gallery Collection

Janes, Alfred 1911–1999, *Still Life – Fruit*, purchased from the artist, 1931, © the copyright holder, photo credit: City & County of Swansea: Glynn Vivian Art Gallery Collection

Janes, Alfred 1911–1999, *Untitled (Portrait of a Man)*, gift from C. Dawson, 1988, © the copyright holder, photo credit: City & County of Swansea: Glynn Vivian Art Gallery Collection

Janes, Alfred 1911–1999, *Mervyn Levy*, purchased from the artist, 1935, © the copyright holder, photo credit: City & County of Swansea: Glynn Vivian Art Gallery Collection

Janes, Alfred 1911–1999, *Hyacinths*, purchased from the artist, 1949, © the copyright holder, photo credit: City & County of Swansea: Glynn Vivian Art Gallery Collection

Janes, Alfred 1911–1999, *Study for a Portrait of Daniel Jones*, purchased

from the Attic gallery, 1996, © the copyright holder, photo credit: City & County of Swansea: Glynn Vivian Art Gallery Collection

Janes, Alfred 1911–1999, *Vernon Watkins*, gift from the Subscription Fund, 1950, © the copyright holder, photo credit: City & County of Swansea: Glynn Vivian Art Gallery Collection

Janes, Alfred 1911–1999, *Blodeuwydd*, gift from Bronwen Holden, 2004, © the copyright holder, photo credit: City & County of Swansea: Glynn Vivian Art Gallery Collection

Janes, Alfred 1911–1999, *Chirrup and Fruit*, purchased from the artist, 1990, © the copyright holder, photo credit: City & County of Swansea: Glynn Vivian Art Gallery Collection

Janes, Alfred 1911–1999, *Still Life – Benedictine Bottle*, purchased from the artist, 1935, © the copyright holder, photo credit: City & County of Swansea: Glynn Vivian Art Gallery Collection

Janes, Alfred 1911–1999, *Still Life – Fruit*, purchased from the artist, 1937, © the copyright holder, photo credit: City & County of Swansea: Glynn Vivian Art Gallery Collection

Janes, Alfred 1911–1999, *Still Life with a Fish*, gift from the Arts Council of Wales, 2002, © the copyright holder, photo credit: City & County of Swansea: Glynn Vivian Art Gallery Collection

Jenkins, Percy Pickard b.1908, *Morning (Swansea Landscape)*, bequeathed by the artist, 1995, © the copyright holder, photo credit: City & County of Swansea: Glynn Vivian Art Gallery Collection

John, Augustus Edwin 1878–1961, *The Tutor*, gift from Richard J. Strick, 1948, © the artist's estate/ Bridgeman Art Library, photo credit: City & County of Swansea: Glynn Vivian Art Gallery Collection

John, Augustus Edwin 1878–1961, *Caitlin*, purchased from the Obelisk Gallery, 1981, © the artist's estate/ Bridgeman Art Library, photo credit: City & County of Swansea: Glynn Vivian Art Gallery Collection

John, Augustus Edwin 1878–1961, *Arenig Mountain*, gift from W. Rufus Lewis, 1953, © the artist's estate/Bridgeman Art Library, photo credit: City & County of Swansea: Glynn Vivian Art Gallery Collection

John, Augustus Edwin 1878–1961, *Irish Coast*, purchased from Leicester Galleries, 1948, © the artist's estate/Bridgeman Art Library, photo credit: City & County of Swansea: Glynn Vivian Art Gallery Collection

John, Augustus Edwin 1878–1961, *L'Hermitage Martigues*, purchased from the artist, 1949, © the artist's estate/Bridgeman Art Library, photo credit: City & County of Swansea: Glynn Vivian Art Gallery Collection

John, Gwen 1876–1939, *The Nun*, purchased from Mathieson Ltd,

1949, photo credit: City & County of Swansea: Glynn Vivian Art Gallery Collection

John, Gwen 1876–1939, *Woman with a Coral Necklace*, gift from the Arts Council of Wales, 2002, photo credit: City & County of Swansea: Glynn Vivian Art Gallery Collection

Johns, John White *Jesus and Martha at the Sepulchre of Lazarus*, gift from P. Gwyn Johns, 1922, photo credit: City & County of Swansea: Glynn Vivian Art Gallery Collection

Johnstone, E. *Alexandra Road, Swansea*, purchased from the Rutland Art Gallery, 1981, photo credit: City & County of Swansea: Glynn Vivian Art Gallery Collection

Jones, Calvert Richard 1804–1877, *Sheep Dog*, purchased from the Colin Lacey Gallery, 1976, photo credit: City & County of Swansea: Glynn Vivian Art Gallery Collection

Jones, Colin 1928–1967, *Funeral, Merthyr*, purchased from the Dillwyn Gallery, 1965, © the copyright holder, photo credit: City & County of Swansea: Glynn Vivian Art Gallery Collection

Jones, Glyn b.1936, *For Macsen*, gift, 1982, © the artist, photo credit: City & County of Swansea: Glynn Vivian Art Gallery Collection

Jones, Jack 1922–1993, *Jack Jones*, purchased from Hugette Jones, © the copyright holder, photo credit: City & County of Swansea: Glynn Vivian Art Gallery Collection

Jones, Jack 1922–1993, *Zoar, Horeb and the Villiers*, purchased from the Taliesin Arts Centre, 1998, © the copyright holder, photo credit: City & County of Swansea: Glynn Vivian Art Gallery Collection

Jones, Jack 1922–1993, *Landore Viaduct*, purchased from the Taliesin Arts Centre, 1992, © the copyright holder, photo credit: City & County of Swansea: Glynn Vivian Art Gallery Collection

Jones, Thomas 1742–1803, *Ruins in Naples*, purchased from Colnaghi & Co. Ltd, photo credit: City & County of Swansea: Glynn Vivian Art Gallery Collection

Jones, Thomas 1742–1803, *On the Road from Albano to Rome*, gift from C. L. Evan-Thomas, 1985, photo credit: City & County of Swansea: Glynn Vivian Art Gallery Collection

Jordaens, Jacob 1593–1678, *Pan and Pipes*, bequeathed by Richard Glynn Vivian, 1911, photo credit: City & County of Swansea: Glynn Vivian Art Gallery Collection

Keith, Alexander active 1808–1874, *The Late John Williams*, gift from William Mansel, 1915, photo credit: City & County of Swansea: Glynn Vivian Art Gallery Collection

Knell, William Adolphus 1802–1875, *Shipping off Oystermouth*, purchased the O'Neil Gallery, 1971, photo credit: City & County of Swansea: Glynn Vivian Art Gallery Collection

Knell, William Calcott 1830–1880, *Fishing Boats Hauling Nets near*

Lowestoft, bequeathed by John Dyer, 1921, photo credit: City & County of Swansea: Glynn Vivian Art Gallery Collection

Lady Malet *Lady with Roses*, bequeathed by Richard Glynn Vivian, 1911, photo credit: City & County of Swansea: Glynn Vivian Art Gallery Collection

Lairesse, Gerard de 1640–1711, *Floral Tributes to Venus*, bequeathed by Richard Glynn Vivian, 1911, photo credit: City & County of Swansea: Glynn Vivian Art Gallery Collection

Landseer, Edwin Henry 1802–1873, *Lord Ellesmere, and His Pony, 'Jack'*, bequeathed by Richard Glynn Vivian, 1911, photo credit: City & County of Swansea: Glynn Vivian Art Gallery Collection

Lanyon, Peter 1918–1964, *Ilfracombe*, purchased Gimpel Fils, 1961, © Sheila Lanyon. All rights reserved, DACS 2013, photo credit: City & County of Swansea: Glynn Vivian Art Gallery Collection

Lawrence, Thomas 1769–1830, *Sir Robert Peel*, gift from Ethel M. Morgan, 1935, photo credit: City & County of Swansea: Glynn Vivian Art Gallery Collection

Lebourg, Albert 1849–1928, *A Wharf on the Seine at Dieppedalle*, gift from François Depeaux, 1911, photo credit: City & County of Swansea: Glynn Vivian Art Gallery Collection

Lees, Derwent 1885–1931, *Welsh Landscape in Winter*, purchased from Rowland, Browse & Delbarco, 1951, photo credit: City & County of Swansea: Glynn Vivian Art Gallery Collection

Leighton, Frederic 1830–1896, *A Spanish View*, bequeathed by Richard Glynn Vivian, 1911, photo credit: City & County of Swansea: Glynn Vivian Art Gallery Collection

Leighton, Frederic 1830–1896, *A Temple on the Nile*, bequeathed by Richard Glynn Vivian, 1911, photo credit: City & County of Swansea: Glynn Vivian Art Gallery Collection

Leighton, Frederic 1830–1896, *Head of a Girl*, bequeathed by Richard Glynn Vivian, 1911, photo credit: City & County of Swansea: Glynn Vivian Art Gallery Collection

Lely, Peter 1618–1680, *Countess of Bedford*, bequeathed by Richard Glynn Vivian, 1911, photo credit: City & County of Swansea: Glynn Vivian Art Gallery Collection

Lewis, Benjamin Archibald 1857–1946, *A Carmarthenshire Farm*, gift from Swansea Art Society, 1938, © the copyright holder, photo credit: City & County of Swansea: Glynn Vivian Art Gallery Collection

Lewis, Edward Morland 1903–1943, *Distant View of Laugharne*, purchased from the London Artists' Association, 1932, © the artist's estate, photo credit: City & County of Swansea: Glynn Vivian Art Gallery Collection

Lewis, Edward Morland 1903–1943, *'Lion Hotel' and Castle, Pembroke*, purchased from the artist, 1935, © the artist's estate, photo credit: City & County of Swansea: Glynn Vivian Art Gallery Collection

Lewis, Edward Morland 1903–1943, *Shandon Church*, gift from the Contemporary Art Society for Wales, 1947, © the artist's estate, photo credit: City & County of Swansea: Glynn Vivian Art Gallery Collection

Lewis, Edward Morland 1903–1943, *The Band Plays*, purchased from the artist, 1935, © the artist's estate, photo credit: City & County of Swansea: Glynn Vivian Art Gallery Collection

Lewis, Edward Morland 1903–1943, *The Beach*, purchased from Rowland, Browse & Delbarco, 1951, © the artist's estate, photo credit: City & County of Swansea: Glynn Vivian Art Gallery Collection

Lewis, Wyndham 1882–1957, *The Convalescent*, gift from Colin Anderson, 1976, © by kind permission of the Wyndham Lewis Memorial Trust (a registered charity), photo credit: City & County of Swansea: Glynn Vivian Art Gallery Collection

Lewis, Wyndham 1882–1957, *Miss Close*, purchased from Leicester Galleries, 1960, © by kind permission of the Wyndham Lewis Memorial Trust (a registered charity), photo credit: City & County of Swansea: Glynn Vivian Art Gallery Collection

Malthouse, Eric James 1914–1997, *Orion*, gift from the Contemporary Art Society for Wales, 1969, © the artist's estate, photo credit: City & County of Swansea: Glynn Vivian Art Gallery Collection

Manson, James Bolivar 1879–1945, *Carreg Cennen Castle*, purchased, 1995, © the artist's estate, photo credit: City & County of Swansea: Glynn Vivian Art Gallery Collection

Martin, Benito Quinquela 1890–1977, *Working at High Pressure*, purchased from the Art Society Bureau, 1930, © the copyright holder, photo credit: City & County of Swansea: Glynn Vivian Art Gallery Collection

Mayer-Marton, George 1897–1960, *Llanthony Valley*, gift, 1951, © estate of George Mayer-Marton. All rights reserved, DACS 2013, photo credit: City & County of Swansea: Glynn Vivian Art Gallery Collection

Mayer-Marton, George 1897–1960, *Girl and Bird*, gift from C. Mayer, 1975, © estate of George Mayer-Marton. All rights reserved, DACS 2013, photo credit: City & County of Swansea: Glynn Vivian Art Gallery Collection

Mayer-Marton, George 1897–1960, *Breakwater, Falmouth Harbour*, gift from C. Mayer, 1975, © estate of George Mayer-Marton. All rights reserved, DACS 2013, photo credit: City & County of Swansea: Glynn

Vivian Art Gallery Collection
Meager, Nigel *Untitled (Seascape)*, purchased, 1992, © the copyright holder, photo credit: City & County of Swansea: Glynn Vivian Art Gallery Collection
Mengs, Anton Raphael 1728–1779, *Madonna della Scodella* (after Correggio) (detail), gift from Captain Bostock, 1911, photo credit: City & County of Swansea: Glynn Vivian Art Gallery Collection
Methuen, Paul Ayshford 1886–1974, *Chinon*, purchased from Leicester Galleries, 1955, © trustees of the Corsham estate, photo credit: City & County of Swansea: Glynn Vivian Art Gallery Collection
Monahan, Richard b.1979, *Portrait with Pencil*, gift from the Friends of the Glynn Vivian Art Gallery, 2006, © the artist, photo credit: City & County of Swansea: Glynn Vivian Art Gallery Collection
Monet, Claude 1840–1926, *Bateaux en Hollande, près de Zaandam*, gift from HM Government, 1974, photo credit: City & County of Swansea: Glynn Vivian Art Gallery Collection
Morgan, Glyn b.1926, *Pontypridd*, gift from the Arts Council of Wales, 2002, © the artist, photo credit: City & County of Swansea: Glynn Vivian Art Gallery Collection
Morris, Carey Boynes 1882–1968, *Landscape with Haystack*, gift from Roderick Howell, 1989, © the artist's estate, photo credit: City & County of Swansea: Glynn Vivian Art Gallery Collection
Morris, Cedric Lockwood 1889–1982, *Llanmadoc Hill, Gower*, purchased from A. Tooth, 1930, © trustees of the Cedric Lockwood Morris Estate/Foundation, photo credit: City & County of Swansea: Glynn Vivian Art Gallery Collection
Morris, Cedric Lockwood 1889–1982, *The Sparrow Hawks*, gift from Arhur Lett-Haines, 1931, © trustees of the Cedric Lockwood Morris Estate/Foundation, photo credit: City & County of Swansea: Glynn Vivian Art Gallery Collection
Morris, Cedric Lockwood 1889–1982, *Pontypridd*, purchased from Leicester Galleries, 1952, © trustees of the Cedric Lockwood Morris Estate/Foundation, photo credit: City & County of Swansea: Glynn Vivian Art Gallery Collection
Morris, Cedric Lockwood 1889–1982, *River Zezere, Portugal*, bequeathed by Esther Grainger, 1991, © trustees of the Cedric Lockwood Morris Estate/ Foundation, photo credit: City & County of Swansea: Glynn Vivian Art Gallery Collection
Morris, Cedric Lockwood 1889–1982, *Margaret's Pots*, gift from the Arts Council of Wales, 2002, © trustees of the Cedric Lockwood Morris Estate/ Foundation, photo credit: City & County of Swansea: Glynn Vivian Art Gallery Collection
Morse-Brown, Sam 1903–2001, *Grey Day, Newquay*, purchased from the artist, 1937, © the copyright holder, photo credit: City & County of Swansea: Glynn Vivian Art Gallery Collection
Morse-Brown, Sam 1903–2001, *Grey Day, Tenby*, gift from Swansea Art Society, 1937, © the copyright holder, photo credit: City & County of Swansea: Glynn Vivian Art Gallery Collection
Muhl, Roger b.1929, *Le champ de colza*, purchased from The Calouste Gulbenkian Foundation, 1963, © ADAGP, Paris and DACS, London 2013, photo credit: City & County of Swansea: Glynn Vivian Art Gallery Collection
Mulloy, Daniel b.1977, *Nikki with Hanging Chair*, purchased from the artist, 1996, © the copyright holder, photo credit: City & County of Swansea: Glynn Vivian Art Gallery Collection
Murata, Eitaro *Landscape of Japan*, gift from the artist, 1930, © the copyright holder, photo credit: City & County of Swansea: Glynn Vivian Art Gallery Collection
Murray, William Grant 1877–1950, *Carreg Cennen Castle*, gift, 1994, © the artist's estate, photo credit: City & County of Swansea: Glynn Vivian Art Gallery Collection
Murray, William Grant 1877–1950, *Gorsedd y Beirdd Abertawe*, gift, 1994, © the artist's estate, photo credit: City & County of Swansea: Glynn Vivian Art Gallery Collection
Murray, William Grant 1877–1950, *The Old Mumbles Train*, purchased from H. E. Quick, 1944, © the artist's estate, photo credit: City & County of Swansea: Glynn Vivian Art Gallery Collection
Murray, William Grant 1877–1950, *Swansea for Business*, gift, 1933, © the artist's estate, photo credit: City & County of Swansea: Glynn Vivian Art Gallery Collection
Murray, William Grant 1877–1950, *Swansea for Pleasure*, gift, 1933, © the artist's estate, photo credit: City & County of Swansea: Glynn Vivian Art Gallery Collection
Murray, William Grant 1877–1950, *Lilac and Laburnum*, gift from the artist, 1944, © the artist's estate, photo credit: City & County of Swansea: Glynn Vivian Art Gallery Collection
Murray, William Grant 1877–1950, *Oxwich Bay*, purchased, 1994, © the artist's estate, photo credit: City & County of Swansea: Glynn Vivian Art Gallery Collection
Myn, Agatha van de 1700–c.1768, *Study of Fruit and Flowers*, bequeathed by Richard Glynn Vivian, 1911, photo credit: City & County of Swansea: Glynn Vivian Art Gallery Collection
Nash, Paul 1889–1946, *Landscape of the Bagley Woods*, purchased from Arthur Tooth & Sons, 1960, © Tate, photo credit: City & County of Swansea: Glynn Vivian Art Gallery Collection
Nash, Thomas John b.1931, *Promontory*, purchased from the Arts Council, 1961, © the copyright holder, photo credit: City & County of Swansea: Glynn Vivian Art Gallery Collection
Neep, Victor 1921–1979, *The Tip*, gift from the Contemporary Art Society for Wales, 1965, © the copyright holder, photo credit: City & County of Swansea: Glynn Vivian Art Gallery Collection
Netscher, Caspar 1639–1684, *Lady with Fruit and Attendant*, bequeathed by Richard Glynn Vivian, 1911, photo credit: City & County of Swansea: Glynn Vivian Art Gallery Collection
Neuschul, Ernst 1895–1968, *Cockle Woman*, gift, 1946, © the artist's estate, photo credit: City & County of Swansea: Glynn Vivian Art Gallery Collection
Neuschul, Ernst 1895–1968, *Untitled (Two Mothers and Babies)*, gift from David Wibberley, 1992, © the artist's estate, photo credit: City & County of Swansea: Glynn Vivian Art Gallery Collection
Neuschul, Ernst 1895–1968, *Untitled (Cockle Picker)*, gift from William Meinel, 1979, © the artist's estate, photo credit: City & County of Swansea: Glynn Vivian Art Gallery Collection
Neyn, Pieter de 1597–1639, *Leyden*, bequeathed by Edgar Hodges, 1984, photo credit: City & County of Swansea: Glynn Vivian Art Gallery Collection
Nicholson, Ben 1894–1982, *October 12th 1952*, gift from the Friends of the Glynn Vivian Art Gallery, 1998, © image unavailable due to copyright restrictions, photo credit: City & County of Swansea: Glynn Vivian Art Gallery Collection
Nicol, Philip b.1953, *Tongue in Cheek*, purchased from the artist, 1987, © the artist, photo credit: City & County of Swansea: Glynn Vivian Art Gallery Collection
Opie, John 1761–1807, *Portrait of a Girl*, bequeathed by Richard Glynn Vivian, 1911, photo credit: City & County of Swansea: Glynn Vivian Art Gallery Collection
Ostade, Adriaen van (follower of) 1610–1685, *Interior of a Tavern*, bequeathed by Richard Glynn Vivian, 1911, photo credit: City & County of Swansea: Glynn Vivian Art Gallery Collection
Panting, Arlie 1914–1994, *Still Life with Mushrooms*, gift from Eve Bletcher, 1999, © the copyright holder, photo credit: City & County of Swansea: Glynn Vivian Art Gallery Collection
Panting, Arlie 1914–1994, *Guild Houses*, gift from Eve Bletcher, 1999, © the copyright holder, photo credit: City & County of Swansea: Glynn Vivian Art Gallery Collection
Panting, Arlie 1914–1994, *Welsh Landscape*, gift from Eve Bletcher, 1999, © the copyright holder, photo credit: City & County of Swansea: Glynn Vivian Art Gallery Collection
Panting, Arlie 1914–1994, *Still Life with Leeks*, gift from Eve Bletcher, 1999, © the copyright holder, photo credit: City & County of Swansea: Glynn Vivian Art Gallery Collection
Parminter, Agnes Vye c.1836–1915, *James Rodgers, JP, Mayor of Swansea (1878)*, gift, 1994, photo credit: City & County of Swansea: Glynn Vivian Art Gallery Collection
Petts, John 1914–1991, *Brenda Chamberlain by Candlelight*, purchased from John Petts, 1975, © the copyright holder, photo credit: City & County of Swansea: Glynn Vivian Art Gallery Collection
Pfeninger, R. E. *R. Glynn Vivian*, bequeathed by Richard Glynn Vivian, 1911, photo credit: City & County of Swansea: Glynn Vivian Art Gallery Collection
Philipson, Robin 1916–1992, *Cockfight Blue*, purchased from the Stone Gallery, 1963, © the artist's estate, photo credit: City & County of Swansea: Glynn Vivian Art Gallery Collection
Phillips, Jane 1957–2011, *Hurricane Charlie*, purchased from the artist, 1986, © the artist's estate, photo credit: City & County of Swansea: Glynn Vivian Art Gallery Collection
Pickersgill, Henry William 1782–1875, *The Hop Pickers*, bequeathed by Richard Glynn Vivian, 1911, photo credit: City & County of Swansea: Glynn Vivian Art Gallery Collection
Piloty, Karl von 1826–1886, *Seated Figure, Germany*, bequeathed by Richard Glynn Vivian, 1911, photo credit: City & County of Swansea: Glynn Vivian Art Gallery Collection
Pissarro, Lucien 1863–1944, *Cefn Bryn, Gower*, gift from W. Rufus Lewis, 1962, © the artist's estate, photo credit: City & County of Swansea: Glynn Vivian Art Gallery Collection
Pitcher, Neville Sotheby 1889–1959, *Tide Time, Swansea*, purchased from the artist, 1939, © the copyright holder, photo credit: City & County of Swansea: Glynn Vivian Art Gallery Collection
Povey, Edward b.1951, *The Herb of the Field (Self Portrait)*, gift from the artist, 2000, © the artist, photo credit: City & County of Swansea: Glynn Vivian Art Gallery Collection
Preece, Patricia 1894–1966, *Interior with Figures*, purchased from the artist, 1935, © Dorothy Hepworth. All rights reserved, DACS 2013, photo credit: City & County of Swansea: Glynn Vivian Art Gallery Collection
Prendergast, Peter 1946–2007, *Carneddi on a Summer's Day*, gift, 1983, © Estate of Peter Prendergast. All rights reserved, DACS 2013, photo credit: City & County of Swansea: Glynn Vivian Art Gallery Collection
Prendergast, Peter 1946–2007, *Bethesda Quarry*, purchased from the Arts Council of Wales, 1983, © Estate of Peter Prendergast. All rights reserved, DACS 2013, photo credit: City & County of Swansea: Glynn Vivian Art Gallery Collection
Prendergast, Peter 1946–2007, *Bethesda Quarry*, gift from the artist, 1983, © Estate of Peter Prendergast. All rights reserved, DACS 2013, photo credit: City & County of Swansea: Glynn Vivian Art Gallery Collection
Prendergast, Peter 1946–2007, *Landscape*, gift from the artist, 1983, © Estate of Peter Prendergast. All rights reserved, DACS 2013, photo credit: City & County of Swansea: Glynn Vivian Art Gallery Collection
Prendergast, Peter 1946–2007, *Landscape Sketch*, gift from the artist, 1983, © Estate of Peter Prendergast. All rights reserved, DACS 2013, photo credit: City & County of Swansea: Glynn Vivian Art Gallery Collection
Priestly, E. active 19th C, *Pecca Falls, Ingleton*, gift, 1994, photo credit: City & County of Swansea: Glynn Vivian Art Gallery Collection
Procter, Dod 1892–1972, *Early Morning, Newlyn*, purchased from the artist, 1929, © the artist's estate/ Bridgeman Art Library, photo credit: City & County of Swansea: Glynn Vivian Art Gallery Collection
Protheroe, Handel 1921–2007, *Penclawdd*, purchased, 1948, © the artist's estate, photo credit: City & County of Swansea: Glynn Vivian Art Gallery Collection
Ranken, William Bruce Ellis 1881–1941, *Macaw and Sunflowers*, gift from Ernest Thesiger, 1946, photo credit: City & County of Swansea: Glynn Vivian Art Gallery Collection
Raphael (copy after) 1483–1520, *Self Portrait*, bequeathed by Richard Glynn Vivian, 1911, photo credit: City & County of Swansea: Glynn Vivian Art Gallery Collection
Rapp, Ginette 1928–1998, *The Beach, Audierne*, purchased from the Adams Gallery, 1956, © the copyright holder, photo credit: City & County of Swansea: Glynn Vivian Art Gallery Collection
Rathmell, Thomas Roland 1912–1990, *Coracle Man*, purchased from the Royal National Eisteddfod, Swansea, 1964, © the artist's estate, photo credit: City & County of Swansea: Glynn Vivian Art Gallery Collection
Rees, John Bromfield Gay 1912–1965, *Still Life with Fruit and Bonbonnière*, gift from the Contemporary Art Society for Wales, 1957, © the copyright holder, photo credit: City & County of Swansea: Glynn Vivian Art Gallery Collection
Reni, Guido 1575–1642, *Susanna and the Elders*, bequeathed by

Richard Glynn Vivian, 1911, photo credit: City & County of Swansea: Glynn Vivian Art Gallery Collection
Reynolds, Alan b.1926, *Nocturne*, purchased from the Howard Roberts Gallery, 1961, © the artist, photo credit: City & County of Swansea: Glynn Vivian Art Gallery Collection
Rhys-James, Shani b.1953, *The Mirror*, purchased from the Martin Tinney Gallery, 1994, © the artist, photo credit: City & County of Swansea: Glynn Vivian Art Gallery Collection
Rhys-James, Shani b.1953, *Head I (Self Portrait)*, purchased from the Martin Tinney Gallery, 2003, © the artist, photo credit: City & County of Swansea: Glynn Vivian Art Gallery Collection
Rhys-James, Shani b.1953, *Head II (Self Portrait)*, purchased from the Martin Tinney Gallery, 2003, © the artist, photo credit: City & County of Swansea: Glynn Vivian Art Gallery Collection
Rhys-James, Shani b.1953, *Head III (Self Portrait)*, purchased from the Martin Tinney Gallery, 2003, © the artist, photo credit: City & County of Swansea: Glynn Vivian Art Gallery Collection
Richards, Anthony b.1962, *Llandeilo*, purchased from the artist, 1991, © the artist, photo credit: City & County of Swansea: Glynn Vivian Art Gallery Collection
Richards, Ceri Giraldus 1903–1971, *The Artist's Wife*, purchased from the New Grafton Gallery, 1981, © estate of Ceri Richards. All rights reserved, DACS 2013, photo credit: City & County of Swansea: Glynn Vivian Art Gallery Collection
Richards, Ceri Giraldus 1903–1971, *Costerwoman*, purchased from Fischer Fine Art Ltd, 1973, © estate of Ceri Richards. All rights reserved, DACS 2013, photo credit: City & County of Swansea: Glynn Vivian Art Gallery Collection
Richards, Ceri Giraldus 1903–1971, *The Force that through the Green Fuse: The Source*, gift from the family of Iorwerth and Elizabeth Jones in their memory, 2007, © estate of Ceri Richards. All rights reserved, DACS 2013, photo credit: City & County of Swansea: Glynn Vivian Art Gallery Collection
Richards, Ceri Giraldus 1903–1971, *The Pianist*, purchased from the Redfern Gallery, 1948, © estate of Ceri Richards. All rights reserved, DACS 2013, photo credit: City & County of Swansea: Glynn Vivian Art Gallery Collection
Richards, Ceri Giraldus 1903–1971, *The Sculptor's Landscape* (homage to Henry Moore), purchased from the Monika Kinley Gallery, 1980, © estate of Ceri Richards. All rights reserved, DACS 2013, photo credit: City & County of Swansea: Glynn Vivian Art Gallery Collection
Richards, Ceri Giraldus 1903–1971, *Bouquet*, gift from the Arts Council of Wales, 2002, © estate of Ceri Richards. All rights reserved, DACS 2013, photo credit: City & County of Swansea: Glynn Vivian Art Gallery Collection
Richards, Ceri Giraldus 1903–1971, *The Artist's Father*, gift from the Contemporary Art Society for Wales, 1961, © estate of Ceri Richards. All rights reserved, DACS 2013, photo credit: City & County of Swansea: Glynn Vivian Art Gallery Collection
Richards, Ceri Giraldus 1903–1971, *The Ravine*, gift from the Contemporary Art Society for Wales, 1961, © estate of Ceri Richards. All rights reserved, DACS 2013, photo credit: City & County of Swansea: Glynn Vivian Art Gallery Collection
Richards, Ceri Giraldus 1903–1971, *La cathédrale engloutie III*, purchased from the Matt Hirsen Gallery, 1960, © estate of Ceri Richards. All rights reserved, DACS 2013, photo credit: City & County of Swansea: Glynn Vivian Art Gallery Collection
Richards, Ceri Giraldus 1903–1971, *Enclosed in Deep Blue*, purchased from the New London Gallery, 1963, © estate of Ceri Richards. All rights reserved, DACS 2013, photo credit. City & County of Swansea: Glynn Vivian Art Gallery Collection
Richards, Ceri Giraldus 1903–1971, *The Lion Hunt*, purchased from the Howard Roberts Gallery, 1965, © estate of Ceri Richards. All rights reserved, DACS 2013, photo credit: City & County of Swansea: Glynn Vivian Art Gallery Collection
Richards, Ceri Giraldus 1903–1971, *The Lion Hunt IV*, gift from Colin Anderson, 1976, © estate of Ceri Richards. All rights reserved, DACS 2013, photo credit: City & County of Swansea: Glynn Vivian Art Gallery Collection
Richards, Ceri Giraldus 1903–1971, *Music of Colours, White Blossom*, gift, © estate of Ceri Richards. All rights reserved, DACS 2013, photo credit: City & County of Swansea: Glynn Vivian Art Gallery Collection
Richards, Ceri Giraldus 1903–1971, *Hammerclavier Theme*, gift from the Contemporary Art Society in memory of curator David Bell (1915–1959), 1960, © estate of Ceri Richards. All rights reserved, DACS 2013, photo credit: City & County of Swansea: Glynn Vivian Art Gallery Collection
Richards, Frances 1903–1985, *Metamorphosis*, gift from the Contemporary Art Society for Wales, 1967, © the copyright holder, photo credit: City & County of Swansea: Glynn Vivian Art Gallery Collection
Ridinger, Johan Elias 1695–1767, *Three Portraits of Countess Ansbach*, bequeathed by Richard Glynn Vivian, 1911, photo credit: City & County of Swansea: Glynn Vivian Art Gallery Collection
Rigaud, John Francis 1742–1810, *Mrs Hartle*, gift from G. Bransby, photo credit: City & County of Swansea: Glynn Vivian Art Gallery Collection
Roberts, Will 1907–2000, *Winter*, gift from the Friends of the Glynn Vivian Art Gallery, 1964, © Will Roberts' estate, photo credit: City & County of Swansea: Glynn Vivian Art Gallery Collection
Roberts, Will 1907–2000, *Public Reading Room*, gift from Friends of the Glynn Vivian Art Gallery, 1987, © Will Roberts' estate, photo credit: City & County of Swansea: Glynn Vivian Art Gallery Collection
Roberts, William Patrick 1895–1980, *Miss Jane Tupper-Carey*, gift from the Contemporary Art Society, 1928, © estate of John David Roberts. By courtesy of The William Roberts Society, photo credit: City & County of Swansea: Glynn Vivian Art Gallery Collection
Roos, Philipp Peter 1657–1706, *Landscape with Bull, Goats and Attendant*, bequeathed by Richard Glynn Vivian, 1911, photo credit: City & County of Swansea: Glynn Vivian Art Gallery Collection
Rowntree, Kenneth 1915–1997, *Vase of Flowers in a Landscape*, gift from the Contemporary Art Society for Wales, 1967, © the artist's estate, photo credit: City & County of Swansea: Glynn Vivian Art Gallery Collection
Rubens, Peter Paul 1577–1640, *Abraham and Melchisedek*, bequeathed by Richard Glynn Vivian, 1911, photo credit: City & County of Swansea: Glynn Vivian Art Gallery Collection
Saunders, Gerald *Cockle Pickers*, gift from the Friends of the Glynn Vivian Art Gallery, 1993, photo credit: City & County of Swansea: Glynn Vivian Art Gallery Collection
Sauvage, Piat Joseph 1744–1818, *Diana and Nymphs*, bequeathed by Richard Glynn Vivian, 1911, photo credit: City & County of Swansea: Glynn Vivian Art Gallery Collection
Sauvage, Piat Joseph 1744–1818, *The Boar Hunt*, bequeathed by Richard Glynn Vivian, 1911, photo credit: City & County of Swansea: Glynn Vivian Art Gallery Collection
Schalcken, Godfried 1643–1706, *Good Night*, bequeathed by Richard Glynn Vivian, 1911, photo credit: City & County of Swansea: Glynn Vivian Art Gallery Collection
Schwabeda, Johann Michael 1734–1794, *Cupids and Fruit*, bequeathed by Richard Glynn Vivian, 1911, photo credit: City & County of Swansea: Glynn Vivian Art Gallery Collection
Schwabeda, Johann Michael 1734–1794, *Cupids and Goat*, bequeathed by Richard Glynn Vivian, 1911, photo credit: City & County of Swansea: Glynn Vivian Art Gallery Collection
Scott, Peter Markham 1909–1989, *Widgeon Asleep in the Noonday Sun*, gift from the Royal Navy Services Association, 1948, © the artist's estate, photo credit: City & County of Swansea: Glynn Vivian Art Gallery Collection
Setch, Terry b.1936, *Once upon a Time there Was…*, gift from the Contemporary Art Society, 2007, © the artist, photo credit: City & County of Swansea: Glynn Vivian Art Gallery Collection
Setch, Terry b.1936, *Explosion III*, purchased from the artist, 1984, © the artist, photo credit: City & County of Swansea: Glynn Vivian Art Gallery Collection
Shanks, Duncan b.1937, *Waterfall*, purchased from the Davies Memorial Gallery, 1988, © the artist, photo credit: City & County of Swansea: Glynn Vivian Art Gallery Collection
Sheppard, Maurice Raymond b.1947, *Gypsy Men Logging in the Wood*, gift from the Contemporary Art Society for Wales, 1996, © the artist/Bridgeman Art Library, photo credit: City & County of Swansea: Glynn Vivian Art Gallery Collection
Sheringham, George 1884–1937, *Mabinogion Series* (design for a silk panel), gift from Mrs George Sheringham, 1938, photo credit: City & County of Swansea: Glynn Vivian Art Gallery Collection
Sickert, Walter Richard 1860–1942, *La Nera*, purchased from Leicester Galleries, 1952, photo credit: City & County of Swansea: Glynn Vivian Art Gallery Collection
Smith, Alan b.1956, *Six Months in a Closet of Rushing Water with Cold Tea and All the Time in the World*, purchased from the artist, 1986, © the copyright holder, photo credit: City & County of Swansea: Glynn Vivian Art Gallery Collection
Smith, Alan b.1956, *Water Tower No.3*, purchased from the artist, 1986, © the copyright holder, photo credit: City & County of Swansea: Glynn Vivian Art Gallery Collection
Smith, Alan b.1956, *Watertower No.2*, purchased from the artist, 1986, © the copyright holder, photo credit: City & County of Swansea: Glynn Vivian Art Gallery Collection
Smith, Alan b.1956, *T piece No.1*, purchased from the artist, 1986, © the copyright holder, photo credit: City & County of Swansea: Glynn Vivian Art Gallery Collection
Smith, Matthew Arnold Bracy 1879–1959, *Winter Landscape, Cornwall*, purchased, 1957, © by permission of the copyright holder, photo credit: City & County of Swansea: Glynn Vivian Art Gallery Collection
Smith, Matthew Arnold Bracy 1879–1959, *Marguerites and Pears*, purchased, 1960, © by permission of the copyright holder, photo credit: City & County of Swansea: Glynn Vivian Art Gallery Collection
Soo Pieng, Cheong 1917–1983, *Abstraction II*, purchased from the Redfern Gallery, 1963, © the copyright holder, photo credit: City & County of Swansea: Glynn Vivian Art Gallery Collection
Spear, Ruskin 1911–1990, *River in Winter*, gift, 1957, © the artist's estate/Bridgeman Art Library, photo credit: City & County of Swansea: Glynn Vivian Art Gallery Collection
Spear, Ruskin 1911–1990, *Winter Evening*, purchased, 1955, © the artist's estate/Bridgeman Art Library, photo credit: City & County of Swansea: Glynn Vivian Art Gallery Collection
Spencer, Stanley 1891–1959, *Garden at Whitehouse, Northern Ireland*, bequeathed by Richard J. Strick, 1974, © the estate of Stanley Spencer 2013. All rights reserved DACS, photo credit: City & County of Swansea: Glynn Vivian Art Gallery Collection
Spencer, Stanley 1891–1959, *Marriage at Cana, Bride and Bridegroom*, purchased, 1958, © the estate of Stanley Spencer 2013. All rights reserved DACS, photo credit: City & County of Swansea: Glynn Vivian Art Gallery Collection
Stapleton, Niemann *Landscape with River and Boy Fishing**, bequeathed by Trevor Jones, 1977, © the copyright holder, photo credit: City & County of Swansea: Glynn Vivian Art Gallery Collection
Stapleton, Niemann *Chiselhurst Church and Landscape*, bequeathed by Trevor Jones, 1977, © the copyright holder, photo credit: City & County of Swansea: Glynn Vivian Art Gallery Collection
Stapleton, Niemann *Whitby*, bequeathed by Trevor Jones, 1977, © the copyright holder, photo credit: City & County of Swansea: Glynn Vivian Art Gallery Collection
Steele-Morgan, Tony 1930–2009, *Tiger Mirror Box*, purchased from the artist, 1997, © the artist's estate, photo credit: City & County of Swansea: Glynn Vivian Art Gallery Collection
Stothard, Thomas 1755–1834, *The Fall*, bequeathed by Richard Glynn Vivian, 1911, photo credit: City & County of Swansea: Glynn Vivian Art Gallery Collection
Stuart, Gordon b.1924, *Daniel Jones*, gift from the Friends of the Glynn Vivian Art Gallery, 1996, © the artist, photo credit: City & County of Swansea: Glynn Vivian Art Gallery Collection
Stuart, Gordon b.1924, *Will Roberts, Painter*, purchased from the Taliesin Arts Centre, 1992, © the artist, photo credit: City & County of Swansea: Glynn Vivian Art Gallery Collection
Swan, Douglas 1930–2000, *Michael Sweeping into Air*, purchased, 1984, © DACS 2013, photo credit: City & County of Swansea: Glynn Vivian Art Gallery Collection

Swan, Douglas 1930–2000, *Michael Sweeping into Air*, purchased, 1984, © DACS 2013, photo credit: City & County of Swansea: Glynn Vivian Art Gallery Collection

Swan, Douglas 1930–2000, *Michael Sweeping into Air*, purchased, 1984, © DACS 2013, photo credit: City & County of Swansea: Glynn Vivian Art Gallery Collection

Tatarczyk, Tomasz *Seven Deadly Sins*, purchased, 1985, © the copyright holder, photo credit: City & County of Swansea: Glynn Vivian Art Gallery Collection

Taylor, Edward Ingram 1855–1923, *Oxwich Bay, Gower*, bequeathed by Sir Geoffrey Taylor, 1976, photo credit: City & County of Swansea: Glynn Vivian Art Gallery Collection

Thomas, J. B. *Farm, Rudry*, gift from the Friends of the Glynn Vivian Art Gallery, 1998, photo credit: City & County of Swansea: Glynn Vivian Art Gallery Collection

Thomson, Henry 1773–1843, *Icarus after His Fall, Found on the Sea Shore*, purchased from Thomas Agnew, 1973, photo credit: City & County of Swansea: Glynn Vivian Art Gallery Collection

Tischbein, Johan Wilhelm *Reuszin und Heinrich XXXVII Juneere Reusz*, bequeathed by Richard Glynn Vivian, 1911, photo credit: City & County of Swansea: Glynn Vivian Art Gallery Collection

Tischbein, Johan Wilhelm *Heinrich der XXXVII Heinrich der XXXIX Junge Reusz*, bequeathed by Richard Glynn Vivian, 1911, photo credit: City & County of Swansea: Glynn Vivian Art Gallery Collection

Toulcher, Sylvia *Picking Out the Coal Seam*, gift from the artist, 1994, © the copyright holder, photo credit: City & County of Swansea: Glynn Vivian Art Gallery Collection

Tuke, Henry Scott 1858–1929, *On the Beach, Bournemouth, March 1882*, bequeathed by Ronald Hedley Smoldon, 1998, photo credit: City & County of Swansea: Glynn Vivian Art Gallery Collection

Tyzack, Michael 1933–2007, *Scarlet Fissure*, purchased from the Howard Roberts Gallery, 1965, © Michael Tyzack, courtesy of Portland Gallery, London, photo credit: City & County of Swansea: Glynn Vivian Art Gallery Collection

Uhlman, Fred 1901–1985, *Welsh Farm*, gift from Richard J. Strick, 1954, © the artist's estate/Bridgeman Art Library, photo credit: City & County of Swansea: Glynn Vivian Art Gallery Collection

unknown artist *Mrs Mary Morgan*, purchased from H. Vivian, photo credit: City & County of Swansea: Glynn Vivian Art Gallery Collection

unknown artist *Jane Ann Edmond*, bequeathed by Mary Elizabeth Clarke Edmond, 1984, photo credit: City & County of Swansea: Glynn Vivian Art Gallery Collection

unknown artist *John Edmond*, bequeathed by Mary Elizabeth Clarke Edmond, 1984, photo credit: City & County of Swansea: Glynn Vivian Art Gallery Collection

unknown artist *View of Swansea*, gift from George L. Crocker, 1943, photo credit: City & County of Swansea: Glynn Vivian Art Gallery Collection

unknown artist *Jacob's Dream*, bequeathed by Richard Glynn Vivian, 1911, photo credit: City & County of Swansea: Glynn Vivian Art Gallery Collection

unknown artist *Landscape with Animals*, bequeathed by Richard Glynn Vivian, 1911, photo credit: City & County of Swansea: Glynn Vivian Art Gallery Collection

unknown artist *Portrait of a Man*, bequeathed by Richard Glynn Vivian, 1911, photo credit: City & County of Swansea: Glynn Vivian Art Gallery Collection

unknown artist *Portrait of a Woman*, bequeathed by Richard Glynn Vivian, 1911, photo credit: City & County of Swansea: Glynn Vivian Art Gallery Collection

unknown artist *The Virgin Mary*, bequeathed by Richard Glynn Vivian, 1911, photo credit: City & County of Swansea: Glynn Vivian Art Gallery Collection

unknown artist *Untitled (mythological subject)*, bequeathed by Richard Glynn Vivian, 1911, photo credit: City & County of Swansea: Glynn Vivian Art Gallery Collection

unknown artist *Untitled (mythological subject)*, bequeathed by Richard Glynn Vivian, 1911, photo credit: City & County of Swansea: Glynn Vivian Art Gallery Collection

unknown artist *Untitled (mythological subject)*, bequeathed by Richard Glynn Vivian, 1911, photo credit: City & County of Swansea: Glynn Vivian Art Gallery Collection

unknown artist *Untitled (A Lady at Her Mirror)*, bequeathed by Richard Glynn Vivian, 1911, photo credit: City & County of Swansea: Glynn Vivian Art Gallery Collection

unknown artist *Untitled (Cavalry Charge)*, gift, 1994, photo credit: City & County of Swansea: Glynn Vivian Art Gallery Collection

unknown artist *Untitled (Landscape)*, gift, 1994, photo credit: City & County of Swansea: Glynn Vivian Art Gallery Collection

unknown artist *Untitled (Landscape)*, gift, 1994, photo credit: City & County of Swansea: Glynn Vivian Art Gallery Collection

unknown artist *Untitled (Landscape)*, gift, 1994, photo credit: City & County of Swansea: Glynn Vivian Art Gallery Collection

unknown artist *Untitled (Landscape)*, bequeathed by Richard Glynn Vivian, 1911, photo credit: City & County of Swansea: Glynn Vivian Art Gallery Collection

unknown artist *Untitled (View of a City)*, gift, 1994, photo credit: City & County of Swansea: Glynn Vivian Art Gallery Collection

unknown artist *Untitled (Woman Carrying a Basket of Flowers on Her Head)*, bequeathed by Richard Glynn Vivian, 1911, photo credit: City & County of Swansea: Glynn Vivian Art Gallery Collection

Varley I, John 1778–1842, *Harlech Castle*, gift from F. J. Nettlefold, photo credit: City & County of Swansea: Glynn Vivian Art Gallery Collection

Vaughan, John Keith 1912–1977, *Warrior*, purchased from the Matthiesen Gallery, 1960, © the estate of Keith Vaughan. All rights reserved, DACS 2013, photo credit: City & County of Swansea: Glynn Vivian Art Gallery Collection

Vicari, Andrew b.1938, *Three Welsh Colliers*, gift, 1994, © the copyright holder, photo credit: City & County of Swansea: Glynn Vivian Art Gallery Collection

Vignet, Henri 1857–1920, *West Front of Rouen Cathedral at Sunset*, gift from François Depeaux, 1911, photo credit: City & County of Swansea: Glynn Vivian Art Gallery Collection

Walters, Evan 1893–1951, *Still Life Study of Fish*, gift from Mary Cleaver, 2008, © the artist's estate, photo credit: City & County of Swansea: Glynn Vivian Art Gallery Collection

Walters, Evan 1893–1951, *Mrs Coombe-Tennant, JP, and Sons, Alexander and Henry*, bequeathed by Mrs Coombe-Tennant, 1957, © the artist's estate, photo credit: City & County of Swansea: Glynn Vivian Art Gallery Collection

Walters, Evan 1893–1951, *Mrs Grant Murray*, gift from Mrs Grant Murray, 1961, © the artist's estate, photo credit: City & County of Swansea: Glynn Vivian Art Gallery Collection

Walters, Evan 1893–1951, *Rear Admiral Walker-Heneage-Vivian*, gift, 1988, © the artist's estate, photo credit: City & County of Swansea: Glynn Vivian Art Gallery Collection

Walters, Evan 1893–1951, *Doctor Edith Anne Evans, née Jones*, gift from the Friends of the Glynn Vivian Art Gallery, 2011, © the artist's estate, photo credit: City & County of Swansea: Glynn Vivian Art Gallery Collection

Walters, Evan 1893–1951, *Blind Pianist*, gift from Erna Meinel, 1953, © the artist's estate, photo credit: City & County of Swansea: Glynn Vivian Art Gallery Collection

Walters, Evan 1893–1951, *Boy with Feather*, purchased from E. Harries, 1927, © the artist's estate, photo credit: City & County of Swansea: Glynn Vivian Art Gallery Collection

Walters, Evan 1893–1951, *Eva*, gift from Howard Elt, 1964, © the artist's estate, photo credit: City & County of Swansea: Glynn Vivian

Art Gallery Collection

Walters, Evan 1893–1951, *Mr William Hopkins, a Welsh Collier*, purchased from the artist, 1926, © the artist's estate, photo credit: City & County of Swansea: Glynn Vivian Art Gallery Collection

Walters, Evan 1893–1951, *Pennard Castle*, purchased from the artist, 1926, © the artist's estate, photo credit: City & County of Swansea: Glynn Vivian Art Gallery Collection

Walters, Evan 1893–1951, *Mr and Mrs Rowlands*, gift from Miss Rowlands, 1973, © the artist's estate, photo credit: City & County of Swansea: Glynn Vivian Art Gallery Collection

Walters, Evan 1893–1951, *Brothers*, purchased from the Brandon Davis Gallery, 1930, © the artist's estate, photo credit: City & County of Swansea: Glynn Vivian Art Gallery Collection

Walters, Evan 1893–1951, *Miner*, gift from Erna Meinel, 1953, © the artist's estate, photo credit: City & County of Swansea: Glynn Vivian Art Gallery Collection

Walters, Evan 1893–1951, *Street Scene*, gift from the Wrexham Arts Centre, 1994, © the artist's estate, photo credit: City & County of Swansea: Glynn Vivian Art Gallery Collection

Walters, Evan 1893–1951, *Portrait of a Young Woman*, gift from Erna Meinel, 1953, © the artist's estate, photo credit: City & County of Swansea: Glynn Vivian Art Gallery Collection

Walters, Evan 1893–1951, *Village Lane, Mumbles*, gift from the Taliesin Arts Centre, 1994, © the artist's estate, photo credit: City & County of Swansea: Glynn Vivian Art Gallery Collection

Walters, Evan 1893–1951, *A Welsh Miner*, gift, 1931, © the artist's estate, photo credit: City & County of Swansea: Glynn Vivian Art Gallery Collection

Walters, Evan 1893–1951, *An Empty Frame*, gift from William Meinel, 1979, © the artist's estate, photo credit: City & County of Swansea: Glynn Vivian Art Gallery Collection

Walters, Evan 1893–1951, *Stout Man with Jug*, gift from Erna Meinel, 1953, © the artist's estate, photo credit: City & County of Swansea: Glynn Vivian Art Gallery Collection

Walters, Evan 1893–1951, *Portrait of a Woman*, gift from B. Mort-Jones, 1994, © the artist's estate, photo credit: City & County of Swansea: Glynn Vivian Art Gallery Collection

Walters, Evan 1893–1951, *Hampstead through a Window*, gift from Erna Meinel, 1953, © the artist's estate, photo credit: City & County of Swansea: Glynn Vivian Art Gallery Collection

Walters, Evan 1893–1951, *The Artist's Mother Asleep*, gift from

Erna Meinel, 1953, © the artist's estate, photo credit: City & County of Swansea: Glynn Vivian Art Gallery Collection

Walters, Evan 1893–1951, *Lady in a Black Hat (Mrs Erna Meinel)*, bequeathed by the sitter, 1992, © the artist's estate, photo credit: City & County of Swansea: Glynn Vivian Art Gallery Collection

Walters, Evan 1893–1951, *Landscape with Farm*, gift from Erna Meinel, 1953, © the artist's estate, photo credit: City & County of Swansea: Glynn Vivian Art Gallery Collection

Walters, Evan 1893–1951, *Girl in Kitchen*, gift from Erna Meinel, 1953, © the artist's estate, photo credit: City & County of Swansea: Glynn Vivian Art Gallery Collection

Walters, Evan 1893–1951, *South Wales Landscape under Cloud*, gift from Erna Meinel, 1953, © the artist's estate, photo credit: City & County of Swansea: Glynn Vivian Art Gallery Collection

Walters, Evan 1893–1951, *The Artist's Mother Reading the Bible*, gift from Erna Meinel, 1953, © the artist's estate, photo credit: City & County of Swansea: Glynn Vivian Art Gallery Collection

Walters, Evan 1893–1951, *Woman Reading*, gift from Erna Meinel, 1953, © the artist's estate, photo credit: City & County of Swansea: Glynn Vivian Art Gallery Collection

Walters, Evan 1893–1951, *Cockle Woman*, gift from Richard J. Strick, 1939, © the artist's estate, photo credit: City & County of Swansea: Glynn Vivian Art Gallery Collection

Walters, Evan 1893–1951, *Self Portrait with Candle*, gift from Erna Meinel, 1953, © the artist's estate, photo credit: City & County of Swansea: Glynn Vivian Art Gallery Collection

Walters, Evan 1893–1951, *Still Life with Cricket Ball*, gift from William Meinel, 1979, © the artist's estate, photo credit: City & County of Swansea: Glynn Vivian Art Gallery Collection

Walters, Evan 1893–1951, *A Study from Life*, gift from William Meinel, 1979, © the artist's estate, photo credit: City & County of Swansea: Glynn Vivian Art Gallery Collection

Walters, Evan 1893–1951, *Colliery Disaster*, gift from William Meinel, 1979, © the artist's estate, photo credit: City & County of Swansea: Glynn Vivian Art Gallery Collection

Walters, Evan 1893–1951, *Miss Thomas*, bequeathed by F. S. H. Thomas, 1987, © the artist's estate, photo credit: City & County of Swansea: Glynn Vivian Art Gallery Collection

Walters, Evan 1893–1951, *Owain and Luned*, gift from William Meinel, 1979, © the artist's estate, photo credit: City & County of Swansea: Glynn Vivian Art Gallery Collection

Walters, Evan 1893–1951, *Boys at Golf*, gift from William Meinel, 1979, © the artist's estate, photo credit: City & County of Swansea: Glynn Vivian Art Gallery Collection

Walters, Evan 1893–1951, *Richard J. Strick*, bequeathed by Richard J. Strick, 1974, © the artist's estate, photo credit: City & County of Swansea: Glynn Vivian Art Gallery Collection

Walters, Evan 1893–1951, *Blackened Face with Reclining Figure*, gift from William Meinel, 1979, © the artist's estate, photo credit: City & County of Swansea: Glynn Vivian Art Gallery Collection

Walters, Evan 1893–1951, *Self Portrait, Green*, gift from William Meinel, 1979, © the artist's estate, photo credit: City & County of Swansea: Glynn Vivian Art Gallery Collection

Walters, Evan 1893–1951, *A Venetian Lady*, gift from William Meinel, 1979, © the artist's estate, photo credit: City & County of Swansea: Glynn Vivian Art Gallery Collection

Walters, Evan 1893–1951, *Abstract with Woman's Head*, gift from William Meinel, 1979, © the artist's estate, photo credit: City & County of Swansea: Glynn Vivian Art Gallery Collection

Walters, Evan 1893–1951, *Abstract Landscape*, gift from William Meinel, 1979, © the artist's estate, photo credit: City & County of Swansea: Glynn Vivian Art Gallery Collection

Walters, Evan 1893–1951, *View through French Windows*, gift from William Meinel, 1979, © the artist's estate, photo credit: City & County of Swansea: Glynn Vivian Art Gallery Collection

Walters, Evan 1893–1951, *Abstract Figures in Landscape*, gift from William Meinel, 1979, © the artist's estate, photo credit: City & County of Swansea: Glynn Vivian Art Gallery Collection

Walters, Evan 1893–1951, *Abstract Figures in Landscape*, gift from William Meinel, 1979, © the artist's estate, photo credit: City & County of Swansea: Glynn Vivian Art Gallery Collection

Walters, Evan 1893–1951, *Abstract Figures Smoking*, gift from William Meinel, 1979, © the artist's estate, photo credit: City & County of Swansea: Glynn Vivian Art Gallery Collection

Walters, Evan 1893–1951, *Abstract Heads in Grey*, gift from William Meinel, 1979, © the artist's estate, photo credit: City & County of Swansea: Glynn Vivian Art Gallery Collection

Walters, Evan 1893–1951, *Abstract Landscape with Figures*, gift from William Meinel, 1979, © the artist's estate, photo credit: City & County of Swansea: Glynn Vivian Art Gallery Collection

Walters, Evan 1893–1951, *Abstract View through Window*, gift from William Meinel, 1979, © the artist's estate, photo credit: City & County of Swansea: Glynn Vivian Art Gallery Collection

Walters, Evan 1893–1951, *Adam and Eve*, gift from William Meinel, 1979, © the artist's estate, photo credit: City & County of Swansea: Glynn Vivian Art Gallery Collection

Walters, Evan 1893–1951, *Breakfast*, gift from William Meinel, 1979, © the artist's estate, photo credit: City & County of Swansea: Glynn Vivian Art Gallery Collection

Walters, Evan 1893–1951, *Child in a High Chair*, gift from the Wrexham Arts Centre, 1994, © the artist's estate, photo credit: City & County of Swansea: Glynn Vivian Art Gallery Collection

Walters, Evan 1893–1951, *Dead Flowers*, gift from William Meinel, 1979, © the artist's estate, photo credit: City & County of Swansea: Glynn Vivian Art Gallery Collection

Walters, Evan 1893–1951, *Double Images No.1*, gift from William Meinel, 1979, © the artist's estate, photo credit: City & County of Swansea: Glynn Vivian Art Gallery Collection

Walters, Evan 1893–1951, *Execution*, gift from William Meinel, 1979, © the artist's estate, photo credit: City & County of Swansea: Glynn Vivian Art Gallery Collection

Walters, Evan 1893–1951, *Figures against a Landscape 1*, gift from William Meinel, 1979, © the artist's estate, photo credit: City & County of Swansea: Glynn Vivian Art Gallery Collection

Walters, Evan 1893–1951, *Figures against a Landscape 2*, gift from William Meinel, 1979, © the artist's estate, photo credit: City & County of Swansea: Glynn Vivian Art Gallery Collection

Walters, Evan 1893–1951, *Flowers in a Vase*, gift from A. P. Cottle, 1986, © the artist's estate, photo credit: City & County of Swansea: Glynn Vivian Art Gallery Collection

Walters, Evan 1893–1951, *Foxgloves*, gift from Erna Meinel, 1953, © the artist's estate, photo credit: City & County of Swansea: Glynn Vivian Art Gallery Collection

Walters, Evan 1893–1951, *Garden Scene with Two Doves*, gift from William Meinel, 1979, © the artist's estate, photo credit: City & County of Swansea: Glynn Vivian Art Gallery Collection

Walters, Evan 1893–1951, *Gardens No.1*, gift from William Meinel, 1979, © the artist's estate, photo credit: City & County of Swansea: Glynn Vivian Art Gallery Collection

Walters, Evan 1893–1951, *Geometric Forms*, gift from William Meinel, 1979, © the artist's estate, photo credit: City & County of Swansea: Glynn Vivian Art Gallery Collection

Walters, Evan 1893–1951, *H. P. Widdup*, purchased from Philip Davies Fine Art, 1996, © the artist's estate, photo credit: City & County of Swansea: Glynn Vivian Art Gallery Collection

Walters, Evan 1893–1951, *Jam Pot*, gift from William Meinel, 1979, © the artist's estate, photo credit: City & County of Swansea: Glynn Vivian Art Gallery Collection

Walters, Evan 1893–1951, *John Jenkins*, gift, 1970, © the artist's estate, photo credit: City & County of Swansea: Glynn Vivian Art Gallery Collection

Walters, Evan 1893–1951, *Les yeux qui rient*, gift from Howard Elt, 1964, © the artist's estate, photo credit: City & County of Swansea: Glynn Vivian Art Gallery Collection

Walters, Evan 1893–1951, *Medea*, gift from William Meinel, 1979, © the artist's estate, photo credit: City & County of Swansea: Glynn Vivian Art Gallery Collection

Walters, Evan 1893–1951, *Mrs Bessie Jones*, gift from Mrs B. Mort-Jones, 1975, © the artist's estate, photo credit: City & County of Swansea: Glynn Vivian Art Gallery Collection

Walters, Evan 1893–1951, *Mrs N. Ledingham as a Young Girl*, gift from N. Ledingham, 1983, © the artist's estate, photo credit: City & County of Swansea: Glynn Vivian Art Gallery Collection

Walters, Evan 1893–1951, *Mumbles Woman in Window*, gift from William Meinel, 1979, © the artist's estate, photo credit: City & County of Swansea: Glynn Vivian Art Gallery Collection

Walters, Evan 1893–1951, *Nude*, gift from Erna Meinel, 1953, © the artist's estate, photo credit: City & County of Swansea: Glynn Vivian Art Gallery Collection

Walters, Evan 1893–1951, *Nude*, gift from Howard Elt, 1964, © the artist's estate, photo credit: City & County of Swansea: Glynn Vivian Art Gallery Collection

Walters, Evan 1893–1951, *Pipe*, gift from William Meinel, 1979, © the artist's estate, photo credit: City & County of Swansea: Glynn Vivian Art Gallery Collection

Walters, Evan 1893–1951, *Portrait of a Lady*, gift from William Meinel, 1979, © the artist's estate, photo credit: City & County of Swansea: Glynn Vivian Art Gallery Collection

Walters, Evan 1893–1951, *Portrait of a Laughing Man*, gift from the Taliesin Arts Centre, 1994, © the artist's estate, photo credit: City & County of Swansea: Glynn Vivian Art Gallery Collection

Walters, Evan 1893–1951, *Portrait of a Woman*, gift, 1994, © the artist's estate, photo credit: City & County of Swansea: Glynn Vivian Art Gallery Collection

Walters, Evan 1893–1951, *Portrait of an Unknown Man**, gift from

William Meinel, 1979, © the artist's estate, photo credit: City & County of Swansea: Glynn Vivian Art Gallery Collection

Walters, Evan 1893–1951, *Pottery Horses*, gift from William Meinel, 1979, © the artist's estate, photo credit: City & County of Swansea: Glynn Vivian Art Gallery Collection

Walters, Evan 1893–1951, *Resolution*, gift from William Meinel, 1979, © the artist's estate, photo credit: City & County of Swansea: Glynn Vivian Art Gallery Collection

Walters, Evan 1893–1951, *Self Portrait*, gift from Erna Meinel, 1953, © the artist's estate, photo credit: City & County of Swansea: Glynn Vivian Art Gallery Collection

Walters, Evan 1893–1951, *Self Portrait*, gift from William Meinel, 1979, © the artist's estate, photo credit: City & County of Swansea: Glynn Vivian Art Gallery Collection

Walters, Evan 1893–1951, *Self Portrait*, gift from William Meinel, 1979, © the artist's estate, photo credit: City & County of Swansea: Glynn Vivian Art Gallery Collection

Walters, Evan 1893–1951, *Self Portrait*, gift from A. P. Cottle, 1986, © the artist's estate, photo credit: City & County of Swansea: Glynn Vivian Art Gallery Collection

Walters, Evan 1893–1951, *Self Portrait*, gift from Elizabeth Iorwerth-Jones, 2004, © the artist's estate, photo credit: City & County of Swansea: Glynn Vivian Art Gallery Collection

Walters, Evan 1893–1951, *Semi-Abstract*, gift from William Meinel, 1979, © the artist's estate, photo credit: City & County of Swansea: Glynn Vivian Art Gallery Collection

Walters, Evan 1893–1951, *Sir William A. Jenkins, JP*, gift from the Trustees Savings Bank, 1986, © the artist's estate, photo credit: City & County of Swansea: Glynn Vivian Art Gallery Collection

Walters, Evan 1893–1951, *Soho*, gift from William Meinel, 1979, © the artist's estate, photo credit: City & County of Swansea: Glynn Vivian Art Gallery Collection

Walters, Evan 1893–1951, *Still Life with Candle*, gift from William Meinel, 1979, © the artist's estate, photo credit: City & County of Swansea: Glynn Vivian Art Gallery Collection

Walters, Evan 1893–1951, *Still Life with Crocuses*, gift from William Meinel, 1979, © the artist's estate, photo credit: City & County of Swansea: Glynn Vivian Art Gallery Collection

Walters, Evan 1893–1951, *The Ascension*, gift from William Meinel, 1979, © the artist's estate, photo credit: City & County of Swansea: Glynn Vivian Art Gallery Collection

Walters, Evan 1893–1951, *Toby Jug and Flowers*, gift from William Meinel, 1979, © the artist's estate,

photo credit: City & County of Swansea: Glynn Vivian Art Gallery Collection

Walters, Evan 1893–1951, *Tree Trunks*, gift from William Meinel, 1979, © the artist's estate, photo credit: City & County of Swansea: Glynn Vivian Art Gallery Collection

Walters, Evan 1893–1951, *Two Heads*, gift from William Meinel, 1979, © the artist's estate, photo credit: City & County of Swansea: Glynn Vivian Art Gallery Collection

Walters, Evan 1893–1951, *Untitled*, gift from William Meinel, 1979, © the artist's estate, photo credit: City & County of Swansea: Glynn Vivian Art Gallery Collection

Walters, Evan 1893–1951, *Waiting for Charon*, gift from William Meinel, 1979, © the artist's estate, photo credit: City & County of Swansea: Glynn Vivian Art Gallery Collection

Walters, Evan 1893–1951, *War Abstract*, gift from William Meinel, 1979, © the artist's estate, photo credit: City & County of Swansea: Glynn Vivian Art Gallery Collection

Walters, Evan 1893–1951, *White Flowers and Apples*, gift from William Meinel, 1979, © the artist's estate, photo credit: City & County of Swansea: Glynn Vivian Art Gallery Collection

Walters, Evan 1893–1951, *William Daniel Rees*, purchased from the artist, 1939, © the artist's estate, photo credit: City & County of Swansea: Glynn Vivian Art Gallery Collection

Walters, Evan 1893–1951, *Woman in an Arch of Trees*, gift, 1994, © the artist's estate, photo credit: City & County of Swansea: Glynn Vivian Art Gallery Collection

Walters, Evan 1893–1951, *Woman Peeling Potatoes*, gift from William Meinel, 1979, © the artist's estate, photo credit: City & County of Swansea: Glynn Vivian Art Gallery Collection

Walters, Evan 1893–1951, *Woman Playing with a Cat*, gift from the Wrexham Arts Centre, 1994, © the artist's estate, photo credit: City & County of Swansea: Glynn Vivian Art Gallery Collection

Watson, Harry 1871–1936, *Summer Day on the Flats*, purchased from the Art Exhibitions Bureau, 1938, photo credit: City & County of Swansea: Glynn Vivian Art Gallery Collection

Webster, Catrin b.1966, *Hafod 2*, gift from Friends of the Glynn Vivian Art Gallery, 2009, © the copyright holder, photo credit: City & County of Swansea: Glynn Vivian Art Gallery Collection

Weight, Carel Victor Morlais 1908–1997, *From Robert Buhler's Cottage*, gift from the Contemporary Art Society for Wales, 1957, © the artist's estate/Bridgeman Art Library, photo credit: City & County of Swansea: Glynn Vivian Art Gallery Collection

West, W. *Wreck off Rocky Coast*, purchased from Regency Antiques, 1972, photo credit: City & County of Swansea: Glynn Vivian Art Gallery Collection

Wilkins, William Powell b.1938, *A Dance*, purchased from the artist, 1993, © the copyright holder, photo credit: City & County of Swansea: Glynn Vivian Art Gallery Collection

Williams, Archie 1922–1993, *Salubrious Passage, Swansea*, gift from the Friends of the Glynn Vivian Art Gallery, 1996, © the copyright holder, photo credit: City & County of Swansea: Glynn Vivian Art Gallery Collection

Williams, B. H. *Untitled*, gift, 1988, photo credit: City & County of Swansea: Glynn Vivian Art Gallery Collection

Williams, Christopher 1873–1934, *A Fresh Morning, Llangranog*, photo credit: City & County of Swansea: Glynn Vivian Art Gallery Collection

Williams, Christopher 1873–1934, *Atalanta*, gift, photo credit: City & County of Swansea: Glynn Vivian Art Gallery Collection

Williams, Christopher 1873–1934, *Branwen*, gift from the artist, 1934, photo credit: City & County of Swansea: Glynn Vivian Art Gallery Collection

Williams, Christopher 1873–1934, *Ceridwen*, gift from the artist, 1934, photo credit: City & County of Swansea: Glynn Vivian Art Gallery Collection

Williams, Christopher 1873–1934, *Coast near Holyhead*, gift, photo credit: City & County of Swansea: Glynn Vivian Art Gallery Collection

Williams, Christopher 1873–1934, *Criccieth Castle*, purchased, photo credit: City & County of Swansea: Glynn Vivian Art Gallery Collection

Williams, Christopher 1873–1934, *Family on Barmouth Island*, gift from Ivor Williams, photo credit: City & County of Swansea: Glynn Vivian Art Gallery Collection

Williams, Christopher 1873–1934, *In North Wales*, gift, photo credit: City & County of Swansea: Glynn Vivian Art Gallery Collection

Williams, Christopher 1873–1934, *Near Merthyr Mawr*, gift, photo credit: City & County of Swansea: Glynn Vivian Art Gallery Collection

Williams, Christopher 1873–1934, *Remorse of Saul*, gift, photo credit: City & County of Swansea: Glynn Vivian Art Gallery Collection

Williams, Christopher 1873–1934, *Santa Maria della Salute, Venice*, gift, photo credit: City & County of Swansea: Glynn Vivian Art Gallery Collection

Williams, Christopher 1873–1934, *View from Arthog*, gift, photo credit: City & County of Swansea: Glynn Vivian Art Gallery Collection

Williams, Emrys b.1958, *Woman on the Promenade*, purchased from Benjamin Rhodes Gallery, Cardiff, 1990, © the artist

Williams, Emrys b.1958, *On the Pier II*, purchased from the artist, 1996, © the artist, photo credit: City & County of Swansea: Glynn Vivian Art Gallery Collection

Williams, Kyffin 1918–2006, *Highgate Schoolboy*, gift from the Contemporary Art Society, 1956, © Llyfrgell Genedlaethol Cymru / The National Library of Wales, photo credit: City & County of Swansea: Glynn Vivian Art Gallery Collection

Williams, Kyffin 1918–2006, *Jack Jones*, purchased from Hugette-Louise Jones, 1997, © Llyfrgell Genedlaethol Cymru / The National Library of Wales, photo credit: City & County of Swansea: Glynn Vivian Art Gallery Collection

Williams, Kyffin 1918–2006, *Deposition*, purchased from Colnaghi & Co., 1948, © Llyfrgell Genedlaethol Cymru / The National Library of Wales, photo credit: City & County of Swansea: Glynn Vivian Art Gallery Collection

Williams, Kyffin 1918–2006, *Eryri (Snowdon)*, purchased from Caerphilly Eisteddfod, 1951, © Llyfrgell Genedlaethol Cymru / The National Library of Wales, photo credit: City & County of Swansea: Glynn Vivian Art Gallery Collection

Williams, Kyffin 1918–2006, *Mountainous Landscape*, gift from the Friends of the Glynn Vivian Art Gallery, 1998, © Llyfrgell Genedlaethol Cymru / The National Library of Wales, photo credit: City & County of Swansea: Glynn Vivian Art Gallery Collection

Williams, Kyffin 1918–2006, *Snowdon from near Harlech*, gift from the Friends of the Glynn Vivian Art Gallery, 1998, © Llyfrgell Genedlaethol Cymru / The National Library of Wales, photo credit: City & County of Swansea: Glynn Vivian Art Gallery Collection

Williams, Kyffin 1918–2006, *Tre'r Ceiri*, purchased, 1948, © Llyfrgell Genedlaethol Cymru / The National Library of Wales, photo credit: City & County of Swansea: Glynn Vivian Art Gallery Collection

Williams, Kyffin 1918–2006, *View of Snowdon in Winter*, gift from the artist, 1953, © Llyfrgell Genedlaethol Cymru / The National Library of Wales, photo credit: City & County of Swansea: Glynn Vivian Art Gallery Collection

Williams, Margaret Lindsay 1888–1960, *Martha, the Artist's Mother*, gift from S. Hall, 1986, © the copyright holder, photo credit: City & County of Swansea: Glynn Vivian Art Gallery Collection

Williams, Penry 1798–1885, *The Assumption of the Virgin* (after Jacopa Cavedone), bequeathed by Richard Glynn Vivian, 1911, photo credit: City & County of Swansea: Glynn Vivian Art Gallery Collection

Williams, Penry 1798–1885, *The Vision of Saint Bruno* (after Guercino), bequeathed by Richard Glynn Vivian, 1911, photo credit: City & County of Swansea: Glynn Vivian Art Gallery Collection

Williams, Penry 1798–1885, *The Visitation* (after Albertinelli), bequeathed by Richard Glynn Vivian, 1911, photo credit: City & County of Swansea: Glynn Vivian Art Gallery Collection

Williams, Penry 1798–1885, *Two Saints* (after Albertinelli), bequeathed by Richard Glynn Vivian, 1911, photo credit: City & County of Swansea: Glynn Vivian Art Gallery Collection

Williams, Penry 1798–1885, *Massacre of the Innocents*, bequeathed by Richard Glynn Vivian, 1911, photo credit: City & County of Swansea: Glynn Vivian Art Gallery Collection

Williams, Penry 1798–1885, *Repose*, bequeathed by Richard Glynn Vivian, 1911, photo credit: City & County of Swansea: Glynn Vivian Art Gallery Collection

Williams, Penry 1798–1885, *Saint John* (after Guercino), bequeathed by Richard Glynn Vivian, 1911, photo credit: City & County of Swansea: Glynn Vivian Art Gallery Collection

Williams, Sue b.1956, *Beach View*, purchased from the artist, 1993, © the artist, photo credit: City & County of Swansea: Glynn Vivian Art Gallery Collection

Williams, Sue b.1956, *Scorched*, purchased from the artist, 1993, © the artist, photo credit: City & County of Swansea: Glynn Vivian Art Gallery Collection

Williams, William 1808–1895, *Fabian's Bay, Swansea, 1844*, gift, 1988, photo credit: City & County of Swansea: Glynn Vivian Art Gallery Collection

Wilson, Frank Avray 1914–2009, *Configuration*, purchased from the Redfern Gallery, 1960, © the artist's estate, photo credit: City & County of Swansea: Glynn Vivian Art Gallery Collection

Wilson, Richard 1713/1714–1782, *Lake Averno*, purchased from Alex Martin, 1943, photo credit: City & County of Swansea: Glynn Vivian Art Gallery Collection

Wilson, Richard 1713/1714–1782, *Landscape with Old Castle*, bequeathed by Richard Glynn Vivian, 1911, photo credit: City & County of Swansea: Glynn Vivian Art Gallery Collection

Wilson, Richard 1713/1714–1782, *River Scene in Italy*, bequeathed by Richard Glynn Vivian, 1911, photo credit: City & County of Swansea: Glynn Vivian Art Gallery Collection

Wilson, Richard 1713/1714–1782, *Solitude*, purchased, 1971, photo credit: City & County of Swansea: Glynn Vivian Art Gallery Collection

Wilson, Richard 1713/1714–1782, *The White Monk*, bequeathed by Richard Glynn Vivian, 1911, photo credit: City & County of Swansea: Glynn Vivian Art Gallery Collection

Wit, Jacob de 1695–1754, *Blind Man's Buff*, bequeathed by Richard Glynn Vivian, 1911, photo credit: City & County of Swansea: Glynn Vivian Art Gallery Collection

Wit, Jacob de 1695–1754, *Decorative Panel* (with putti), bequeathed by Richard Glynn Vivian, 1911, photo credit: City & County of Swansea: Glynn Vivian Art Gallery Collection

Wit, Jacob de 1695–1754, *Decorative Panel*, bequeathed by Richard Glynn Vivian, 1911, photo credit: City & County of Swansea: Glynn Vivian Art Gallery Collection

Wit, Jacob de 1695–1754, *Decorative Panel with Three Portraits*, bequeathed by Richard Glynn Vivian, 1911, photo credit: City & County of Swansea: Glynn Vivian Art Gallery Collection

Wit, Jacob de 1695–1754, *Decorative Panel with Two Central Figures*, bequeathed by Richard Glynn Vivian, 1911, photo credit: City & County of Swansea: Glynn Vivian Art Gallery Collection

Wit, Jacob de 1695–1754, *Triumphal Procession*, bequeathed by Richard Glynn Vivian, 1911, photo credit: City & County of Swansea: Glynn Vivian Art Gallery Collection

Wit, Jacob de 1695–1754, *Triumphal Procession*, bequeathed by Richard Glynn Vivian, 1911, photo credit: City & County of Swansea: Glynn Vivian Art Gallery Collection

Wolkowsky *The Vintage in Umbria*, bequeathed by Mrs Coombe-Tennant, 1957, © the copyright holder, photo credit: City & County of Swansea: Glynn Vivian Art Gallery Collection

Wright, John b.1931, *Out of the Hills*, gift from the Contemporary Art Society for Wales, 1965, © the copyright holder, photo credit: City & County of Swansea: Glynn Vivian Art Gallery Collection

Zajac, Ryszard b.1929, *Umbrian Landscape*, purchased from Cassel Gallery, 1964, © the copyright holder, photo credit: City & County of Swansea: Glynn Vivian Art Gallery Collection

Zobole, Ernest 1927–1999, *Ystrad and People No.1*, gift from the Contemporary Art Society for Wales, 1965, © the artist's estate, photo credit: City & County of Swansea: Glynn Vivian Art Gallery Collection

Zobole, Ernest 1927–1999, *Landscape around December*, gift from the Arts Council of Wales, 2002, © the artist's estate, photo credit: City & County of Swansea: Glynn Vivian Art Gallery Collection

Zobole, Ernest 1927–1999, *Painter and Subject Matter No.7*, gift from the Contemporary Art Society for Wales, 2006, © the artist's estate, photo credit: City & County of Swansea: Glynn Vivian Art Gallery Collection

Gower Heritage Centre

Jones, D. B. R. *Three Cliffs Bay, Gower*, © the copyright holder

Marchant, David *Three Cliffs Bay, Gower*, © the copyright holder

Maggie's Swansea

Prendergast, Peter 1946–2007, *Over the Hill*, donated by the artist's family, © the copyright holder

Weil, Barbara b.1933, *Forest of Love*, donated by the artist, © the artist

Swansea Metropolitan University

Cox, Richard C. b.1946, *Red Beard Diptych, I*, © the artist

Cox, Richard C. b.1946, *Red Beard Diptych, III*, © the artist

Cox, Richard C. b.1946, *Red Beard Series Black*, © the artist

Cox, Richard C. b.1946, *Red Beard Series Blue*, © the artist

Donovan, James b.1974, *Tower Colliery Miner*, © the copyright holder

Donovan, James b.1974, *Tower Colliery Miner*, © the copyright holder

Donovan, James b.1974, *Tower Colliery Miners*, © the copyright holder

unknown artist *Abstract (in Mustard and Blue)**, © the copyright holder

unknown artist *Abstract (in Red and Black)**, © the copyright holder

unknown artist *Apocalyptic Scene 1*, © the copyright holder

unknown artist *Apocalyptic Scene 2*, © the copyright holder

unknown artist *Apocalyptic Scene 3*, © the copyright holder

unknown artist *Choppy Sea**, © the copyright holder

unknown artist *Man with Closed Eyes**, © the copyright holder

Swansea Museum

Adams, Edward active 1880–1884, *'Inchmaru'*, bequeathed

Adams, Edward active 1880–1884, *'Inchgarvie'*, bequeathed

Birchall, H. B. active 19th C, *Pilot Cutter 'Tom Rosser'*, bequeathed

Brandon, A. K. *Brigantine 'Agnes Ellen'*, purchased

Butler, William 1824–1870, *Loughor Glass Works*, bequeathed

Butler, William 1824–1870, *Kidwelly Castle*, purchased

Butler, William 1824–1870, *Loughor Castle and Town*, bequeathed

Buttersworth, Thomas 1768–1842, *HMS 'Daedalus'*, unknown acquisition method

Carter, William 1863–1939, *Caroline Julia Talbot Dillwyn Llewelyn*, gift

Carter, William 1863–1939, *John Talbot Dillwyn Llewelyn*, gift

Collection Addresses

Carmarthenshire (Sir Gaerfyrddin)

Carmarthen

Carmarthenshire Museums Service Collection:

> Carmarthenshire County Museum
> Abergwili, Carmarthen SA31 2JG
> Telephone 01267 228696

> Carmarthen County Hall
> Carmarthen SA31 1JP
> Telephone 01267 234567

> Carmarthen Guildhall
> Guildhall Square, Carmarthan SA31 1PR
> Telephone 01267 222233

> Llanelli Town Hall
> Town Hall Square, Llanelli SA15 3DD
> Telephone 01554 774352

> Parc Howard Museum and Art Gallery
> Felinfoel Road, Llanelli SA15 3LJ
> Telephone 01554 772029

University of Wales Trinity Saint David:

> Trinity St David, Lampeter
> Founder's Library
> Lampeter Campus, Lampeter SA48 7ED
> Telephone 01570 422351

> Trinity University College, Carmarthen
> College Road, Carmarthen SA31 3EP
> Telephone 01267 676767

Llandovery

Llandovery Town Council:
> Llandovery Heritage Centre
> King's Road, Llandovery SA20 0AW
> Telephone 01550 720693

> Llandovery Heritage Centre
> King's Road, Llandovery SA20 0AW
> Telephone 01550 720693

Llandovery Library
Town Hall, Market Square, Llandovery SA20 0AA
Telephone 01550 721626

Neath Port Talbot (Castell-nedd Port Talbot)

Neath

Neath Antiquarian Society
Neath Antiquarian Society Archives
Neath Mechanics' Institute, 4 Church Place
Neath SA11 3LL
Telephone 01639 620139

Neath Port Talbot College
Dwr-y-Felin Road, Neath SA10 7RF
Telephone 01639 648000

Port Talbot

Neath Port Talbot County Borough Council:

> Reginald Street Library
> Port Talbot SA13 1YY
> Telephone 01639 899829

> Cefn Coed Colliery Museum
> Blaenant Colliery Site, Neath Road, Crynant
> Neath SA10 8SN
> Telephone 01639 750556

> Margam Castle
> Margam Country Park, Margam
> Port Talbot SA13 2TJ
> Telephone 01639 881635

> Neath Port Talbot Civic Centre
> Port Talbot SA13 1PJ
> Telephone 01639 686868

> Neath Town Hall
> Church Place, Neath SA11 3LL

South Wales Miners' Museum
Afan Forest Park, Cynonville, Port Talbot SA13 3HG
Telephone 01639 850564

Pembrokeshire (Sir Benfro)

Haverfordwest

Haverfordwest Town Museum
Castle House, Haverfordwest SA61 2EF
Telephone 01437 763087

Pembrokeshire County Council's Museums Service:

> Scolton Manor Museum
> Scolton Manor Museum and Country Park
> Spittal, Haverfordwest SA62 5QL
> Telephone 01437 731328

> Haverfordwest Registry Office
> Tower Hill, Haverfordwest SA61 1SS
> Telephone 01437 775176

> Pembrokeshire County Council County Hall
> Haverfordwest SA61 1TP
> Telephone 01437 764551

Milford Haven

Milford Haven Heritage and Maritime Museum
The Old Custom House, The Docks,
Milford Haven SA73 3AF
Telephone 01646 694496

Pembroke Dock

Pembroke Dock Sunderland Trust
The Fleet Surgeon's House
1 The Terrace, Royal Dockyard
Pembroke Dock SA72 6YH
Telephone 01646 684220

Puncheston

Puncheston School
Aelybryn, Puncheston SA62 5RL
Telephone 01348 881321

Tenby

Tenby Museum & Art Gallery
Castle Hill, Tenby SA70 7BP
Telephone 01834 842809

Tenby Town Council
De Valence Pavilion, Upper Frog Street, Tenby SA70 7JD
Telephone 01834 842730

Swansea (Abertawe)

Swansea

Abertawe Bro Morgannwg University Health Board:

> Morriston Hospital
> Heol Maes Eglwys, Morriston, Swansea SA6 6NL
> Telephone 01792 702222

> Gellinudd Hospital
> Lon Catwyg, Gellinudd, Pontardawe
> Swansea SA8 3DX
> Telephone 01792 862221

> Gorseinon Hospital
> Gorseinon, Swansea SA4 4UU
> Telephone 01792 702222

> Princess of Wales Hospital
> Coity Road, Bridgend CF31 1RQ
> Telephone 01656 752752

> Singleton Hospital
> Sketty Lane, Sketty, Swansea SA2 8QA
> Telephone 01792 205666

Glynn Vivian Art Gallery:

> Glynn Vivian Art Gallery
> Alexandra Road, Swansea SA1 5DZ
> Telephone 01792 516900

> Brangwyn Hall
> Guildhall, Swansea SA1 4PE
> Telephone 01792 635432

Gower Heritage Centre
Park Mill, Gower, Swansea SA3 2EH
Telephone 01792 371206

Maggie's Swansea
Singleton Hospital, Sketty Lane, Sketty, Swansea SA2 8QA
Telephone 01792 200000

Swansea Metropolitan University
Mount Pleasant, Swansea SA1 6ED
Telephone 01792 481000

Swansea Museum:

Swansea Museum
Victoria Road, The Maritime Quarter
Swansea SA1 1SN
Telephone 01792 653763

The Museum Collections Centre
Cross Valley Link Road, Landore
Swansea SA1 2JT
Telephone 01792 653763

The Tramshed
Dylan Thomas Square, The Maritime Quarter
Swansea SA1 1RR
Telephone 01792 653763

Acknowledgements

The Public Catalogue Foundation would like to thank the individual artists and copyright holders for their permission to reproduce for free the paintings in this catalogue. Exhaustive efforts have been made to locate the copyright owners of all the images included within this catalogue and to meet their requirements. Copyright credit lines for copyright owners who have been traced are listed in the Further Information section.

The Public Catalogue Foundation would like to express its great appreciation to the following organisations for their kind assistance in the preparation of this catalogue:

Bridgeman Art Library
Flowers East
Marlborough Fine Art
National Association of Decorative & Fine Arts Societies (NADFAS)
National Gallery, London
National Portrait Gallery, London
Royal Academy of Arts, London
Tate

Index of Artists

In this catalogue, artists' names and the spelling of their names follow the preferred presentation of the name in the Getty Union List of Artist Names (ULAN) as of February 2004, if the artist is listed in ULAN.

The page numbers next to each artist's name below direct readers to paintings that are by the artist; are attributed to the artist; or, in a few cases, are more loosely related to the artist being, for example, 'after', 'the circle of' or copies of a painting by the artist. The precise relationship between the artist and the painting is listed in the catalogue.

The Public Catalogue Foundation

The Public Catalogue Foundation is a registered charity. It was launched in 2003 to create a photographic record of the entire national collection of oil, tempera and acrylic paintings in public ownership in the United Kingdom.

Whilst our public galleries and civic buildings hold arguably the greatest collection of oil paintings in the world, over 80 per cent of these are not on view. Few collections have a complete photographic record of their paintings let alone a comprehensive illustrated catalogue. What is publicly owned is not publicly accessible.

The Foundation is publishing a series of fully illustrated, county-by-county catalogues that will cover, eventually, the entire national UK collection. To date, it has published over 30 volumes, presenting over 72,000 paintings.

In partnership with the BBC, the Foundation will make its database of the entire UK collection of 200,000 oil paintings available online through a new website called *Your Paintings*. The website was launched in the summer of 2011.

Your Paintings (*www.bbc.co.uk/arts/yourpaintings*) offers a variety of ways of searching for paintings as well as further information about the paintings and artists, including links to the participating collections' websites. For those interested in paintings and the subjects they portray *Your Paintings* is an unparalleled learning resource.

Collections benefit substantially from the work of the Foundation, not least from the digital images that are given to them for free following photography, and from the increased recognition that the project brings. These substantial benefits come at no financial cost to the collections.

The Foundation is funded by a combination of support from individuals, charitable trusts, companies and the public sector although the latter provides less than 20 per cent of the Foundation's financial support.

Supporters

Master Patrons

The Public Catalogue Foundation is greatly indebted to the following Master Patrons who have helped it in the past or are currently working with it to raise funds for the publication of their county catalogues. All of them have given freely of their time and have made an enormous contribution to the work of the Foundation.

Peter Andreae (*Hampshire*)
Sir Henry Aubrey-Fletcher, Bt, Lord Lieutenant of Buckinghamshire (*Buckinghamshire*)
Sir Nicholas Bacon, DL, High Sheriff of Norfolk (*Norfolk*)
Sir John Bather, Lord Lieutenant of Derbyshire (*Derbyshire*)
The Hon. Mrs Bayliss, JP, Lord Lieutenant of Berkshire (*Berkshire*)
Ian Bonas (*County Durham*)

Peter Bretherton (*West Yorkshire: Leeds*)
Michael Brinton, Lord Lieutenant of Worcestershire (*Worcestershire*)
Sir Hugo Brunner, KCVO, JP (*Oxfordshire*)
Mr John Bush, OBE, Lord-Lieutenant of Wiltshire (*Wiltshire*)
Lady Butler (*Warwickshire*)
Richard Compton (*North Yorkshire*)
George Courtauld, DL, Vice Lord Lieutenant of Essex (*Essex*)

The Countess of Darnley, Lord Lieutenant of Herefordshire (*Herefordshire*)

The Marquess of Downshire (*North Yorkshire*)

Martin Dunne, Lord Lieutenant of Warwickshire (*Warwickshire*)

Sir Henry Elwes, KCVO, Lord-Lieutenant of Gloucestershire (*Gloucestershire*)

Jenny Farr, MBE, DL (*Nottinghamshire*)

John Fenwick (*Tyne & Wear Museums*)

Mark Fisher, MP (*Staffordshire*)

Patricia Grayburn, MBE, DL (*Surrey*)

The Earl of Halifax, KStJ, JP, DL (*East Riding of Yorkshire*)

Lord Roy Hattersley, PC (*South Yorkshire: Sheffield*)

Algy Heber-Percy, Lord Lieutenant of Shropshire (*Shropshire*)

The Lady Mary Holborow, Lord Lieutenant of Cornwall (*Cornwall*)

Sarah Holman (*Warwickshire*)

Tommy Jowitt (*West Yorkshire*)

Alderman Sir David Lewis, The Rt Hon. The Lord Mayor of London, 2007–2008 (*The City of London*)

Sir Michael Lickiss (*Cornwall*)

Magnus Linklater (*Scotland*)

Lord Marlesford, DL (*Suffolk*)

Dr Bridget McConnell (*Glasgow*)

Lady Sarah Nicholson (*County Durham*)

Malcolm V. L. Pearce, MP (*Somerset*)

Sir John Riddell, Lord Lieutenant of Northumberland (*Northumberland*)

Venetia Ross Skinner (*Dorset*)

The Most Hon. The Marquess of Salisbury, PC, DL (*Hertfordshire*)

Julia Somerville (*Government Art Collection*)

Tim Stevenson, OBE, Lord Lieutenant of Oxfordshire (*Oxfordshire*)

Phyllida Stewart-Roberts, OBE (*East Sussex*)

Lady Juliet Townsend, Lord Lieutenant of Northamptonshire (*Northamptonshire*)

Leslie Weller, DL (*West Sussex*)

Sir Samuel C. Whitbread, KCVO, Lord Lieutenant of Bedfordshire (*Bedfordshire*)

Financial support

The Public Catalogue Foundation is particularly grateful to the following organisations and individuals who have given it generous financial support since the project started in 2003.

National Sponsor

Christie's

Benefactors (£10,000–£50,000)

The 29th May 1961 Charitable Trust
Arts Council England
The Barbour Trust
Binks Trust
City of Bradford Metropolitan District Council
Deborah Loeb Brice Foundation
The Bulldog Trust
A. & S. Burton 1960 Charitable Trust
Christie's
City of London Corporation
The John S. Cohen Foundation
Covent Garden London
Creative Scotland
Department for Culture, Media and Sport

Sir Harry Djanogly, CBE
Mr Lloyd Dorfman
Dunard Fund
The Elmley Foundation
Fenwick Ltd
Fidelity UK Foundation
Marc Fitch Fund
The Foyle Foundation
J. Paul Getty Jr Trust
Hampshire County Council
The Charles Hayward Foundation
Peter Harrison Foundation
Mr Robert Hiscox
Hiscox plc
David Hockney, CH, RA
ICAP plc

The Jordan Charitable Foundation
Kent County Council
The Linbury Trust
The Manifold Trust
Paul Mellon Centre for Studies in
   British Art
The Mercers' Company
Robert Warren Miller
Mr & Mrs A. Mittal
The Monument Trust
Miles Morland
Allan and Carol Murray
National Gallery Trust
Stavros Niarchos Foundation
Norfolk County Council
Northern Rock Foundation
Nottingham City Council
Malcolm V. L. Pearce, MP
P. F. Charitable Trust
The Pilgrim Trust

Provident Financial
RAB Capital plc
The Radcliffe Trust
Renaissance East Midlands
Renaissance West Midlands
Renaissance Yorkshire
Saga Group Ltd
Scottish Government
The Bernard Sunley Charitable
   Foundation
Townsend Family Trust
University College, London
University of Leeds
The Walker Trust
The Wolfson Foundation
Sir Siegmund Warburg's Voluntary
   Settlement
Garfield Weston Foundation
Mr & Mrs A. H. Wilkinson
The Wixamtree Trust

Series Patrons
(Minimum donation of £2,500)

James & Lindsay Adam
Sir John Bather
Harry Bott
Janey Buchan
Mrs Rhona Callander
Dr Peter Cannon-Brookes
The John S. Cohen Foundation
Bushey Museum in memory of
   Lavender Watson
Mr Lloyd Dorfman
Lord Douro
Jenny Farr, MBE, DL
Mrs Greta Fenston
The FIRS Trust
Glasgow Museums
Patricia Grayburn, MBE, DL
G. Laurence Harbottle
R. K. Harrison Insurance Services
   Limited
Paul & Fiona Hart
Paul & Kathrine Haworth
Lord & Lady Heseltine
Patrik Holden & Lin Hinds
Neil Honebon

Michael Jacobson
Grace Jenkins
Dr David Johnson, DL
The Keatley Trust
John Kendall, Esq.
Michael A. Lambert, CBE
David & Amanda Leathers
Miles Morland
Allan & Carol Murray
North East Regional Museums Hub
The University of Northampton
Nottingham Civic Society
Richard & Amika Oldfield
The Roper Family Charitable Trust
Adam Sedgwick
Sir Harry & Lady Soloman
Stuart M. Southall
Simon Still
Chloe Teacher
University of Surrey
David & Cissy Walker
Tony Wilkinson
Mr & Mrs Jo Windsor
Mr & Mrs Charles Wyvill

Catalogue Patrons
(£1,000–£10,000)

The 29th May 1961 Charitable Trust
ACE Study Tours
Adams & Remers
Marcus & Kate Agius
The AIM Foundation
D. C. R. Allen
John Alston, CBE

Amberley Castle
The Astor Foundation
The Aylesford Family Charitable
   Trust
Chairman of Cornwall County
   Council, Mrs Doris Anson, OBE, JP
Archant Ltd

Christopher & Catherine Foyle
Freemasons of Derbyshire
The Friends of Historic Essex
The Friends of the Laing Art Gallery
The Friends of the Royal Pavilion,
    Art Gallery & Museums, Brighton
The Friends of Southampton's
    Museums, Archives and Galleries
The Friends of Sunderland Museums
The Friends of York Art Gallery (E. J.
    Swift Bequest)
Philip Gibbs
The Hon. H. M. T. Gibson's Charity
    Trust
Lewis & Jacqueline Golden
The Goldsmiths' Company
Gorringes
Charles Gregson
The Grocers' Company
The Gulland Family
David Gurney
Philip Gwyn
Sir Ernest Hall
The Earl of Halifax, KStJ, JP, DL
The W. A. Handley Charity Trust
The Hartnett Charitable Trust
Hazlitt, Gooden & Fox Ltd
Heartwood Wealth Management Ltd
The Trustees of the King Henry VIII
    Endowed Trust, Warwick
The Rt Hon. the Lord Heseltine, CH,
    PC & Lady Heseltine
The Lady Hind Trust
Hobart Charitable Trust
Edward and Anna Hocknell
David Hockney CH, RA
Patrick Holden & Lin Hinds
Mrs Michael Hollingbery
The Holman Family
Mr & Mrs A. Holman-West
The Honourable Company of
    Gloucestershire
The Hope Scott Trust
David & Prue Hopkinson
Major & Mrs Bill Hutchinson
His Honour Gabriel Hutton
Isle of Wight Council
The J. and S. B. Charitable Trust
Alan & Penny Jerome
James & Lucilla Joll Charitable Trust

Mr & Mrs Peter Jones
Tommy Jowitt
The Keatley Trust
Kent Messenger Group
Garrett Kirk, Jr
Mr John Kirkland, OBE & Mrs
    Sheila Kirkland
Robert Kirkland
Kirklees Council
The David Laing Foundation
Landau Foundation
Lord Lea of Crondall, OBE
The Leche Trust
Leeds Art Collections Fund
Leeds City Council
Leeds Philosophical and Literary
    Society
The Hon. David Legh, DL
Lord Leverhulme's Charitable Trust
Mr & Mrs John Lewis
Mark & Sophie Lewisohn
Tom Lugg & the Lane Family
The Orr Mackintosh Foundation
The MacRobert Trust
Maidstone Borough Council
John Manser
Mr & Mrs Derek Mapp
Walter & Barbara Marais
The Marlay Group
Marshall Charitable Trust
Stephen & Carolyn Martin
Tom & Anne Martin
The Medlock Charitable Trust
The Piet Mendels Foundation
MLA East of England
MLA North East of England
Museums Galleries Scotland
Mr Paul Myners
Rupert Nabarro
Nancie Massey Charitable Trust
Newcastle City Council
Bryan Norman
Lord & Lady Northampton
The University of Northampton
NP Aerospace Ltd
Oakmoor Trust
Jasper & Virginia Olivier
The Orr Mackintosh Foundation
Mr Christopher Oughtred
The Owen Family Trust

Sir Idris Pearce
Roger Neville Russ Peers
The Pennycress Trust
Perkins Family
The Lord & Lady Phillimore
Mrs Margaret Pollett
Simon & Ursula Pomeroy
The Portland Family
Portsmouth City Council
George Pragnell Ltd
The Prince Philip Trust Fund for the
  Royal Borough of Windsor and
  Maidenhead
Provident Financial plc
Mr John Rank
Rathbone Investment Management
  Ltd
The Hans and Märit Rausing
  Charitable Trust
Roger & Jane Reed
Renaissance North East
Renaissance South East
Renaissance South West
Michael Renshall, CBE, MA, FCA
Sir John Riddell
Sir Miles & Lady Rivett-Carnac
Rockley Charitable Trust
Rolls-Royce plc
The Roper Family Charitable Trust
Rothschild Foundation
Royal Cornwall Museum
Graham & Ann Rudd
Sir Nigel Rudd
Russell New
The J. S. & E. C. Rymer Charitable
  Trust
The Earl St Aldwyn
The Sammermar Trust
Scarfe Charitable Trust
Andrew & Belinda Scott
The Trustees of the Finnis Scott
  Foundation
Shaftesbury PLC
Mr W. Sharpe
The Shears Foundation
Robert Shields, DL
Smith & Williamson

South West of England Regional
  Development Agency
Caroline M. Southall
Stuart M. Southall
Southampton City Council
The Jessie Spencer Trust
Hugh & Catherine Stevenson
Mrs Andrew Stewart-Roberts, OBE
Mr Michael Stone
Mr Peter Stormonth Darling
The Stratford-upon-Avon Town
  Trust
Strutt and Parker
Suffolk County Council, through the
  Association for Suffolk Museums
Surrey County Council
The John Swire 1989 Charitable
  Trust
The Tanner Trust
Tennants Auctioneers
Tesco Charity Trust
The Thistle Trust
Prof. Caroline Tisdall
Trusthouse Charitable Foundation
Gladwyn Turbutt
TWM Business Partners
Tyne & Wear Museums
University College Falmouth
University of Derby
University of Essex
David & Grizelda Vermont
Wakefield Metropolitan District
  Council
Robert & Felicity Waley-Cohen
The Peggy Walker Charitable Trust
The Walland Trust Fund
John Wates Charitable Trust
Leslie Weller, DL
The Welton Foundation
West Sussex County Council
Mr & Mrs David Wigglesworth
Wilkin & Sons Ltd
Mr & Mrs Jo Windsor
Peter Wolton Charitable Trust
Michael J. Woodhall, FRICS
Sir Philip Wroughton
Mrs Angela Yeoman

Notes

Notes

Notes

Notes

Notes